AQA
GCSE Mathematics
Modular

Sue Chandler Ewart Smith

Foundation

Module 5

www.heinemann.co.uk

✓ Free online support
✓ Useful weblinks
✓ 24 hour online ordering

01865 888058

Heinemann

Inspiring generations

D0480766

Heinemann is an imprint of Harcourt Education Limited, a company incorporated in
England and Wales, having its registered office: Halley Court, Jordan Hill, Oxford OX2 8EJ.
Registered company number: 3099304

www.harcourt.co.uk

Heinemann is the registered trademark of Harcourt Education Limited

Text © Harcourt Education Limited, 2007

First published 2007

12 11 10 09 08 07
10 9 8 7 6 5 4 3 2 1

British Library Cataloguing in Publication Data is available from the British Library on
request.

ISBN 978 0 435807 23 8

Typeset by Tech-Set Ltd
Original illustrations © Harcourt Education Limited, 2007
Illustrated by Phil Garner
Cover design by mccdesign ltd
Cover photo: Digital Vision ©
Printed in the United Kingdom by Scotprint

Acknowledgements
Harcourt would like to thank those schools who gave invaluable help in the development
and trialling of this course.

The author and publisher would like to thank the following individuals and organisations
for permission to reproduce photographs:

Photos.com pp **26**, **101**, **139**; Getty Images/PhotoDisc pp **48**, **80**, **118**, **125**; Masterfile p **52**;
Morguefile p **104**; Alamy Images p **161**

Every effort has been made to contact copyright holders of material reproduced in this
book. Any omissions will be rectified in subsequent printings if notice is given to the
publishers.

There are links to relevant websites in this book. In order to ensure that the links are
up-to-date, that the links work, and that the sites are not inadvertently linked to sites
that could be considered offensive, we have made the links available on the Heinemann
website at www.heinemann.co.uk/hotlinks. When you access the site, the express code
is 7238P.

How to use this book

This book is designed to give you the best possible preparation for your AQA GCSE Module 5 Examination. The authors are experienced writers of successful school mathematics textbooks and each book has been exactly tailored to your GCSE maths specification.

Finding your way around

To help you find your way around when you are studying and revising use the

- **contents list** – this gives a detailed breakdown of the topics covered in each chapter
- **list of objectives** at the start of each chapter – this tells you what you will learn in the chapter
- **list of prerequisite knowledge** at the start of each chapter – this tells you what you need to know before starting the chapter
- **index** – on page 270 – you can use this to find any topic covered in this book.

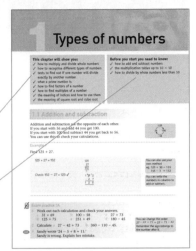

Remembering key facts

At the end of each chapter you will find

- **a summary of key points** – this lists the key facts and techniques covered in the chapter
- **grade descriptions** – these tell you which techniques and skills most students need to be able to use to achieve each exam grade
- **a glossary** – this gives the definitions of the mathematical words used in the chapter.

Exercises and practice papers

- **Worked examples** show you exactly how to answer exam questions.
- **Tips and hints** highlight key techniques and explain the reasons behind the answers.
- **Exam practice** questions work from the basics up to exam level. Hints and tips help you achieve your highest possible grade.
- The icon (UAM) against a question is Using and Applying mathematics.
- **Examination practice papers** on page 239 helps you prepare for your written examination.
- **Answers** for all the questions are included at the end of the book.

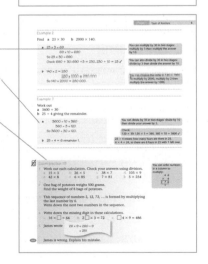

Enrichment, communication and technology

- **Enrichment tasks** throughout the book will help you practice your mathematical skills.
- **ICT tasks** will highlight opportunities to use computer programs and the Internet to help your understanding of mathematical topics.
- **Class discussion** sections allow you to talk about problems and what techniques you might use to solve them.

Contents

10 Shapes 2

11 Sequences

12 Volumes

13 Pythagoras' theorem

14 Coordinates and graphs

15 Using graphs

16 Transformations

17 Enlargement

1 Types of numbers

This chapter will show you:
- ✓ how to multiply and divide whole numbers
- ✓ how to recognise different types of numbers
- ✓ tests to find out if one number will divide exactly by another number
- ✓ what a prime number is
- ✓ how to find factors of a number
- ✓ how to find multiples of a number
- ✓ the meaning of indices and how to use them
- ✓ the meaning of square root and cube root

Before you start you need to know:
- ✓ how to add and subtract numbers
- ✓ the multiplication tables up to 10 × 10
- ✓ how to divide by whole numbers less than 10

1.1 Addition and subtraction

Addition and subtraction are the opposite of each other.
If you start with 56 and add 44 you get 100.
If you start with 100 and subtract 44 you get back to 56.
You can use this to check your calculations.

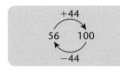

Example 1

Find 125 + 27.

125 + 27 = 152

$$\begin{array}{r} 125 \\ 27 \\ \hline 152 \\ \scriptstyle 1 \end{array}$$

Check: 152 − 27 = 125 ✓

$$\begin{array}{r} 1\,{}^{4}\!\!\not{5}\,{}^{1}2 \\ 2\ 7 \\ \hline 1\ 2\ 5 \end{array}$$

> You can also use your own method
> eg. 125 + 30 = 155
> 155 − 3 = 152

> You can write the numbers in columns to add or subtract.

Exam practice 1A

1. Work out each calculation and check your answers.
   - a 31 + 69
   - b 100 − 58
   - c 27 + 73
   - d 125 + 75
   - e 251 + 49
   - f 180 − 45

> You can change the order:
> 27 − 42 + 73 = 27 + 73 − 42
> Remember the sign belongs to the number after it.

2. Calculate a 27 − 42 + 73   b 360 − 110 − 45.

3. Sandy wrote '24 − 5 + 8 = 11.'
   Sandy is wrong. Explain her mistake.

4 Find the missing digit in each calculation.

a $2\square + 78 = 100$ b $100 - \square7 = 53$

c $4 - \square + 7 = 2$ d $18\square - 74 = 106$

e $2 + 2 + 2 + 2 = \square$ f $2\square5 + 75 = 300$

5 Abdul wrote

> $4 + 5 + 2 = 6 + 7 = 13$

UAM Abdul is wrong. Explain his mistake.

1.2 Multiplication and division

Multiplication is the same as adding the same number several times:

7×8 means '7 lots of 8', or $8 + 8 + 8 + 8 + 8 + 8 + 8$.

You need to know the multiplication tables to write down

$7 \times 8 = 56$ without having to add all the 8s.

When a number is multiplied by 10, 100, 1000, … the digits move 1, 2, 3, … columns to the left on a place value diagram.

10 000 s	1000 s	100 s	10 s	units
			4	7
		4	7	0
4	7	0	0	0

47×10 (points to third row)
47×1000 (points to fourth row)

When you divide a number by 10, 100, 1000, … the digits move 1, 2, 3, … columns to the right on a place value diagram.

10 000 s	1000 s	100 s	10 s	units
8	6	0	0	0
	8	6	0	0
			8	6

$86\,000 \div 10$ (points to second row)
$86\,000 \div 1000$ (points to third row)

Multiplication and division are the opposite of each other.
If you multiply 7 by 8 the answer is 56
If you divide 56 by 8 you get back to 7.
You can use this to check your answers.

The order in which you multiply numbers does not matter:

$4 \times 9 \times 6$ is the same as $6 \times 9 \times 4$.

However the order does matter when you are dividing:

$15 \div 3$ is not the same as $3 \div 15$.

Class discussion

a Amy said 'I find 7×8 by finding $64 - 8$. Why does this give the right answer?

b Leo said 'I find 7×8 by doubling 7 three times. How does this work?

c Aisha wrote
$27 \times 19 = 27 \times 20 - 27$
$= 540 - 27 = 513$.
This is correct. Why does it work?

d Here are three ways of finding
7×6: $\quad 7 \times 3 \times 2$
$\quad\quad\quad\quad 6 \times 6 + 6$
$\quad\quad\quad\quad 7 \times 5 + 7$
Why do all of these give the right answer?
What other ways are there of finding 7×6?

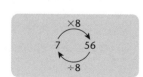

Example 2

Find   **a** 23 × 30   **b** 2000 × 140.

a 23 × 3 = 69
              69 × 10 = 690
       So 23 × 30 = 690.
       Check: 690 ÷ 30: 690 ÷ 3 = 230, 230 ÷ 10 = 23 ✓

> You can multiply by 30 in two stages: multiply by 3 then multiply the answer by 10.

> You can also divide by 30 in two stages: divide by 3 then divide the answer by 10.

b 140 × 2 = 280
              280 × 1000 = 280 000
       So 140 × 2000 = 280 000.

> You can change the order to 140 × 2000. To multiply by 2000, multiply by 2 then multiply the answer by 1000.

Example 3

Work out
a 3600 ÷ 30
b 25 ÷ 4 giving the remainder.

a   3600 ÷ 10 = 360
              360 ÷ 3 = 120
       So 3600 ÷ 30 = 120.

> You can divide by 30 in two stages: divide by 10 then divide your answer by 3.

> Check:
> 120 × 30: 120 × 3 = 360, 360 × 10 = 3600 ✓

b 25 ÷ 4 = 6 remainder 1.

> 25 ÷ 4 means how many fours are there in 25.
> 6 × 4 = 24, so there are 6 fours in 25 with 1 left over.

Exam practice 1B

1 Work out each calculation. Check your answers using division.
   a 15 × 3   **b** 26 × 5   **c** 38 × 7   **d** 103 × 9
   e 42 × 8   **f** 6 × 85   **g** 7 × 81   **h** 5 × 254

> You can write numbers in a column to multiply:
> ```
>     4 6
>   ×   6
>   -----
>   2 7 6
>     3
> ```

2 One bag of potatoes weighs 500 grams.
   Find the weight of 8 bags of potatoes.

3 This sequence of numbers 2, 12, 72, … is formed by multiplying the last number by 6.
   Write down the next two numbers in the sequence.

4 Write down the missing digit in these calculations.
   a 16 × ☐ = 64   **b** 2☐ × 3 = 72   **c** ☐4 × 9 = 486

5 James wrote   26 × 9 = 260 − 9
                          = 251

   James is wrong. Explain his mistake.

6   Write down the value of:
    a   37 × 10   b   35 × 1000   c   120 × 100   d   27 × 10 000
    e   28 × 20   f   200 × 56   g   131 × 3000   h   5000 × 74

7   Jason said '230 × 47 = 1081'.
    Explain how you know he must be wrong.

8   Work out each calculation. Check your answers using
    multiplication.
    a   45 ÷ 5   b   64 ÷ 4   c   54 ÷ 6   d   243 ÷ 9
    e   259 ÷ 7   f   184 ÷ 8   g   5700 ÷ 100   h   280 ÷ 20

> You can divide the hundreds first, then the tens, then the units:
> $$\frac{3\ 8}{7)26^56}$$

9   Freya has to pack 68 balls into boxes. Each box holds 10 balls.
    Mark said 'You need 6 boxes.'
    Explain why Mark is wrong.

10 Work out each calculation giving the remainder when there is
    one.
    a   32 ÷ 5   b   53 ÷ 4   c   112 ÷ 10   d   132 ÷ 11
    e   128 ÷ 16   f   240 ÷ 15   g   250 ÷ 8   h   170 ÷ 13

11 Work out:
    a   3 × 2 × 3   b   5 × 2 × 3   c   4 × 4 × 2
    d   2 × 2 × 3 × 7   e   3 ÷ 4 × 8   f   7 × 4 ÷ 2
    g   6 × 3 ÷ 2   h   2 ÷ 3 × 6 ÷ 2

> To find 3 × 2 × 3, multiply the first two numbers then multiply the answer by 3.

12 Jenny wrote

    3 × 2 × 4 = 12 × 8
            = 96

> You can change the order to make the calculation easier. Remember that each × or ÷ sign belongs to the number after it.
> 3 ÷ 4 × 8 = 3 × 8 ÷ 4

    Explain why Jenny's answer is wrong.

1.3 Order of operations

When a calculation contains a mixture of brackets, +, −, × and ÷,
remember the order of operations:

Brackets first → Then multiplication and division → Then addition and subtraction

---

Example 4

Work out 4 + (2 + 5) × 3.

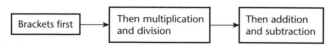

4 + (2 + 5) × 3 = 4 + 7 × 3 = 4 + 21 = 25

Work out 2 + 5 first.   Find 7 × 3 next.

Exam practice 1C

1   Work out:
   a $2 + 4 \times 6$ b $7 \times (4 - 3)$ c $5 + 24 \div 12$
   d $24 \div 8 - 3$ e $7 \times (2 + 6)$ f $9 - 3 + 6 \times 2$

2   Calculate:
   a $(7 + 2) \times 2$ b $3 \times 2 - 4 \div 2$ c $6 + 8 \div 4 + 6$
   d $20 \div (9 - 4)$ e $(7 + 9) \times 2$ f $5 \times (4 + 6) \div 2$

> You cannot change the order of a calculation when it has a mixture of + or − signs and × or ÷ signs.

1.4 Types of whole numbers

The **whole numbers** are 0, 1, 2, 3, 4, ...
The **counting numbers** are 1, 2, 3, 4, ...

> Counting numbers are also called **natural numbers**.

Even numbers end in 0, 2, 4, 6 or 8.
An even number is divisible exactly by 2.

Odd numbers end in 1, 3, 5, 7 or 9.
An odd number is not divisible exactly by 2.

> Divides exactly means there is no remainder.

A **prime number** is only divisible exactly by 1 and itself.

A **factor** of a number is divisible exactly into the number. When a factor is a prime number it is called a **prime factor**.
Two or more numbers can have the same factor. This is called a **common factor**.

> 2 is a factor of 8 because $8 \div 2 = 4$.
> 2 is not a factor of 9 because $9 \div 2$ is not a whole number.
> The factors of 12 are 1, 2, 3, 4, 6 and 12.
> The prime factors of 12 are 2 and 3.

> These tests for divisibility are useful when you are looking for factors.
> - Any even number is divisible exactly by 2.
> - A number is divisible by 3 if its digits add up to a number that is divisible by 3.
>   So 171 is divisible by 3 as $1 + 7 + 1 = 9$ and $9 \div 3 = 3$.
> - Any number ending in 5 or zero is divisible by 5.
>   So 230 and 155 are divisible exactly by 5.
> - A number is divisible by 9 if its digits add up to a number that is divisible by 9.
>   So 261 can be divided by 9 as $2 + 6 + 1 = 9$ and $9 \div 9 = 1$.

When a number is multiplied by a whole number the answer is a **multiple** of the first number.
A number that is a multiple of two or more numbers is called a **common multiple**.

> 35 is a multiple of 5 because $5 \times 7 = 35$.
> You can list the multiples of a number by multiplying it by 1, 2, 3, ...
> So the multiples of 5 are:
>   5, 10, 15, 20, ...

Example 5

From the numbers in the cloud write down:
a   a factor of 52   b   a multiple of 16   c   the prime numbers.

3   5   13   25
34   58   64

a 13	Look for a number that divides into 52 exactly: 3 doesn't and 5 doesn't but 13 does: $52 \div 13 = 4$.
b 64	Write down the multiples of 16 until you find one in the list: 16, 32, 48, 64, ...
c 3, 5, 13	25 is not a prime number because it is divisible by 5. 34, 58 and 64 are not prime numbers because they all are divisible by 2.

Example 6

Find **a** all the factors of 8   **b** the common factors of 8 and 20.

> **a**   The factors of 8 are 1, 2, 4, 8.

Remember that 1 and 8 are factors of 8. You can find the others by seeing which numbers divide exactly into 8.

> **b**   The factors of 20 are 1, 2, 4, 5, 10, 20.
>   The common factors of 8 and 20 are 1, 2 and 4.

List the factors of 20. The common factors are the numbers in both lists.

Example 7

Write 36 as the product of prime factors.

> $36 = 6 \times 6$
> $= 2 \times 3 \times 2 \times 3$

Start by writing 36 as the **product** of any two factors. Then write each factor that is not a prime as the product of two factors. Repeat this until all the factors are prime.

Example 8

Find a common multiple of 8 and 20.

> 8, 16, 24, 32, **40**, 48, …
> 20, **40**, …
> 40 is a common multiple of 8 and 20.

List the multiples of 8 and 20 until you find a number that is in both lists.

Exam practice 1D

1 From the numbers in the cloud write down:
   a the even numbers   b the odd numbers
   c the prime numbers   d the multiples of 3

2 Write down all the factors of
   a 14   b 24   c 56   d 27.

3 Write down the prime numbers between 0 and 20.

Remember that 1 is not a prime number.

4 Write these numbers as a product of prime factors:
   a 40   b 28   c 56

5 a Eddie said '45 is a multiple of 7'.
      Is Eddie right? Give a reason for your answer.
   b 21 is a multiple of 7. Write down another multiple of 7.

6 From the numbers in the cloud write down:
   a two factors of 28   b a prime factor of 44
   c two multiples of 5   d the prime numbers

7 Jane said 'When you add any two prime numbers the answer is an even number.'
   Give an example to show that Jane is wrong.

8 a Write down all the factors of 15.
   b Find the common factors of 15 and 18.

9 Find the common factors of
   a 14 and 21   b 8 and 12.

10 Find a common multiple of
    a 8 and 12   b 10 and 15   c 8 and 16.

11 a Write down the multiples of 17 between 30 and 60.
    b Find a common multiple of 17 and 3.

12 From the numbers in this star write down:
    a two common factors of 16 and 24
    b an odd number that is not a prime number
    c two common multiples of 4 and 12
    d a prime factor of 34
    e an even number that is a multiple of 7

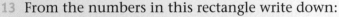

8   24
21 12 14
17   36
   2

13 From the numbers in this rectangle write down:
    a an even number that is factor of 360
    b a multiple of 90
    c a prime factor of 38
    d an odd number that is a multiple of 9
    e an odd number that is a factor of 360

46   60   63
  270   300
25   15   19

Class discussion
- Lisa said 'I can find the factors of 26 by trying all the numbers from 1 to 26 to see which of them divides into 26 exactly.'
  Why does she not need to try all these numbers?
- Robert said 'The sum of any two prime numbers is an even number'. He made an assumption. What was it and why is it wrong?

Enrichment task

You can use a grid like this to find the prime numbers from 0 to 100.

1	2	3	4	5	6	7	8	9	10
11	12	13	14	15	16	17	18	19	20
21	22	23	24	25	26	27	28	29	30
31	32	33	34	35	36	37	38	39	40
41	42	43	44	45	46	47	48	49	50
51	52	53	54	55	56	57	58	59	660
61	62	63	64	65	66	67	68	69	70
71	72	73	74	75	76	77	78	79	80
81	82	83	84	85	86	87	88	89	90
91	92	93	94	95	96	97	98	99	100

This is known as the Sieve of Eratosthenes after a mathematician living in Alexandria in the Second Century BC.

The first two columns of even numbers have been crossed out for you.

You will need a copy of this grid:
- 2 is the first prime number. Shade it in. Cross out all the other numbers that are multiples of 2.
- 3 is the next prime number. Shade this square. Now cross out all the other numbers that are multiples of 3.

- 5 is the next prime number. Shade this square then cross out all the other numbers that are multiples of 5.
- Carry on doing this until there are no more squares to cross out. The numbers that are left are the prime numbers. Shade them in.

Write down answers to these questions.

a Why has 1 been crossed out?

b When you get to 11, all the multiplies of 11 have already been crossed out. Give a reason why.

1.5 Squares, cubes and roots

A number is **squared** when it is multiplied by itself.

6×6 is called 6 squared.

The answer is a **square number**.

36 is a square number because $6 \times 6 = 36$.

> $1^2 = 1, 2^2 = 4, 3^2 = 9, 4^2 = 16,$
> $5^2 = 25, 6^2 = 36, 7^2 = 49,$
> $8^2 = 64, 9^2 = 81, 10^2 = 100,$
> $11^2 = 121, 12^2 = 144, 13^2 = 169,$
> $14^2 = 196, 15^2 = 225$

A number is **cubed** when three of them are multiplied together.

$3 \times 3 \times 3$ is called 3 cubed.

The answer is called a **cube number**.

27 is a cube number because $3 \times 3 \times 3 = 27$.

> $1^3 = 1, 2^3 = 8, 3^3 = 27, 4^3 = 64,$
> $5^3 = 125, 6^3 = 216, 7^3 = 343,$
> $8^3 = 512, 9^3 = 729, 10^3 = 1000$

When a number is squared, the starting number is called the **square root**.

$5 \times 5 = 25$, so 5 is a square root of 25.

The symbol $\sqrt{\ }$ means 'square root': $\sqrt{25} = 5$

> When you multiply two negative numbers the answer is positive. So a positive number has two square roots. One is positive and the other is negative:
> $-5 \times -5 = 25$, so -5 is also a square root of 25.

When a number is cubed, the starting number is called the **cube root**.

$2 \times 2 \times 2 = 8$ so 2 is the cube root of 8.

> $\sqrt{\ }$ always gives the positive square root of a number.

You need to know the squares of the numbers from 1 to 15 and the cubes of the numbers 2, 3, 4, 5 and 10.

Example 9

Write down   **a** the square root of 49   **b** the cube root of 125

a 7

> You know that 7 squared is 49, so the square root of 49 is 7.

b 5

> You know that 5 cubed is 125 so the cube root of 125 is 5.

Exam practice 1E

1 Write down the value of :

  a 4 squared   **b** 4 cubed   **c** the square root of 64

  d 9 squared   **e** 10 cubed   **f** the cube root of 216

UAM

2 Jacob said that 8 is a square number because 4 × 2 = 8.
   Explain why Jacob is wrong.

3 Write down the value of:
   a the square root of 100   b the cube root of 1000
   c 15 squared   d the square of 13

4 Write down the value of:
   a $\sqrt{81}$ b $\sqrt{121}$ c $\sqrt{144}$ d $\sqrt{225}$ e $\sqrt{196}$

UAM

5 Emily said that 9 is a cube number because 9 ÷ 3 = 3.
   Explain why Emily is wrong.

6 Jodi said that the square root of any even number is an even
   number.
   Give an example to show that Jodi is wrong.

UAM

7 From the numbers in the circle write down
   a a square number
   b a cube number
   c three prime numbers
   d a multiple of 7
   e a factor of 26.

11   39
29   42   81
     13   125
40   34

8 Carol said that 64 is a square number and a cube number.
   Explain why she is correct.

UAM

9 From the numbers in this cloud write down:
   a the value of 200 − 48
   b the square root of 10 000
   c the cube of 5
   d a prime number

97   152   125
225   196
100   57

1.6 Indices

Indices is the plural of index.

Indices are used to write expressions such as 3 × 3 × 3 × 3 in a
shorter form.

This number is called
the **index** or **power**.

You write $3 \times 3 \times 3 \times 3 = 3^4$

This number is called
the **base**.

You say '3 to the power 4' or '3 to the 4'

When the power is 2 or 3,
special names are used:
5^2 is called 'five squared'
and 5^3 is called 'five cubed'.
5^1 means there is only one 5,
so $5^1 = 5$

Example 10

Write 5 × 5 × 5 × 5 × 5 × 5 using index notation.

$5 \times 5 \times 5 \times 5 \times 5 \times 5 = 5^6$

There are six lots of five
multiplied together.

Example 11

Find the value of   **a** 2^4 **b** $3^2 \times 2^4$.

a $2^4 = 2 \times 2 \times 2 \times 2$
  $= 4 \times 2 \times 2$
  $= 8 \times 2 = 16$
b $3^2 = 9$ and $2^4 = 16$
  $3^2 \times 2^4 = 9 \times 16 = 144$

Exam practice 1F

1 Write each of the following using index notation.
   a 2×2 b $4 \times 4 \times 4$
   c $7 \times 7 \times 7 \times 7$ d $10 \times 10 \times 10 \times 10 \times 10$

2 Find the value of:
   a 2^5 b 7^2 c 3^3 d 10^4 e 10^6

3 David said the value of 4^3 was 12.
   David is wrong. Explain his mistake

4 Write in index form:
   a $2 \times 2 \times 7 \times 7$ b $3 \times 3 \times 3 \times 2 \times 2$
   c $2 \times 3 \times 3 \times 5 \times 2 \times 5$ d $7 \times 7 \times 7 \times 3 \times 5 \times 7 \times 3$
   e $13 \times 5 \times 13 \times 5 \times 13$ f $3 \times 5 \times 5 \times 3 \times 7 \times 3 \times 7$

5 Find the value of:
   a $2^3 \times 3^2$ b $3^2 \times 10^2$ c $5^2 \times 2^2 \times 7^1$ d $5^1 \times 3^3 \times 4^1$

7^1 means 7.

6 Kinga wrote '$3^2 \times 2^3 = 6^5$ '
   Is Kinga correct? Give a reason for your answer.

7 Find the value of: a $(2^2)^3$ b $(10^3)^2$

Remember that you work out the inside of the brackets first.

8 Hassan wrote $(5^2)^3 = 10^3$.
   This is wrong. Explain the mistake that Hassan made.

9 a Write these numbers as powers of 10.
     i 10   ii 1000   iii 100 000   iv 1 000 000 000
   b Write these numbers in words.
     i 100   ii 10 000   iii 2 000 000   iv 500 500

10 Which is greater, 5^2 or $\sqrt{121}$?
    Explain your answer.

11 Write these numbers as powers of 2.
    a 2   b 4   c 32   d 64

12 Which is greater, 5^3 or 3^5?
    Explain your answer.

13 Write these numbers as a product of their prime factors using index notation.
    a 36   b 24   c 28   d 100

14 Write these numbers in order of size, smallest first:
    4^3, $\sqrt{169}$, 14^2, $\sqrt{225}$, 2^4

Summary of key points

- Addition and subtraction are the opposite of each other.
- Multiplication and division are the opposite of each other.
- When a calculation involves a mixture of brackets, +, −, × and ÷, work in the order: brackets, then multiplication and division, then addition and subtraction.
- The factors of a number include 1 and the number itself.
- The multiples of a number include the number itself.
- A prime factor is a factor that is a prime number.

Most students who get GRADE E or above can:
- find the cube of a number
- work out the value of a calculation given in index notation
- recognise a prime number.

Most students who get GRADE C can also:
- write a number as the product of its prime factors.

Glossary

Base	the number which is raised to a power: in 5^4, 5 is the base
Common factor	a number that divides exactly into two or more numbers
Common multiple	a number which two or more numbers will divide into exactly
Counting number	one of the numbers 1, 2, 3, 4, …
Cubed	three of the same number multiplied together: $5^3 = 5 \times 5 \times 5$
Cube number	the answer to a whole number that is cubed
Cube root	the number which when cubed gives the original number: the cube root of 8 is 2
Even number	a number that divides exactly by 2
Factor	a number that divides exactly into a given number
Index (plural indices)	tells you how many of the base number to multiply together
Multiple	the product of any whole number and the given number
Natural number	a counting number
Odd number	a number that does not divide exactly by 2
Power	another word for index
Prime factor	a factor of a number that is also a prime number
Prime number	a number that only has two factors, 1 and itself
Product	the result of multiplying numbers
Squared	a number multiplied by itself
Square number	the product of a number multiplied by itself once
Square root	a number which when multiplied by itself gives the original number: the square root of 16 is 4
Whole number	any of the numbers 0, 1, 2, 3, 4, …

2 Fractions, decimals and percentages

This chapter will show you:
- ✓ how to find equivalent fractions
- ✓ how to find a fraction of a quantity
- ✓ how to order a set of fractions and decimals according to size
- ✓ what the reciprocal of a number is and how to find it
- ✓ how to convert between fractions, decimals and percentages
- ✓ how to round a number
- ✓ the meaning of standard form

Before you start you need to know:
- ✓ how to add and subtract whole numbers
- ✓ how to multiply and divide by a whole number

2.1 Fractions

A **fraction** is used to represent part of a quantity.

The top number is called the **numerator**. It tells you the number of parts.

The fraction 'two-fifths' is written as $\frac{2}{5}$.

The bottom number is called the **denominator**. It tells you how many equal-sized parts the whole has been divided into.

Example 1

a Write down the fraction of this shape that is shaded.

b Shade $\frac{2}{5}$ of this diagram.

a $\frac{1}{6}$

One of the six squares is shaded.

b

There are 5 equal size squares. $\frac{2}{5}$ is two of these squares. Shade any two squares

Exam practice 2A

1   Write down the fraction of each shape that is shaded.

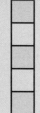

a b c

d e f

g h i

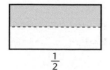 2   Copy each shape and shade the fraction asked for.

a $\frac{1}{4}$ b $\frac{3}{4}$ c $\frac{5}{6}$

d $\frac{3}{4}$ e $\frac{3}{10}$

   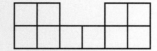

f $\frac{5}{9}$ g $\frac{3}{8}$ h $\frac{5}{12}$

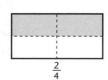 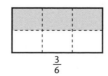 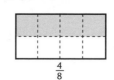

 3   Greg said that half this shape is shaded.
Explain why he is wrong.

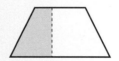

2.2 Equivalent fractions

Equivalent fractions give the same sized part of a quantity.

$\frac{1}{2}$ $\frac{2}{4}$ $\frac{3}{6}$ $\frac{4}{8}$

The same sized part of each rectangle is shaded. So $\frac{1}{2}$, $\frac{2}{4}$, $\frac{3}{6}$ and $\frac{4}{8}$ are
equivalent fractions.

You get an equivalent fraction when you multiply or divide the
numerator and denominator of a fraction by the same number.

Example 2

a Write down a fraction equivalent to $\frac{2}{3}$.

b Complete these equivalent fractions.   **i** $\frac{3}{7} = \frac{12}{\square}$ **ii** $\frac{2}{\square} = \frac{10}{25}$

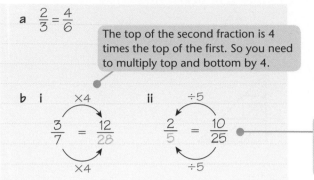

a $\frac{2}{3} = \frac{4}{6}$

The top of the second fraction is 4 times the top of the first. So you need to multiply top and bottom by 4.

Multiply top and bottom by any number, for example 2:

$$\frac{2}{3} = \frac{4}{6}$$ ×2 ... ×2

b i ×4
$$\frac{3}{7} = \frac{12}{28}$$
×4

ii ÷5
$$\frac{2}{5} = \frac{10}{25}$$
÷5

You need to divide the top of the second fraction by 5 to get the top of the first fraction. So you also need to divide the bottom of the second fraction by 5 to get the bottom of the first fraction.

You can compare the size of two fractions by changing them to equivalent fractions with the same denominator.

Example 3

Which is larger, $\frac{2}{5}$ or $\frac{3}{8}$?

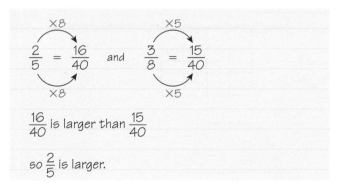

×8
$$\frac{2}{5} = \frac{16}{40}$$ and $\frac{3}{8} = \frac{15}{40}$ ×5
×8   ×5

You need a common multiple of 5 and 8 for the denominator of the equivalent fractions.
Multiples of 5: 5, 10, 15, 20, 25, 30, 35, 40, ...
Multiples of 8: 8, 16, 24, 32, 40, ...

$\frac{16}{40}$ is larger than $\frac{15}{40}$

so $\frac{2}{5}$ is larger.

Exam practice 2B

1 Copy and complete these equivalent fractions.

    a $\frac{2}{5} = \frac{6}{\square}$ **b** $\frac{2}{3} = \frac{\square}{6}$ **c** $\frac{1}{3} = \frac{\square}{9}$ **d** $\frac{3}{8} = \frac{6}{\square}$

    e $\frac{4}{\square} = \frac{8}{14}$ **f** $\frac{3}{\square} = \frac{12}{16}$ **g** $\frac{\square}{5} = \frac{12}{20}$ **h** $\frac{\square}{8} = \frac{9}{24}$

2 Write a fraction that is equivalent to

    a $\frac{2}{7}$ **b** $\frac{7}{12}$ **c** $\frac{5}{8}$ **d** $\frac{1}{6}$.

3 $\frac{4}{9}$ is equivalent to $\frac{8}{18}$. Find another fraction equivalent to $\frac{4}{9}$.

4 Find a fraction equivalent to $\frac{15}{20}$ with a smaller numerator and denominator.

Class discussion

How you can tell that $\frac{7}{12}$ is larger than $\frac{1}{2}$? Which of these fractions are larger than $\frac{1}{2}$ and which are less than $\frac{1}{2}$:

$\frac{5}{13}, \frac{9}{10}, \frac{7}{15}, \frac{4}{7}, \frac{17}{24}$?

5 Write each fraction as an equivalent fraction with a
  denominator of 12.

  a $\frac{1}{3}$ b $\frac{3}{4}$ c $\frac{5}{6}$

6 Write each fraction as an equivalent fraction with a
  denominator of 30.

  a $\frac{5}{6}$ b $\frac{4}{5}$ c $\frac{2}{3}$

7 Copy and complete these equivalent fractions.

  a $\frac{2}{3} = \frac{\square}{9} = \frac{8}{\square}$ b $\frac{3}{4} = \frac{\square}{12} = \frac{15}{\square}$

  c $\frac{\square}{5} = \frac{6}{\square} = \frac{12}{20}$ d $\frac{2}{\square} = \frac{\square}{12} = \frac{16}{24}$

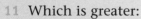

8 Copy each shape and shade the fraction asked for.

  a $\frac{2}{3}$ b $\frac{1}{4}$

> In part **a** the shape is divided into 6 equal squares. Find a fraction equivalent to $\frac{2}{3}$ with a denominator of 6. The numerator of this fraction tells you how many squares to shade.

  c $\frac{5}{6}$ d $\frac{3}{8}$

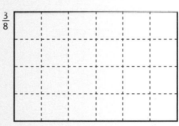

  e $\frac{3}{4}$ f $\frac{2}{7}$

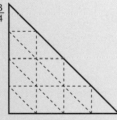

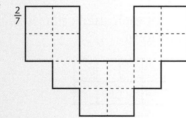

9 Write $\frac{2}{3}$ and $\frac{7}{9}$ as equivalent fractions with denominator 9.
  Which fraction is larger?

10 Kate said that $\frac{4}{9}$ is smaller than $\frac{5}{12}$.
   Explain why Kate is wrong.

11 Which is greater:

  a $\frac{1}{3}$ or $\frac{2}{5}$ b $\frac{1}{2}$ or $\frac{4}{9}$

  c $\frac{3}{4}$ or $\frac{4}{5}$ d $\frac{2}{3}$ or $\frac{3}{4}$.

> You must show your working.

12 Write these fractions in order of size with the smallest first.

  a $\frac{2}{5}, \frac{1}{4}, \frac{3}{10}$ b $\frac{5}{6}, \frac{7}{9}, \frac{11}{18}$

2.3 Simplifying fractions

You **simplify a fraction** by finding an equivalent fraction with a smaller numerator and denominator.

The fraction is in its **simplest form** when the numerator and denominator are as small as possible.

> This is also called **cancelling the fraction**.

> **Lowest possible terms** is another way of describing a fraction in its simplest form.

Example 4

Give $\frac{20}{40}$ in its simplest form.

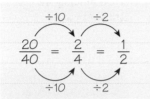

Exam practice 2C

1   Give each fraction in its simplest form.

a $\frac{2}{4}$ b $\frac{6}{8}$ c $\frac{4}{6}$ d $\frac{4}{12}$

e $\frac{6}{9}$ f $\frac{9}{12}$ g $\frac{12}{15}$ h $\frac{18}{36}$

i $\frac{24}{36}$ j $\frac{13}{65}$ k $\frac{90}{360}$ l $\frac{14}{196}$

m $\frac{15}{75}$ n $\frac{9}{45}$ p $\frac{70}{100}$ q $\frac{45}{180}$

2   Write down the fraction of each shape that is shaded. Give your answers in their simplest form.

a   b   c

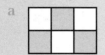 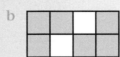

d   e   f

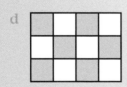 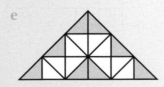 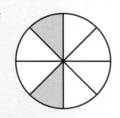

g   h   i

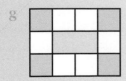 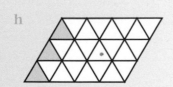 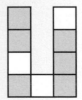

3   Which of these fractions are not equal to $\frac{1}{4}$?

$\frac{3}{12}$ $\frac{5}{15}$ $\frac{7}{28}$ $\frac{25}{100}$ $\frac{20}{100}$ $\frac{12}{36}$ $\frac{11}{44}$

2.4 Fractions of quantities

To find a fraction of a quantity, divide the quantity by the denominator. Then multiply the answer by the numerator.

Example 5

Find $\frac{2}{5}$ of £30.

$30 \div 5 = 6$

$\qquad 6 \times 2 = 12$

$\frac{2}{5}$ of £30 = £12.

> The denominator of $\frac{2}{5}$ is 5: divide 30 by 5. Then multiply the answer by 2.

Exam practice 2D

1 Find:

   a $\frac{3}{5}$ of £25   b $\frac{3}{4}$ of £44   c $\frac{3}{8}$ of 32 metres

   d $\frac{5}{12}$ of 48 litres   e $\frac{7}{20}$ of 400 people   f $\frac{11}{100}$ of 500 kg

> Do not forget to give units with your answers.

2 There were 16 sweets in a bag.
   Henry took $\frac{5}{8}$ of the sweets.
   How many sweets did Henry take?

3 The area of this shape is 25 square centimetres.
   $\frac{4}{5}$ of the area is shaded.
   What is the area of the shaded part?

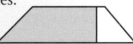

4 The price of a cinema ticket is £12.
   Booking on-line takes $\frac{1}{3}$ off this price.
   What is the price of a ticket booked on-line?

> Read the question carefully. Make sure you know what you are asked to find.

5 a What fraction of this shape is shaded?
   b How many more squares need to be
      shaded so that $\frac{2}{5}$ of the shape is shaded?

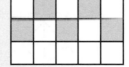

6 The distance from York to London is 208 miles.
   The distance from Penzance to London is one and half times as
   far. What is the distance from Penzance to London?

2.5 Decimals

The position of a digit in a number is called its **place value**. It tells you the value of that digit.

Decimal numbers are written with a decimal point after the units.

You can write decimal numbers in a place value diagram.

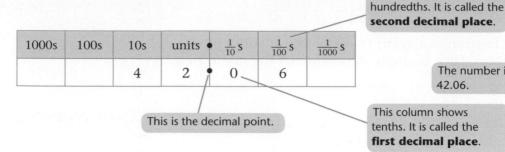

This column shows hundredths. It is called the **second decimal place**.

1000s	100s	10s	units •	$\frac{1}{10}$s	$\frac{1}{100}$s	$\frac{1}{1000}$s
		4	2 •	0	6	

The number is 42.06.

This is the decimal point.

This column shows tenths. It is called the **first decimal place**.

Comparing decimals

You can compare the size of decimals by looking at the figures in each place value.

Example 6

Which is larger, 5.14 or 5.104?

5.14 is larger.

5.104 has more digits than 5.14 but that does not mean that 5.104 is larger than 5.14.
Look first at the number of units – they are the same.
Next look at the number of tenths – they are also the same.
Next look at the number of hundredths – 4 is larger than 0 so 5.14 is larger than 5.105.

Converting decimals to fractions

The positions of the figures after the decimal point tell you their value.
You can use this to write decimals as fractions.

Example 7

Write 0.35 as a fraction.

$$0.35 = \frac{35}{100} \xrightarrow[\div 5]{\div 5} \frac{7}{20}$$

0.35 is 3 tenths and 5 hundredths, or 35 hundredths. Write this as a fraction and simplify.

Adding and subtracting decimals

You can add and subtract decimals in the same way that you add and subtract whole numbers.

If you write decimals in a column, make sure the decimal points line up.

Example 8

On Monday Abul spent £1.85 on fares, £2.56 on lunch and 75p on a newspaper.
a   How much did he spend on Monday?
b   Abul had £15 at the start of Monday.
    How much did he have at the end of the day?

a   1.85
   2.56
   <u>0.75</u>
   5.16

He spent £5.16

> You need to add £1.85, £2.56 and 75p.
> Quantities must be in the same unit so write 75p as £0.75.

b   15.00
   <u>−5.16</u>
   9.84

> Fill in empty columns after the decimal point with noughts.

> You need to subtract £5.16 from £15.

He had £9.84 left.

Multiplying and dividing decimals by 10, 100, 1000, …

You can multiply and divide a decimal number using the same rules as you do for whole numbers.

When a number is multiplied by 10, 100, 1000, … the figures move 1, 2, 3, … places to the left on a place value diagram.

When a number is divided by 10, 100, 1000, … the digits move 1, 2, 3, … places to the right on a place value diagram.

10 000 s	1000 s	100 s	10 s	units •	$\frac{1}{10}$ s	$\frac{1}{100}$ s	$\frac{1}{1000}$ s
			3	2 • 1			
	3	2	1	0 •			
				0 • 3	2	1	

32.1 × 100

32.1 ÷ 100

Exam practice 2E

1   Which is the larger:
   a   0.29 or 0.32   b   2.7 or 0.9   c   5.146 or 5.149?

2   Convert these decimals to fractions. Give your answers in their simplest form.
   a   0.5   b   0.25   c   0.125   d   0.4
   e   0.75   f   0.28   g   0.375

3   The train fare from Manchester Victoria to Burnage is £1.60 for an adult and 45p for a child.
   What is the total cost for two adults and one child for the train journey from Manchester Victoria to Burnage?

4 Here is a bus route with distances.

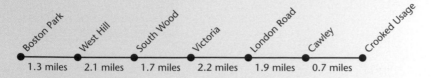

Boston Park — 1.3 miles — West Hill — 2.1 miles — South Wood — 1.7 miles — Victoria — 2.2 miles — London Road — 1.9 miles — Cawley — 0.7 miles — Crooked Usage

a   Jason travelled on the bus from West Hill to Victoria.
    How long was his journey?
b   How far does the bus travel from one end of its route to the other?
c   The bus takes 2 minutes to travel 1 mile.
    i   How long does the bus take to travel from Boston Park to London Road?
    ii The bus takes half as long again to travel this route in the rush hour.
        How many minutes does the bus take to travel from Boston Park to London Road in the rush hour?

5 Work out:
a 2.5×100 b 1.62×10 c 38.5×1000 d 0.175×100
e $48 \div 100$ f $17.5 \div 100$ g $2.8 \div 10$ h $0.17 \div 10$

6 Reet buys 100 packs of envelopes at £1.35 each.
Calculate the total cost.

7 This table gives the price of some ink cartridges.

Catalogue number	Colour	Price, £
154	●	11.35
217	●●●	17.62
176	●	14.80
218	●	10.54
219	●	10.54
220	●	10.54

a   James bought two cartridges: catalogue numbers 154 and 217. Find the total cost.
b   Nikki bought three cartridges: catalogue numbers 176, 218 and 219. Find the total cost.
c   There is a special offer:

SAVE $\frac{1}{5}$ when you buy any five cartridges.

Aisha buys two 154 cartridges and one each of 218, 219 and 220.
How much does Aisha save?

2.6 Rounding numbers

You can round a number to a given place value by drawing a line after that place value.
Then look at the figure after the line.
If it is less than 5, round down.
If it is 5 or more, round up.

Giving a number to the nearest tenth is called **rounding to one decimal place** or **correcting to one decimal place**.
Giving a number to the nearest hundredth is called **rounding to two decimal places**.

You can also round a number to its first significant figure.
The **first significant figure** in a number is the first digit that is not zero.

Example 9

Give   **a**   2561 to the nearest 100
       b   2.382 correct to 2 decimal places
       c   0.0272 correct to 1 significant figure.

a   25|61 = 2600 to the nearest 100.

> Draw a line after the hundreds.

> 6 is more than 5, so round up to the next 100.

b   2.38|2 = 2.38 correct to 2 d.p.

> Draw a line after the second decimal place. d.p. is short for decimal place.

> 2 is less than 5, so round down to the hundredth given.

c   0.02|52 = 0.03 to 1 s.f.

> s.f. is short for significant figure.

> This is the first significant figure. The next digit is 5 so round up 2 to 3.

Converting fractions to decimals

You can convert a fraction to a decimal by dividing the numerator by the denominator.

Example 10

Convert to a decimal: **a** $\frac{5}{8}$ **b** $\frac{2}{3}$ to 3 decimal places.

a
$$\frac{0.6\,2\,5}{8)5.0^20^40}$$
$\frac{5}{8} = 0.625$

> This is exact.

b
$$\frac{0.6\,6\,6\,6}{3)2.0^20^20^20}$$
$\frac{2}{3} = 0.666|6... = 0.667$ to 3 d.p.

> Add noughts after the decimal point to continue the division.

> This never stops. To give an answer to 3 d.p., you can stop after the fourth decimal place.

Recurring decimals

Some fractions convert exactly to decimals, like $\frac{5}{8}$.

All other fractions convert to a decimal that goes on for ever, like $\frac{2}{3}$.

The digits in these decimals have a repeating pattern.
They are called **recurring decimals**.

> A recurring decimal is written with a dot over the repeating digit.
> $0.6666... = 0.\dot{6}$
> When there is a pattern of repeating digits, you write dots over the first and last digits in the pattern.
> $0.215215215... = 0.\dot{2}1\dot{5}$

Example 11

a Write 1.234 343 4... as a recurring decimal using dot notation.
b Give 0.1455̇ correct to 4 d.p.

> **a** 1.234 343 4... = 1.2̇3̇4̇

The digits 34 repeat.

> **b** = 0.1̇45̇5̇ = 0.1455|455... = 0.1455... correct to 4 d.p.

Write more than four decimal places.

Reciprocals

When the product of two numbers is 1, each number is called the **reciprocal** of the other.

$\frac{1}{3} \times 3 = 1$ so $\frac{1}{3}$ is the reciprocal of 3 and 3 is the reciprocal of $\frac{1}{3}$.

You can find the reciprocal of a fraction by turning the fraction upside down.

The reciprocal of $\frac{2}{5}$ is $\frac{5}{2}$.

You can find the reciprocal of a number by dividing 1 by that number.

0 does not have a reciprocal because you cannot divide by 0.

The reciprocal of 4 is $1 \div 4 = \frac{1}{4} = 0.25$.

Exam practice 2F

1 **a** Round these numbers to the nearest ten.
   i 255   **ii** 4772   **iii** 20 504   **iv** 97

   b Round these numbers to 1 d.p.
   i 24.58   **ii** 2.615   **iii** 56.69   **iv** 0.217

   c Round these numbers to 2 d.p.
   i 0.2721   **ii** 22.8085   **iii** 4.5001   **iv** 0.00955

   d Round these number to one significant figure.
   i 253   **ii** 5.21   **iii** 0.662   **iv** 0.0207

2 Vijay worked out the area of a rectangle on his calculator.
The display showed 25.4674.
Give this number correct to 2 decimal places.

3 Give these recurring decimals to 3 decimal places.
   a 0.3̇   **b** 0.07̇   **c** 1.1̇4̇   **d** 5.12̇4̇

4 Convert these fractions to decimals.
   a $\frac{5}{8}$ **b** $\frac{3}{5}$ **c** $\frac{7}{10}$ **d** $\frac{17}{20}$

5 Convert these fractions to decimals giving your answers to 2 d.p.
   a $\frac{3}{7}$ **b** $\frac{5}{6}$ **c** $\frac{1}{9}$ **d** $\frac{3}{11}$

6 Which is larger:
   a $\frac{1}{3}$ or 0.3   **b** 0.25 or $\frac{1}{5}$ **c** $\frac{7}{10}$ or 0.22   **d** 1.45 or $1\frac{5}{8}$?

Convert the fraction to a decimal. Then compare the decimals.

7 Lim said that $\frac{1}{6}$ = 0.16
Explain why Lim is wrong.

8 Find $\frac{2}{3}$ of £20. Give your answer to the nearest penny.

9 Write down the reciprocal of each number. Give an exact answer.

   a   2   b $\frac{3}{5}$ c $\frac{2}{3}$ d   5   e   1.5

> For part **e**, find an equivalent fraction to $\frac{1}{1.5}$ that has a whole number as the denominator.

10 Write down the reciprocal of each number. Give your answer as a decimal to 1 d.p.

   a   9   b $\frac{3}{7}$ c $\sqrt{36}$ d $\frac{3}{5}$ e   8

11 Jack said that 0.5 is the reciprocal of 5.
   Explain why Jack is wrong.

UAM

2.7 Converting between percentages, decimals and fractions

'**Percent**' means 'out of 100'.

> 30% means '30 out of 100'.

You can convert a percentage to a fraction by writing the percentage over 100 and removing the % sign.

> $30\% = \frac{30}{100} = \frac{3}{10}$

You do the opposite to convert a fraction to a percentage: multiply the fraction by 100 and add a % sign.

> $\frac{3}{10} = \frac{3}{10} \times 100\%$
> $= 0.3 \times 100\% = 30\%$

You can convert a percentage to a decimal by dividing the percentage by 100 and removing the % sign.

> $30\% = 30 \div 100 = 0.3$

You do the opposite to convert a decimal to a percentage: multiply the decimal by 100 and add a percentage sign.

> $0.3 = 0.3 \times 100\% = 30\%$

Example 12

Convert $12\frac{1}{2}\%$ to   **a**   a decimal   **b**   a fraction.

a $12\frac{1}{2}\% = 12.5\% = 12.5 \div 100$
              $= 0.125$

> To convert $12\frac{1}{2}\%$ to a decimal start by writing it as 12.5%.

b $12\frac{1}{2}\% = \dfrac{12\frac{1}{2}}{100} = \dfrac{25}{200}$
            $= \dfrac{5}{40} = \dfrac{1}{8}$

> Multiply top and bottom by 2 to give an equivalent fraction with a whole number denominator. Then simplify the fraction.

Example 13

Convert to percentages: **a**   0.36   **b** $\frac{2}{5}$

a $0.36 = 0.36 \times 100\% = 36\%$

b $\frac{2}{5} = \frac{2}{5} \times 100\%$
      $= 2 \times 20\%$
      $= 40\%$

> To find $\frac{2}{5}$ of 100, divide 100 by 5 then multiply the answer by 2.

Exam practice 2G

1 Convert to decimals:
   a 25%   b 45%   c 17.5%   d $7\frac{1}{2}$%   e 5.4%

2 Convert to fractions in their simplest form:
   a 50%   b 25%   c 60%   d 37.5%   e $33\frac{1}{3}$%

3 Convert to percentages:
   a 0.46   b 0.52   c 1.5   d 0.265   e 0.75
   f $\frac{3}{4}$ g $\frac{4}{5}$ h $\frac{7}{10}$ i $\frac{5}{8}$ j $2\frac{1}{2}$

WWW 4 Copy and complete this table.

Percentage	Fraction	Decimal
20%		
	$\frac{7}{8}$	
		1.75
62.5%		

5 Jon wrote

$$33\% = \frac{1}{3}$$

UAM Explain why Jon is wrong.

6 Mischa got 12 out of 20 questions correct.
   What percentage did Mischa get correct?

7 Which is larger, 45% or $\frac{5}{8}$?
UAM Give a reason for your answer.

8 Arrange these in order of size, smallest first.
   0.72, $\frac{2}{5}$, 52%

2.8 Finding percentages

You can find a percentage of a quantity by first dividing the quantity
by 100 to find 1%.

You can sometimes use these facts as a short cut:
   $10\% = \frac{1}{10}$, $100\% = 1$, $25\% = \frac{1}{4}$, $50\% = \frac{1}{2}$

Example 14

Work out   a 40% of £250   b 150% of 80 kg   c 5.3% of £5000.

   a 10% of £250 = £250 ÷ 10 = £25
      40% of £250 = 4 × £25 = £100

40% = 4 × 10%. So
find 10% by dividing
by 10 then multiply
your answer by 4.

b 100% of 80 = 1 × 80 = 80
  50% of 80 = $\frac{1}{2}$ of 80 = 40
  150% of 80 kg = 120 kg.

> 150% = 100% + 50%

c 5000 ÷ 100 = 50
  5.3 × 50 = 265
  5.3% of £5000 = £265

> 1% of £5000 is £50.
> So 5.3% of £5000 is
> 5.3 × £50 = £265.

Exam practice 2H

1 Calculate:
   a 30% of £200   b 10% of 80p   c 60% of £20
   d 5% of 2000 kg   e 300% of £20   f 25% of 80 metres
   g 70% of £2.50   h 10% of £1.10 i 75% of £1

2 The first edition of a dictionary has 350 pages.
   The second edition of the dictionary has 10% more pages.
   How many more pages are there in the second edition?

3 Amy sells a bike on the internet for £50.
   The web site charges 5% of this price.
   a Find the charge.
   b How much does Amy get?

4 An old car travels for 200 miles on a full tank of petrol.
   A new version of this car goes 25% further on a full tank.
   How many more miles does the new car go?

5 2000 people watched the first football game in a knockout
   competition.
   40% more people watched the final game.
   How many people watched the final game?

6 The area of this shape is
   150 square centimetres.
   60% of the area is shaded.
   Find the unshaded area.

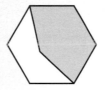

> **Class discussion**
>
> Dwain found $2\frac{1}{2}$% of 50.
> This is his working:
>   10% = 5
>   5% = 2.5
> $2\frac{1}{2}$% = 1.25
> **a** How did Dwain get his answer?
> **b** How can you find 7½ % of 450?
> **c** What is the easiest way of finding $17\frac{1}{2}$% of £1200?
> **d** Finding $17\frac{1}{2}$% of a sum of money is a common calculation in business. Why is this?

> Read the question carefully. Make sure you know what you are asked to find.

2.9 Estimating

You can **estimate** the value of a calculation by rounding each
number to its first significant figure.

Example 15

Estimate the value of 28.5 × 34.6.

2|8.5 = 30 to 1 s.f and 3|4.6 = 30 to 1 s.f.
28.5 × 34.6 ≈ 30 × 30 = 900

> The symbol ≈ means
> 'is approximately equal
> to'.

You can estimate the value of a square root by finding the nearest square number to the number under the square root sign.

Example 16

a Estimate the value of $\sqrt{90}$.
b Which is larger, $\sqrt{90}$ or 2^3.
   Explain your answer.

a $\sqrt{90} \simeq \sqrt{81} = 9$

b $2^3 = 2 \times 2 \times 2 = 8$.
   $\sqrt{90}$ is larger than 2^3 because $\sqrt{90} > \sqrt{81} = 9$ and $9 > 8$.

> The symbol $>$ means 'is greater than'.

Using a calculator

When you use your calculator, estimate your answer first. This will tell you if your calculator answer is likely to be right.

When an answer is not exact, the display will fill with digits. Write down one more digit than you need.

> You will be told how many decimal places to give your answer to.

If the calculator buttons shown in the hint boxes don't provide the right answer please refer to the calculator's manual.

Example 17

a Find $\sqrt{140}$ to 2 d.p.
b Which is larger, $\frac{5}{13}$ or 0.4?
c Find 4.7% of £963. Give your answer to the nearest penny.

a Estimate: $\sqrt{140} \simeq \sqrt{144} = 12$
   $\sqrt{140} = 11.83|2... = 11.83$ to 2 d.p.

> Press
> √ 1 4 0 . =

b $\frac{5}{13} = 0.384...$
   0.4 is larger than 0.384..., so 0.4 is larger than $\frac{5}{13}$.

> Press
> 5 ÷ 1 3 =

c 4.7% of £963 = £45.261 = £45.26 to the nearest penny.

> Press
> 9 6 3 × 4 . 7 % =

Example 18

490 oranges are packed into boxes.
Each box holds 24 oranges.
a How many boxes are needed?
b How many more oranges are there space for?

a $490 \div 24 = 20.4...$
   21 boxes are needed.

> This shows there are 20 lots of 24 in 490 with some left over. One more box is needed for these.

b $24 \times 21 = 504$

> This gives the number of oranges that will fit into 21 boxes.

   $504 - 490 = 14$
   14 oranges

> This is the number of spaces left.

When the answer is very large, the calculator shows a number in **standard form**.

A number in standard form is a number between 1 and 10, multiplied by a power of 10.

> 1.5×10^3 is in standard form.
> 15×10^2 is not.

Example 19

Write 2.8×10^4 as an ordinary number.

$2.8 \times 10\,000 = 28\,000$

> $10^4 = 10 \times 10 \times 10 \times 10 = 10\,000$

Exam practice 2I

1. Find an estimate for:
   a $(2.7)^2$ b $\sqrt{51}$ c $479 \div 92$ d 205×497
   e $\sqrt{201}$ f 9.3^2 g $(2.2)^3$ h $\sqrt{8}$

2. Darsha said '$\sqrt{3}$ is less than 2.'
   Is she right?
   Give a reason for your answer. Do not use a calculator.

3. Convert these fractions to decimals. Give your answers to 2 d.p.
   a $\frac{4}{7}$ b $\frac{8}{11}$ c $\frac{5}{12}$ d $\frac{1}{15}$ e $\frac{3}{17}$

4. Convert these fractions to percentages. Give your answers to 1 d.p.
   a $\frac{7}{12}$ b $\frac{3}{7}$ c $\frac{5}{9}$ d $\frac{1}{11}$ e $\frac{31}{64}$

5. Find the reciprocal of each of the following.
   Give your answers to 2 d.p.
   a 0.45   b 14   c $\sqrt{61}$ d $(2.7)^2$ e $\sqrt{2.1 + 1.6}$

6. Write these in order of size, smallest first:
   a 0.59, 78%, $\frac{1}{11}$ b 80%, 1.2, $\frac{8}{15}$

> It is easier to compare numbers when they are in the same form. Decimals can be compared easily, so convert the percentage and the fraction to decimals.

7. Which is larger, 2.4% or $\frac{1}{20}$? Give a reason for your answer.

8. Which is smaller, $\sqrt{31}$ or $(5.1)^2$?
   Give a reason for your answer.

9. Zak buys 99 bottles of water for 47p each.
   a Find the total cost. Give your answer in pounds.
   b Zak packs these bottles into boxes holding 12 bottles each.
      i How many boxes does he need?
      ii How many more bottles does he need to buy to fill all the boxes?

10. Write the following as ordinary numbers.
    a 2.5×10^3 b 4.1×10^2 c 7.3×10^4 d 1.25×10^3

11. Use your calculator to find the values of these calculations:
    Give your answers as ordinary numbers.
    a $\frac{5000}{(0.0002)^2}$ b $(360\,000)^2$ c $\frac{(300)^2}{(0.008)^2}$

> For part **a** your calculator display will show something like 1.25¹¹
> It means 1.25×10^{11}.

Summary of key points

- You can find equivalent fractions by multiplying or dividing the top and bottom of a fraction by the same number.
- To find a fraction of a quantity, divide the quantity by the denominator and multiply the answer by the numerator.
- You can convert a fraction to a decimal by dividing the numerator by the denominator. The decimal will be either exact or recurring.
- You can convert a decimal to a fraction by writing it as a number of tenths, hundredths, thousandths, … : $0.215 = \frac{215}{1000}$.
- You round a number to a given place value by looking at the next digit. If it is 5 or more, round up. If it is less than 5, round down.
- You can convert percentages to fractions or decimals by dividing the percentage by 100 and removing the % sign. You do the opposite to convert a fraction or a decimal to a percentage:

- You can find a percentage of a quantity by first dividing it by 100 to find 1%.
- You can estimate the value of a calculation by rounding each number to 1 significant figure.

Most students who get GRADE E or above can:
- write a mixture of fractions, decimals and percentages in order of size
- convert between fractions, decimals and percentages
- find fractions and percentages of quantities.

Most students who get GRADE C can also:
- find the reciprocal of a number
- estimate the value of a calculation.

Glossary

Cancel a fraction	find an equivalent fraction with smaller numerator and denominator
Decimal place	the position of a digit to the right of a decimal point
Denominator	the bottom number in a fraction
Equivalent fraction	a fraction that is the same size but with different numerator and denominator
Estimate	find an approximate value
Fraction	part of a quantity
First significant figure	the first digit in a number that is not zero
Lowest possible terms	when a fraction has been simplified as far as possible
Numerator	the top number in a fraction

Glossary (continued)

Percent	out of 100
Place value	the value of the position of the digit
Reciprocal	the result when 1 is divided by a given number
Recurring decimal	a decimal where the digits after the decimal point have a repeating pattern
Rounding	giving a number to a given accuracy such as to the nearest ten or one decimal place
Simplify a fraction	find an equivalent fraction with smaller numerator and denominator
Simplest form	a fraction whose numerator and denominator are as small as possible
Standard form	a number between 1 and 10 multiplied by a power of 10

3 Algebra

3.1 Simplifying expressions

Algebra is a part of mathematics in which letters are used to represent unknown numbers or quantities, or numbers that can vary.

An **expression** is any collection of letters and numbers without an equals sign.

Simplifying an expression means writing it in as short a form as possible.

When you multiply letters you can leave out the multiplication sign.

You can also use indices when a letter is multiplied by itself.
So $q \times q \times q$ can be written as q^3.

> Using letters and symbols instead of words can make writing much shorter: 'the cost is equal to four times the number of apples' can be written as '$C = 4 \times n$' when you use C for the cost and n for the number of apples.

> $l \times b$ is an expression.

> $2a$ means $2 \times a$.
> $3pq$ means $3 \times p \times q$.
> $5x^2$ means $5 \times x \times x$.

Example 1

Simplify: **a** $x \times y$　**b** $b \times 3b$　**c** $5a \times 4a$

a $x \times y = xy$

> You do not know what numbers x or y stand for so you cannot simplify any further.

b $b \times 3b = b \times 3 \times b$
$= 3 \times b \times b$
$= 3b^2$

> The letters represent numbers, so the rules of arithmetic apply. You can change the order of the multiplication so that the letters are together and the numbers are together.

c $5a \times 4a = 5 \times a \times 4 \times a$
$= 5 \times 4 \times a \times a$
$= 20 \times a^2 = 20a^2$

Example 2

Simplify: **a** $6x \div 2$ **b** $3b \div 3$

a $6x \div 2 = 3x$

b $3b \div 3 = b$

> You can change the order. Remember that the sign belongs to the number after it.
> $6x \div 2 = 6 \times x \div 2 = 6 \div 2 \times x = 3 \times x$

> $3b \div 3 = 3 \times b \div 3 = 3 \div 3 \times b = 1 \times b$

Exam practice 3A

1 Simplify:
   a $2 \times x$ b $3 \times y$ c $a \times 4$ d $t \times 2$
   e $x \times z$ f $x \times x$ g $v \times v$ h $x \times t$

2 Simplify:
   a $3 \times 2x$ b $5 \times 2x$ c $3 \times 6x$ d $5x \times 6$
   e $4 \times 3y$ f $2a \times 2$ g $4 \times 3t$ h $7y \times 3$

3 Amir wrote '$2x \times 4x = 8x$.'
   Amir is wrong. Explain why.

4 Simplify:
   a $4x \div 2$ b $6y \div 3$ c $8a \div 2$ d $10s \div 2$
   e $2x \div 2$ f $9b \div 3$ g $4s \div 4$ h $8x \div 8$

5 Simplify:
   a $3a \times 5a$ b $3p \times 5p$ c $2x \times 4x$ d $5a \times 4a$
   e $x \times x \times x$ f $3s \times 2t$ g $p \times p \times p$ h $x \times x \times y$

Did you know

that the word algebra probably comes from the title of a book written by an Arabian mathematician in the 9th century? The book is called Al-jabr-W'almuqabala.

3.2 Collecting like terms

A **term** in an **expression** is any collection of numbers and letters that are not separated by plus or minus signs. So the terms in the expression $2y^2 - 3y + 5$ are $2y^2$, $3y$ and 5.

> A term that is just a number, such as 5, is called a **constant**.

Like terms contain exactly the same combination of letters. So x and $3x$ are like terms but x and x^2 are not.

> **Like terms** can have different numbers in them but they must have exactly the same combination of letters.

Like terms can be added or subtracted to give a single term. So $3x + 5x$ can be simplified to $8x$. This is called collecting like terms.

> $3x$ means $x + x + x$
> and $5x$ means $x + x + x + x + x$.
> Adding them gives 8 lots of x, or $8x$.

Example 3

Simplify: **a** $2x + 3x + 5x$ **b** $5 + 2x - x$ **c** $5pq - 2qp$

a $2x + 3x + 5x = 5x + 5x$

$= 10x$

> These are all like terms so you can add them.

> 5 and x are not like terms so this cannot be simplified.

b $5 + 2x - x = 5 + x$

> $2x$ and x are like terms so they can be collected.

c $5pq - 2qp = 5pq - 2pq$

$= 3pq$

> These are like terms.

> The order in which you multiply does not matter, so $2qp = 2pq$.

Exam practice 3B

1 Which of these are like terms?
   a $2x, 3y, 7, 10x, x^2$
   b $y^2, xy, y^3, 5y, 2y^2$
   c $4x, 5y, x^2, 6x, 2, 3x^3$
   d $3a^2, 5ab, 2a, 4a^2, 7a$

2 Write down the like terms in each expression:
   a $2 + 3x - x$
   b $2t - 4 + 3t$
   c $2y - 4 + 5y$
   d $x - 2x - 4$
   e $3y + 6 - 2y$
   f $x^2 - 3x + 5x$
   g $ab - 2a + b - 2a$
   h $5x^2 - 4 + 2x^2$
   i $4 - 2x + 2 + 5y$

> You can change the order from
> $4x - 5x + 2x$ to
> $4x + 2x - 5x$
> Remember that the sign goes with the term after it.

3 Simplify:
   a $2x + x$
   b $3x - x$
   c $5y + 4y$
   d $2x + x + x$
   e $3x - 2x + x$
   f $4x - 5x + 2x$
   g $3a + 4a + 2a$
   h $7q + 3q - 2q$
   i $5n - 2n + 3n$
   j $7x - 12x + 9x$
   k $15a + 4a - 18a$
   l $6t - 15t + 20t$

4 Simplify:
   a $6 + 2a - 3a + 3$
   b $7x + x + 13 - 8$
   c $3x - y + 2x + 2y$
   d $9p - 6 + 3p - 4$
   e $4a - 2b + 7a + 4b$
   f $2x + 5 - x - 1$
   g $5a + 8 - 2a + 2$
   h $2x + y + 5x + 5y$
   i $ab - 2a + 6a + 4ab$

> There are two sets of like terms in these expressions. You can collect each set.

5 Rachael wrote '$2x + x = x^3$'
   She is wrong. Explain her mistake.

6 Simplify:
   a $x^2 + 6x + 2x$
   b $a^2 + 2a + a$
   c $2a^2 - 6a + 8a$
   d $x^2 - xy + 3xy$
   e $5p^2 - 2p + 4p$
   f $3y - y^2 - 2y$
   g $7x^2 + 3x + 7x + 4$
   h $a^2 + 2a + 9a + 8$
   i $4t^2 - 3t + 8 + 5t$

3.3 Adding and subtracting negative numbers

When you take away a positive number you can end up with a negative answer.

> To add a positive number move to the right on the number line. To add a negative number move to the left on the number line.

Example 4

Simplify: **a** $3 - 5$ **b** $-x - 4x$

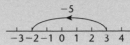

a $3 - 5 = -2$

You can use a number line to help. Move 5 places to the left.

-5

$-3\ -2\ -1\ 0\ 1\ 2\ 3\ 4$

b $-x - 4x = -5x$

$- x - 4x$ is the same as $- 1x - 4x$

These are the rules for adding and subtracting negative numbers.

Adding a negative number is the same as subtracting a positive number.

Subtracting a negative number is the same as adding a positive number.

Example 5

Simplify: **a** $2 + (-5)$ **b** $2 - (-x)$

Putting brackets round the negative number make it easier to see the two signs.

a $2 + (-5) = 2 - 5$

$= -3$

Adding -5 is the same as subtracting 5.

b $2 - (-x) = 2 + x$

These are not like terms so they cannot be simplified.

Subtracting $-x$ is the same as adding x.

Exam practice 3C

1 Simplify:

a $2 - 7$
b $-4 - 6$
c $5 - 8$
d $-7 + 2$
e $4 - 5$
f $-9 - 2$
g $-2a + 6a$
h $4x - 5x$
i $-2y - 3y$

You can use a number line to help you.

2 Simplify:

a $8 + (-7)$
b $3 + (-6)$
c $-2 + (-3)$
d $-3 + (-4)$
e $8 + (-10)$
f $3x + (-2x)$
g $10x + (-7x)$
h $4a + (-7a)$
i $b + (-9b)$

Adding -7 is the same as subtracting 7.

3 Simplify:

a $4 - (-4)$
b $-3 - (-7)$
c $5 - (-6)$
d $-5 - (-1)$
e $-2 - (-6)$
f $8x - (-3x)$
g $10y + (-8y)$
h $-11a - (-2a)$
i $-8p - (-6p)$

Subtracting -3 is the same as adding 3.

4 Simplify:

a $6 - 9 + 4$
b $11x - 4x - 9x$
c $-3y - 3y + 7y$
d $-3 - 4 + 7$
e $-4t + 2t + 5t$
f $-4d + 6d - 8d$
g $7x^2 - 3x - 4x + 4$
h $a^2 - 2a - 3a + 8$
i $4t^2 - 3t + 8 - 5t$

Be careful. $-3y - 3y$ is not subtracting a negative number.

5 Simplify:

a $4 - 2a - 3a$
b $7x + 2x - 11$
c $3x - y - 2y$
d $9p + 5 - 12p$
e $4x - 2y - 5x$
f $2x + 2 - 4x$
g $5 - (-2s) + 3s$
h $5x + 3x - (-8)$
i $3y - (-2y) + 2x$

6 Kwame wrote '$-2x - 2x = 4x$.'
He is wrong. Explain his mistake.

UAM

3.4 Multiplying and dividing with negative numbers

When two numbers are multiplied or divided:

If the signs are the same, the answer is positive.

If the signs are different, the answer is negative.

Example 6

Find: **a** $2 \times (-3)$ **b** $(-4x) \div 2$ **c** $-2x \times (-3x)$

a $2 \times (-3) = -6$

$2 \times 3 = 6$.
The signs are different so the answer is negative.

b $(-4x) \div 2 = -2x$

$4x \div 2 = 2x$.
The signs are different so the answer is negative.

c $-2x \times (-3x) = 6x^2$

$2x \times 3x = 6x^2$.
The signs are the same so the answer is positive.

Exam practice 3D

1 Find:

   a $3 \times (-4)$
   b $(-2) \times (-4)$
   c $(-4) \times (-5)$
   d $(-4) \times (-4)$
   e $6 \times (-3)$
   f $(-3) \times 5$
   g $(-8) \times 2$
   h $(-5) \times (-5)$
   i $8 \div (-4)$
   j $(-10) \div (-5)$
   k $(-14) \div 2$
   l $(-20) \div (-4)$

2 Simplify:

   a $2x \times (-4)$
   b $(-2x) \times 3$
   c $8x \times (-2)$
   d $4y \div (-2)$
   e $(-6a) \div (-2)$
   f $(-10a) \div 5$
   g $(-2x) \div 2$
   h $(-3a) \times (-2)$
   i $(-2t) \times 5t$
   j $3a \times (-b)$
   k $(-x) \times (-y)$
   l $(-5t) \times (-3t)$

3 Simplify:

   a $2 \times (-2) \times (-3)$
   b $2 \times (-2) \times (-2)$
   c $2 \times (-2a) \times (-2b)$
   d $x \times (-x) \times 2$
   e $(-3x) \times 4 \times (-2y)$
   f $5a \times 2a \div (-2)$

> When you multiply three numbers you can start by multiplying any two together first.

4 Simplify:

   a $(-4 + 2) \times (-7)$
   b $8 - (-3) \times 5$
   c $(2 - 10) \div (-4 \times 2)$
   d $(-x + 3x) \times (-2)$
   e $12y + 3y \times (-6)$
   f $(5b - 8b) \div (2 - 5)$
   g $(3a - 5a) \div (-2)$
   h $(x - 5x) \div (9 - 5)$
   i $12t \div (15 - 3)$

> Remember, work out the inside of the brackets first then do multiplication and division before addition and subtraction.

5 Write true or false for each of these calculations:

   a '$2x \times x = 3x$'
   b '$2x - x = x$'
   c '$2x - 2y = x - y$'
   d '$-2 \times (-x) = 2x$'
   e '$3a - a = 3$'
   f '$3x + 2y = 5xy$'

3.5 Multiplying and dividing numbers written in index notation

You can multiply together powers of the *same* number by adding the powers.

Example 7

Simplify: **a** $2^3 \times 2^2$ **b** $x^3 \times x^4$

a $2^3 \times 2^2 = 2^{3+2} = 2^5$

2^3 and 2^2 are both powers of 2 so add the powers.

b $x^3 \times x^4 = x^{3+4} = x^7$

x^3 and x^4 are both powers of x so you can add the powers.

You can divide different powers of the *same* number by subtracting the powers.

Example 8

Simplify: **a** $2^5 \div 2^2$ **b** $p^6 \div p^4$

a $2^5 \div 2^2 = 2^{5-2} = 2^3$

You are dividing so subtract the powers.

b $p^6 \div p^4 = p^{6-4} = p^2$

You cannot use these rules when the base numbers are different. This means that you can not simplify $5^3 \times 3^2$ or $x^3 \div x^2$.

Note that $5^3 \div 5^3 = 5^{3-3} = 5^0$

But $\frac{5^3}{5^3} = 1$, so $5^0 = 1$. In fact (any number)$^0 = 1$.

Exam practice 3E

1 Write as a single expression in index form.
   a $3^5 \times 3^2$ b $7^5 \times 7^3$ c $5^4 \times 5^3$ d $x^3 \times x^2$
   e $x^5 \times x^2$ f $a^4 \times a^2$ g $t^3 \times t^5$ h $p^5 \times p$ $p = p^1$

2 Franz said that $x^4 \times x^2 = x^8$.
   a Explain why Franz is wrong.
   b Write $x^4 \times x^2$ as a single power of x.

3 Simplify:
   a $3^5 \div 3^2$ b $2^5 \div 2^3$ c $7^4 \div 7^3$ d $3^7 \div 3^4$
   e $x^8 \div x^3$ f $x^6 \div x^2$ g $x^3 \div x^3$ h $y^6 \div y^4$
   i $4^3 \times 4$ j $p^4 \times p$ k $3^4 \div 3$ l $x^3 \div x$

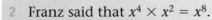
You can write 4 as 4^1

4 Write as a single power:
   a $(2^3)^2$ b $(x^2)^4$ $(2^3)^2 = 2^3 \times 2^3$

5 **a** Tim wrote that $(y^3)^2 = y^5$.
   Is Tim correct? Explain your answer.
   b Poppy wrote that $b^7 \div b^2 \times b^4 = b^7 \div b^6$
   Explain why Poppy is wrong.

6 Simplify:
   a $x^2 \times y$ b $2x^2 \times x$ c $x^2 \times 4x$
   d $n \times 3n^2$ e $a \times 2b \times a$ f $2a \times b \times c$
   g $4c \times b \times 2c$ h $2a^2 \times 3b \times a$

7 Simplify:
   a $7^3 \times 7^2 \div 7^5$ b $x^3 \times x^4 \div x^2$ c $2 \times x^3 \times x^4$
   d $a^5 \div a^3 \times a^2$ e $3x^4 \times x^2$ f $3x^4 \div x^2$
   g $2x^4 \times x^5$ h $4x^2 \times x^6$ i $x^4 \times 3x^3$
   j $8t^4 \div t^2$ k $2v^4 \times 3v^3$ l $4b^4 \div b^3$
   m $\dfrac{5^2 \times 5^7}{5^4}$ n $\dfrac{x^4 \times x^3}{x^2}$ p $\dfrac{a^4 \times a^6}{a^5}$

   $\dfrac{5^2 \times 5^7}{5^4}$ means $(5^2 \times 5^7) \div 5^4$

8 Write true or false for each calculation.
   a $x^3 \times x^3 = x^6$ b $6b^8 \div b^2 = 3b^4$ c $4x^2 \div x = 16$

3.6 Multiplying out brackets

The expression $3(2x - 7)$ means 3 multiplied by everything inside the bracket. So $3(2x - 7) = 3 \times 2x - 3 \times 7 = 6x - 21$
This process is called **multiplying out** the brackets.

> Multiplying out the brackets is sometimes called **expanding** the brackets.

Example 9

Multiply out the brackets: **a** $x(2x - 3)$ **b** $5(x - 2) - x(2x - 4)$

a $x(2x - 3) = 2x^2 - 3x$
   $x \times 2x$ $x \times (-3)$

b $5(x - 2) - x(2x - 4) = 5x - 10 - 2x^2 + 4x$
   $5 \times x$ 5×-2 $-x \times 2x$ $-x \times -4$

$= 9x - 10 - 2x^2$

> Multiply out each bracket.
> Remember that
> $-x \times -4 = +4x$
> Collect like terms.

The expression $(2x - 5)(x + 4)$ means each term in the second bracket is multiplied by each term in the first bracket.
So $(2x - 5)(x + 4) = 2x(x + 4) - 5(x + 4)$
$\qquad\qquad\qquad\quad = 2x^2 + 8x - 5x - 20$
$\qquad\qquad\qquad\quad = 2x^2 + 3x - 20$

> You can use a grid like this:
>
> | | x | 4 |
> |---|---|---|
> | $2x$ | $2x^2$ | $8x$ |
> | -5 | $-5x$ | -20 |

Example 10

Expand and simplify $(3x - 2)(2x - 5)$.

$$(3x-2)(2x-5) = 3x(2x-5) - 2(2x-5)$$
$$= 6x^2 - 15x - 4x + 10$$
$$= 6x^2 - 19x + 10$$

If you are confident you can leave out the second step.

Exam practice 3F

1   Multiply out and simplify:

a $5(x + 2)$ b $3(2x - 3)$ c $4(2a + 6)$

d $2(5 - 3x)$ e $7(2 - x)$ f $5(2a - 3b)$

g $4y(7 - 3y)$ h $2x(4 - x)$ i $3x(2 - 6x)$

j $2x(3 - y)$ k $3a(a + 2b)$ l $2pq(3p - 2q)$

m $x(x^2 + 2)$ n $y(2y^2 - 3)$ p $a^2(a + 1)$

2   Multiply out and simplify:

a $3(3 - a) - a(5 - 2a)$ b $3x(x - 3) - 2(4 - x)$

c $2(x - 5y) + 4(x + y)$ d $x(x + 5) + 2(x + 5)$

e $3x(x + 1) - 2(x + 1)$ f $4x(2x - 1) - 3(2x - 1)$

g $x(x - y) + 2y(x + 3y)$ h $6(x - 2y) - (x + y)$

i $x(2 - x) - (4 - 3x)$

Remember to collect like terms.

$-(x + y)$ is the same as $-1(x + y)$.

3   Multiply out and simplify:

a $(x - 4)(x + 1)$ b $(a - 7)(a + 5)$ c $(x + 3)(x + 4)$

d $(y + 4)(y + 2)$ e $(x - 2)(x + 5)$ f $(b + 5)(b + 7)$

g $(x - 1)(x - 2)$ h $(p + 5)(p - 4)$ i $(a - 4)(a - 3)$

4   Multiply out and simplify:

a $(2x + 1)(x + 1)$ b $(x + 2)(2x + 3)$ c $(3x + 2)(x + 4)$

d $(2s - t)(3s + 2t)$ e $(7y + 3)(2y + 9)$ f $(4t - 1)(t - 3)$

g $(x - 2)(x + 2)$ h $(3x + 1)(3x - 1)$ i $(2 - y)(5 - 2y)$

j $(x + 3)^2$ k $(x - 5)^2$ l $(2x + 1)^2$

m $(3x - 1)^2$ n $(2x + 3)^2$ p $(4 - 3x)^2$

$(x + 3)^2$ means $(x + 3)(x + 3)$.

3.7 Factors

A factor of an algebraic term is a number, letter or term that divides into it exactly.

$2x = 2 \times x$ so 2 and x are factors of $2x$. 1 and $2x$ are also factors of $2x$.

Two terms can have the same factor. This is called a common factor.

You can see the factors when you put the multiplication signs in.

Example 11

Find the common factors of   **a** $4x$ and x^2 **b** $6x$ and 9.

---

a $4x = 2 \times 2 \times x$: Factors of $4x$ are 1, 2, 4, **x**, 2x, 4x

$x^2 = x \times x$: Factors of x^2 are 1, **x**, x^2

1 and x are the common factors.

> Write down the factors of each term.

> A common factor is a number or letter that is in both products.

b   Factors of $6x$ are 1, 2, **3**, 6, x, 2x, 3x, 6x

Factors of 9 are 1, **3**, 9

1 and 3 are common factors.

Factorising an expression means writing it as the product of factors.
When an expression has two or more terms, you need to find a
common factor of all the terms.

Example 12

Factorise: **a** $x^2 - 3x$ **b** $6x + 10$

---

a x is a common factor of x^2 and $3x$.

$x^2 - 3x = (x \times x) - (3 \times x)$

$\qquad = x(x - 3)$

Check: $x(x - 3) = x^2 - 3x$ ✓

> The common factor is written outside the bracket with the remaining factors inside.

> You can check by multiplying out the brackets.

b   2 is a common factor of $6x$ and 10.

$6x + 10 = (\mathbf{2} \times 3 \times x) + (\mathbf{2} \times 5)$

$\qquad = 2(3x + 5)$

Check: $2(3x + 5) = 6x + 10$ ✓

Exam practice 3G

1   Write down the factors of each term:
   a   4   b   12   c $3x$ d $14x$ e x^2 f $2t^2$

2   Write down the common factors of:
   a   2 and $4x$ b $6a$ and 3   c $5x$ and 10
   d $3s$ and 12   e x^2 and $2x$ f $4x$ and 12

3   Factorise:
   a $3x + 6$ b $3x - 12$ c $8x + 4$ d $2x + 6$
   e $10 + 5x$ f $16b + 8$ g $7x - 14$ h $5x + 5$ ●————— $5 = 5 \times 1$
   i $4b + 12$ j $3y + 9$ k $9x - 18$ l $14 - 21x$

4   Factorise:
   a $x^2 + 3x$ b $a^2 - 2a$ c $x^2 + 5x$ d $t^2 - 6t$
   e $v^2 + 2v$ f $2x - x^2$ g $4x + x^2$ h $5x - x^2$
   i $2x^2 - x$ j $2a^2 + 5a$ k $6x - 2x^2$ l $4x + 2x^2$

5 Factorise:
   a $2x + 2y$ b $x^2 - xy$ c $5a + 10b$ d $ab + ac$
   e $2x^2 + xy$ f $xy + y^2$ g $2x^2 + 4y^2$ h $x^3 - 2x$

6 Factorise:
   a $2x + 2y + 4$ b $2a + 4b - 2c$ c $4a^2 + 2a - 8$
   d $3xy + 6x + 12$ e $3x + 6x^2 + 9$ f $ab + ac + ad$

> You need to find a common factor of all three terms.

3.8 Substitution

You can find the value of an expression when you know the numbers that the letters stand for. You do this by replacing the letters with the numbers. This is called **substitution**.

Example 13

Find the value of $a^2 - 5b$ when
a $a = 7$ and $b = 6$ **b** $a = -2$ and $b = -3$

a $a^2 - 5b = 7^2 - 5 \times 6$
$\qquad = 49 - 30$
$\qquad = 19$

> Replace a by 7 and b by 6. $5b$ means $5 \times b$. Remember that you do multiplication first.

b $a^2 - 5b = (-2)^2 - 5(-3)$
$\qquad = 4 + 15$
$\qquad = 19$

> Put the negative numbers in brackets. Remember that when you multiply two negative numbers, the answer is positive.

Exam practice 3H

1 Find the value of $2x - 7$ when
   a $x = 8$ b $x - 2$ c $x = -2$.

2 Work out the value of $5x + 7$ when
   a $x = 3$ b $x = -2$ c $x = -1$.

3 Find the value of $5 - 2x$ when
   a $x = 2$ b $x = 6$ c $x = -2$.

4 Calculate the value of $x^2 + 5$ when
   a $x = 3$ b $x = 2$ c $x = -3$.

5 Find the value of $x^2 + x$ when
   a $x = 2$ b $x = 0$ c $x = -1$.

6 Find the value of $4x + 3y$ when
   a $x = 2$ and $y = 2$ b $x = 1$ and $y = 3$ c $x = 2$ and $y = -3$.

7 Find the value of $2a - 3b$ when
   a $a = 8$ and $b = 2$
   b $a = 4$ and $b = 2$
   c $a = 2$ and $b = -2$.

8 Find the value of lw when
   a $l = 3$ and $w = 2$
   b $l = 4$ and $w = 1.5$
   c $l = 1.5$ and $w = 0.5$.

9 Calculate the value of $\frac{1}{2}bh$ when
   a $b = 6$ and $h = 1$
   b $b = 4$ and $h = 2.5$
   c $b = 1.5$ and $h = 5$.

10 Find the value of $a - b - 4c$ when
   a $a = 8$, $b = 2$ and $c = 1$ b $a = 3$, $b = 2$ and $c = 3$.

11 Work out the value of $\frac{1}{2}h(a + b)$ when
   a $h = 6$, $a = 3$ and $b = 2$ b $h = 4$, $a = 1.5$ and $b = 2.5$
   c $h = 3$, $a = 7$ and $b = 5$ d $h = 1.5$, $a = 3$ and $b = 5$.

12 Find the exact value of $2\pi r$ in terms of π when
   a $r = 3$ b $r = 1.5$ c $r = 9$.

13 Find the exact value of $\pi r^2 h$ in terms of π when
   a $r = 2$ and $h = 3$ b $r = 3$ and $h = 2$ c $r = 6$ and $h = 1.5$.

> This means you must leave π in your answer.
> For example when $r = 6$,
> $2\pi r = 2 \times \pi \times 6$
> $ = 2 \times 6 \times \pi$
> $ = 12\pi$.

Summary of key points

- $2x$ means $2 \times x$.
- You can add or subtract like terms.
- Adding a negative number is the same as subtracting a positive number.
- Subtracting a negative number is the same as adding a positive number.
- When two numbers are multiplied or divided:
  if the signs are the same, the answer is positive: $(-2) \times (-3) = 6$
  if the signs are different, the answer is negative: $(+2) \times (-3) = -6$.
- You can multiply together powers of the same number by adding the powers; $2^3 \times 2^4 = 2^7$.
- You can divide different powers of the same number by subtracting the powers; $3^5 \div 3^2 = 3^3$.
- When the product of two brackets is multiplied out, each term in the second bracket is multiplied by each term in the first bracket.
- when you factorise an expression, look for common factors of each term.

Most students who get GRADE E or above can:
- simplify expressions such as
  $2x - 3y + 7x + 8y$.

Most students who get GRADE C can also:
- simplify expressions containing indices such as $x^3 \times x^5$
- expand and simplify expressions containing brackets
- factorise an expression with two terms.

Glossary

Constant	a fixed value
Expanding	multiplying all the terms inside the brackets by the term outside
Expression	a collection of letters and numbers without an equals sign
Factorising	writing an expression as a product of factors
Like terms	containing exactly the same combination of letters
Multiplying out	same as expanding
Simplifying	writing in as short a form as possible
Substitution	replacing letters by numbers
Term	a collection of letters and numbers that are not separated by plus or minus signs

4 Equations and inequalities

This chapter will show you:
✓ what an equation is
✓ how to solve equations algebraically
✓ how to write an expression using letters
✓ how to form equations
✓ how to use trial and improvement to solve equations
✓ what an inequality is
✓ how to solve an inequality

Before you start you need to know:
✓ how to multiply and divide numbers
✓ how to add and subtract positive and negative numbers
✓ how to simplify an expression
✓ how to multiply out brackets
✓ the meaning of a fraction

4.1 Equations

An **expression** is any collection of letters and numbers without an equals sign.

When two expressions are equal for any values of the letters, it is called an **identity**.

An **equation** always has an equals sign. Usually the two expressions are equal when the letter stands for some numbers but not all numbers. **Solving** the equation means finding those numbers.

> $a + b = b + a$ is an identity because $b + a$ is another way of writing $a + b$.

> 3 is the only value of x for which $x + 2 = 5$

There are two ways of thinking of an equation to solve it.

Think of $x + 3 = 5$ as a Balance:

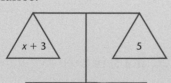

To keep the balance, do the same to both sides.
To get x on its own you need to subtract 3 from both sides:
$x + 3 - 3 = x$
$\quad 5 - 3 = 2$
So $x = 2$.

Think of $x + 3 = 5$ as a Number Machine:

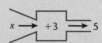

To find what goes in, reverse the number machine: go in the opposite direction and use the reverse instruction.

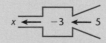

$5 - 3 = 2$, so $x = 2$.

> The solution can be a positive or negative number. It can also be a fraction or a mixed number.

Use which ever method you are used to.

Example 1

Solve the equation $x - 6 = 16$.

$x - 6 = 16$
$x = 16 + 6$
$x = 22$
Check: $22 - 6 = 16$ ✓

$x \xrightarrow{-6} 16$ or $x - 6 + 6 = 16 + 6$
$x \xleftarrow{+6} 16$ $x = 22$

The solution may be a negative number.

Example 2

Solve the equation $7 + t = 5$.

$7 + t = 5$
$t = 5 - 7$
$t = -2$
Check: $7 + (-2) = 7 - 2 = 5$ ✓

$7 + t$ is the same as $t + 7$.

The letter may be subtracted.

Example 3

Solve the equation $7 - x = 4$.

$7 - x = 4$
$7 = 4 + x$ or $4 + x = 7$
$x = 7 - 4$
$x = 3$
Check: $7 - 4 = 3$ ✓

$7 = 4 + x$ is the same as $4 + x = 7$.

Exam practice 4A

1 Solve the equations.
   a $x + 5 = 12$ b $x - 6 = 17$ c $x + 7 = 15$
   d $x - 9 = 4$ e $x + 12 = 24$ f $c - 6 = 14$
   g $x + 4 = 16$ h $a - 8 = 12$ i $p - 2 = 10$

2 Solve the equations.
   a $x + 5 = 3$ b $a + 7 = 6$ c $t + 15 = 6$
   d $a + 3 = 2$ e $x + 4 = 1$ f $x + 2 = 0$

3 Solve the equations.
   a $3 + t = 15$ b $18 + x = 25$ c $7 = x + 5$
   d $10 - x = 8$ e $25 - x = 14$ f $12 - t = 5$
   g $3 + x = 2$ h $13 = y + 15$ i $9 - y = 12$
   j $14 - x = 16$ k $p + 20 = 35$ l $15 = 12 - x$

4.2 Multiples and fractions of x

When an equation has a multiple or fraction of x you can use the fact that multiplication and division are the opposite of each other to undo (reverse) the multiplication or division.

Example 4

Solve the equations: **a** $3x = 18$ **b** $\frac{x}{3} = 5$

a $3x = 18$

$x = 18 \div 3$

$x = 6$

Check: $3 \times 6 = 18$ ✓

> $3x$ means $3 \times x$
>
> $x \xrightarrow{\times 3} 18$ or $3x \div 3 = 18 \div 3$
>
> $x \xleftarrow{\div 3} 18$

b $\frac{x}{3} = 5$

$x = 5 \times 3$

$x = 15$

Check: $15 \div 3 = 5$ ✓

> $\frac{x}{3}$ means $x \div 3$
>
> $x \xrightarrow{\div 3} 5$
>
> $x \xleftarrow{\times 3} 5$

Exam practice 4B

1 Solve these equations:

a $5x = 20$	b $4x = 32$	c $2x = 24$
d $3x = 180$	e $5x = 100$	f $5d = 2$ ●
g $50 = 5x$	h $360 = 9q$	i $2x = 7$
j $10a = 40$	k $3y = 10$ ●	l $4x = 3$ ●

> Give your answer as a fraction.

> Give your answers as mixed numbers.

2 a i   Simplify $3x + 2x$.
     ii Solve the equation $3x + 2x = 15$.
   b i   Simplify $x + 2x + 4x$.
     ii Solve the equation $x + 2x + 4x = 21$.
   c i   Simplify $5x - 2x$.
     ii Solve the equation $5x - 2x = 12$.

3 Solve these equations:

a $x + 3x = 40$	b $3x + 4x = 14$
c $5x - 2x = 7$	d $3x + 2x + x = 180$
e $4x + x + 4x = 90$	f $7x - 3x + x = 360$

4 Solve these equations:

a $\frac{x}{2} = 5$	b $\frac{x}{5} = 4$	c $\frac{x}{3} = 12$	d $\frac{y}{6} = 2$
e $\frac{b}{7} = 5$	f $\frac{t}{10} = 6$	g $\frac{x}{9} = 4$	h $5 = \frac{x}{8}$
i $4 = \frac{x}{7}$	j $6 = \frac{k}{4}$	k $4 = \frac{b}{12}$	l $\frac{x}{2} = 2.5$

4.3 Equations with more than one step

Example 5

Solve: **a** $2x + 3 = 9$ **b** $\frac{x}{3} - 5 = 2$

a $2x + 3 = 9$
   $2x = 9 - 3$
   $2x = 6$
   $x = 6 \div 2$
   $x = 3$
   Check: $2 \times 3 + 3 = 6 + 3 = 9$ ✓

$x \xrightarrow{\times 2} \xrightarrow{+3} 9$ or   subtract 3 from both sides:
$x \xleftarrow{\div 2} \xleftarrow{-3} 9$ $2x + 3 - 3 = 9 - 3$
                                                    $2x = 6$
                          divide both sides by 2: $2x \div 2 = 6 \div 2$
                                                         $x = 3$

b $\frac{x}{3} - 5 = 2$
   $\frac{x}{3} = 2 + 5$ Add 5 to both sides.
   $\frac{x}{3} = 7$
   $x = 7 \times 3 = 21$ Multiply both sides by 3.
   Check: $\frac{21}{3} - 5 = 7 - 5 = 2$ ✓

Exam practice 4C

1 Solve these equations:
   a $2x + 5 = 9$ b $3x + 2 = 5$ c $2x - 1 = 5$
   d $5y - 4 = 6$ e $2x + 1 = 5$ f $4a - 2 = 7$
   g $6x + 4 = 22$ h $5b - 9 = 6$ i $7x + 3 = 17$
   j $4s + 3 = 19$ k $8t - 2 = 7$ l $10x - 3 = 2$

   Give your answer
   to part **f** as a mixed
   number.

2 Solve these equations:
   a $5 = 3 + 2x$ b $4 = 3p - 5$ c $6x + 9 = 3$
   d $2x + 7 = 3$ e $2 = 3x - 2$ f $15 = 4 + 11x$
   g $13 = 9t + 4$ h $5 = 6s + 4$ i $15 = 10a + 20$
   j $7x + 6 = 5$ k $14 = 2 + 5x$ l $4x + 11 = 2$

3 Solve these equations:
   a $\frac{x}{5} + 2 = 4$ b $\frac{p}{6} - 3 = 2$ c $2 + \frac{x}{5} = 3$
   d $\frac{s}{7} - 2 = 1$ e $2 = 1 + \frac{x}{3}$ f $\frac{x}{2} + 5 = 2$
   g $\frac{t}{3} + 7 = 2$ h $7 = 3 + \frac{x}{5}$ i $3 - \frac{x}{2} = 2$
   j $5 - \frac{k}{4} = 1$ k $8 = 2 - \frac{x}{3}$ l $\frac{2x}{3} = 5$

4 Jodie wrote
   Jodie's solution is wrong.
   Explain her mistake.

   $2x - 4 = 6$
   $2x = 2$
   $x = 1$

UAM

5   Abdul wrote $2x - 4 = 6$
                  $x = 6 + 4 = 10 = 5$
    The answer is correct but the working is not.

    Explain why.

4.4 Writing expressions

You can write word problems using letters and numbers.

You need to use the clues in the words to decide how the letters and numbers are connected.

Example 6

Envelopes cost n pence each. Write down an expression for the cost of 20 envelopes.

> Remember that an expression is a collection of letters, numbers and $+$, $-$, $\times$, and $\div$ signs. There is no equals sign.

> 20 × n pence
> or 20n pence

> 20 envelopes cost 20 times the price of 1 envelope.

You are not always given the letters.
You can choose any letter to stand for the unknown number.

Example 7

John thinks of a number. He doubles the number and then adds three.
Write down an expression for John's answer.

> Let x be the number that John thinks of.
> Double the number is 2x.
> John's answer is 2x + 3.   Now add 3.

> Write down what your letter stands for.

> Double means multiply by 2. So the expression is 2x.

Exam practice 4D

1   Soap costs c pence a bar.
    Write an expression for the cost of 5 bars of soap.

2   Apples cost 30 pence each.
    Write an expression for the cost of n apples.

3   A stick was x cm long. A piece 3 cm long is cut off the stick.
    Write an expression for the length of the stick now.

4   Some groceries ordered over the internet cost £C. The delivery charge is £5.
    Write an expression for the total cost.

5 Freya buys 2 books online costing £*p* each. There is a charge of £4 for postage. Find an expression for the total cost.

6 Write an expression for the distance round the sides of this rectangle.

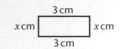

> Simplify your answer.

7 There are *x* pens in one box. There are *y* pens in another box. Jasmine takes 2 pens out of one box and 1 pen out of the other box.
   Write an expression for the total number of pens now in the two boxes.

8 One orange costs *a* pence. One apple costs *b* pence,
   Write an expression for the total cost of 5 oranges and 4 apples.

9 Write an expression for the distance round the sides of this shape.

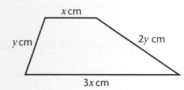

> The distance around a shape is also called the perimeter.

10 Write an expression for the answer in each of the following.
   a Imran thinks of a number and then adds 4.
   b Roger thinks of a number and trebles it.
   c Greg thinks of a number and subtracts 6.
   d Gaby thinks of a number. She doubles it and adds 5.
   e Maryam thinks of a number. She halves it and subtracts 10.

> Remember to say what your letter stands for.

11 These two boxes both contain the same number of beads.

 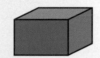

   Marco takes 10 beads out of one of the boxes.
   Write an expression for the total number of beads left in the two boxes.

> Choose a letter to stand for the number of beads in each box before Marco takes any beads out.

12 A chocolate muffin costs 5 pence more than a plain muffin. Write an expression for the cost of 1 chocolate muffin and 1 plain muffin.

> You are not told the cost of either type of muffin, so choose a letter to stand for the cost of one of them.

4.5 Forming equations

You form an equation when you can put an equals sign between two expressions.

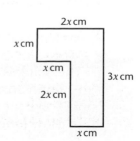

Example 8

a Write an expression for the distance round this shape.
b The distance round the shape is 45 cm.
   Form an equation using this information.
c Solve the equation to find the value of *x*.

a $(2x + 3x + x + 2x + x + x)$ cm = $10x$ cm

> The distance round the shape is the sum of the lengths of the sides. Write these down then collect the like terms.

b $10x = 45$

> The expression for the distance is $10x$ cm. You are told that the distance is 45 cm. This means that $10x$ and 45 are equal. You can write this as an equation.

c $10x = 45$

$\quad x = 45 \div 10$

$\quad x = 4.5$

Check: $10 \times 4.5 = 45$ ✓

Sometimes you are not asked to form an expression first or given a letter for the unknown number.

Example 9

Karla thinks of a number. She multiplies it by 5 and then subtracts 8.
The answer is 27.
What is the number?

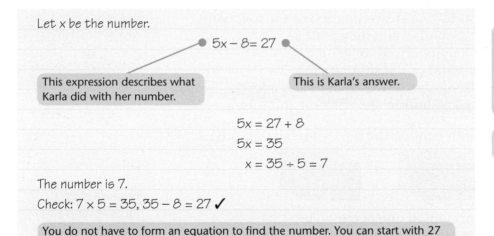

Let x be the number.

$$5x - 8 = 27$$

This expression describes what Karla did with her number.

This is Karla's answer.

> You can form an equation by writing the expression for what Karla did with her number equal to her answer.

$$5x = 27 + 8$$

$$5x = 35$$

$$x = 35 \div 5 = 7$$

> Now solve the equation.

The number is 7.

Check: $7 \times 5 = 35$, $35 - 8 = 27$ ✓

> You do not have to form an equation to find the number. You can start with 27 and then reverse what Karla did to the number: $27 + 8 = 35$ then $35 \div 5 = 7$. If you do it this way you must show your working in the examination.

Exam practice 4E

1 Pears cost 25 pence each.
   a Write an expression for the cost of n pears.
   b The total cost of n pears is 300 pence.
      i Write an equation using this information.
      ii Solve your equation to find the value of n.

2 A plank is 4 m long. A piece x m long is cut off the plank.
   a Write an expression for the length of the plank now.
   b The plank is now 2.5 m long.
      i Form an equation using this information.
      ii Solve the equation to find the value of x.
      iii How long is the piece cut from the plank?

3 Buns cost c pence each.
   a Write an expression for the cost of 20 buns.
   b 20 buns cost £3.
      i   Form an equation using this information.
      ii Solve the equation to find the value of c.
      iii What is the cost of 1 bun?

> You need to work in the same units, so convert £3 to pence.

4 Two pieces of rope are tied together.

5 m x m

   The total length is 8.5 m.
   Write an equation and solve it to find the value of x.

5 Five boxes of apples each contain x apples. Sufi takes 25 apples.
   a Write an expression for the total number of apples left in the boxes.
   b There are 105 apples left.
      Form an equation and solve it to find the value of x.
   c How many apples were there originally in total?

6 Jason buys 3 batteries priced at c pence each.
   He pays with a £2 coin.
   a Find an expression for the change Jason gets.
   b He gets 80 p change.
      Write an equation and solve it to find the value of c.
   c How much did each battery cost?

> Convert £2 to pence.

7 The distance round this shape is 58 cm.
   Find the length of the shortest side.

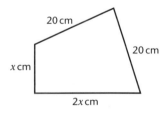

20 cm
20 cm
x cm
$2x$ cm

8 Find the number in each of the following:
   a Rob thinks of a number. He doubles it and then subtracts 10. The answer is 16.
   b Carol thinks of a number. She halves it and then adds 4. The answer is 8.
   c Kingston thinks of a number. He subtracts 3 times his number from 25. His answer is 7.
   d Nazreen thinks of a number. She adds six times the number to 30. Her answer is 42.

9 The sizes of three angles are $x°$, $2x°$ and $3x°$. They add up to 360°.
   Find the size of the smallest angle.

10 The sizes of three angles are $x°$, $x° + 10°$ and $x° + 20°$. They add up to 180°.
   Find the size of the smallest angle.

11 The sizes of five angles are $x°$, $2x°$, $3x°$, $x°$ and $3x°$. They add up to 540°.
   Find the sizes of all the angles.

4.6 Equations with the letter on both sides of the equals sign

You need to be able to solve equations with a letter term on both sides.

Example 10

Solve these equations: **a** $2x - 3 = x + 4$ **b** $3 + 5x = 17 - 2x$

a
$$2x - 3 = x + 4$$
$$2x - 3 - x = 4$$
$$x - 3 = 4$$
$$x = 4 + 3$$
$$x = 7$$
Check: $2 \times 7 - 3 = 11$, $7 + 4 = 11$ ✓

> You need to have the x terms on the same side of the equation.
> Start by subtracting x from both sides:
> $2x - 3 - x = x - 3$ and $x + 4 - x = 4$

b
$$3 + 5x = 17 - 2x$$
$$3 + 5x + 2x = 17 - 2x + 2x$$
$$3 + 7x = 17$$
$$7x = 17 - 3$$
$$7x = 14$$
$$x = 14 \div 7$$
$$x = 2$$
Check: $3 + 5 \times 2 = 13$, $17 - 2 \times 2 = 13$ ✓

Collect like terms

Add $2x$ to both sides.

Exam practice 4F

1 Solve these equations:

  a $2x + 1 = x + 5$ b $2x + 3 = x + 1$

  c $2x + 3 = x + 9$ d $3x + 4 = 2x - 1$

  e $2x - 4 = x + 7$ f $5x - 2 = 2x + 7$

  g $7x + 4 = 3x + 16$ h $3 - x = 2x + 4$

> Remember that solutions can be fractions or negative numbers.

> If two expressions are equal, it does not matter which one you write first. You can write the equation in part **h** as $2x + 4 = 3 - x$.

2 Solve these equations:

  a $5x + 2 = 4 + x$ b $3 - 5x = 2x + 4$

  c $6x + 4 = 2x + 7$ d $2x - 3 = x - 7$

  e $4 + 3x = 9 - 2x$ f $2 - x = 8 - 7x$

  g $1 - 3x = 2 - 2x$ h $5 - 4x = 8 - 7x$

3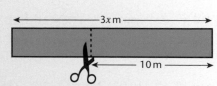

A piece is cut off each of these lengths of carpet.

  a Write an expression for the length of red carpet left.

  b Write an expression for the length of green carpet left.

  c The two pieces of carpet left are the same length.
     Form an equation and solve it to find the value of x.

  d How long was the green carpet before the piece was cut off?

4.7 Equations with brackets

When there is a bracket in an equation you must multiply out the bracket first.

Example 11

Solve the equations   **a** $3(2x - 4) = 18$ **b** $5(x - 2) - 2(2x - 4) = 16$

a $3(2x - 4) = 18$

$6x - 12 = 18$

$6x = 18 + 12$

$6x = 30$

$x = 30 \div 6 = 5$ Check: $3(2 \times 5 - 4) = 3(10 - 4) = 18$

> Start by multiplying out the bracket

b $5(x - 2) - 2(2x - 4) = 16$

$5x - 10 - 4x + 8 = 16$

$x - 2 = 16$

$x = 16 + 2 = 18$ Check: $5(18 - 2) - 2(36 - 4) = 80 - 64 = 16$

> Multiply out the brackets. Remember $-2 \times (-4) = +8$

> Collect like terms.

Example 12

Solve the equation $\dfrac{2x - 4}{3} = 3$.

$\left(\dfrac{2x - 4}{3}\right) = 3$

$2x - 4 = 3 \times 3$

$2x - 4 = 9$

$2x = 9 + 4$

$2x = 13$

$x = 13 \div 2 = 6\frac{1}{2}$ Check: $\dfrac{2 \times 6\frac{1}{2} - 4}{3} = \dfrac{13 - 4}{3} = \dfrac{9}{3} = 3$

> Put brackets round the numerator. $\dfrac{(2x - 4)}{3}$ means $(2x - 4) \div 3$.
>
> Multiply both sides by 3 first.

Exam practice 4G

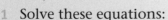

1 Solve these equations:

 a $4(3x - 1) = 20$ b $2(5x + 1) = 7$ c $7(x - 2) = 5$

 d $3(5x + 1) = 33$ e $6(2 - x) = 12$ f $2(3 - 2x) = 16$

 g $7 = 2(x - 1)$ h $4 = 2(2x - 1)$ i $15 = 3(3x + 2)$

2 Solve these equations:

 a $3x + 9 = 2(x + 7)$ b $4(x - 2) = 3x + 1$

 c $7x + 3 = 3(x - 5)$ d $5x + 17 = 3(x + 6)$

 e $3 - 2(x + 5) = 4$ f $6 + 3(x - 2) = 5$

 g $1 + x + 2(3x - 1) = 5$ h $2(x + 1) = x + 6$

 i $3(x - 2) = 2(x + 8)$ j $2(x - 1) - 4(2 - 2x) = 3$

 k $3(2x + 4) = 1 - 7x$ l $4x - 2 = 5(x - 3)$

 m $3 - 2x = 1 - 3(1 - 3x)$ n $1 - 2(x + 4) = 5 + 3(2x - 1)$

> **Class discussion**
>
> What happens when you are asked to solve $6x - 3 = 3(2x) - 1$? What sort of special equation is it?

3   Solve these equations:

  a $\dfrac{(x-1)}{3} = 1$ b $\dfrac{(2x+1)}{3} = 5$ c $\dfrac{(1-x)}{2} = 3$

  d $\dfrac{2x-1}{4} = 6$ e $\dfrac{4-3x}{2} = 1$ f $\dfrac{2a-9}{7} = 5$

4   The bus fare for an adult is x pence.
    The fare for a child is 50p less than this.
  a   Write down an expression for the cost of 3 child fares.
  b   The cost of three child fares is 210p.
       Form an equation using this information and solve it.
  c   What is an adult fare?

5   Gaby thinks of a number. She doubles the number and
    subtracts 4.
    She then multiplies her result by 3. Her answer is 24.
    What is the number?

6   Tom writes:

$$4 - 2(x - 3) = 1$$
$$4 - 2x - 6 = 1$$
$$2 - 2x = 1$$
$$2 = 1 + 2x$$
$$1 = 2x \text{ so } x = \tfrac{1}{2}$$

    He has made two mistakes.
    Describe these mistakes.

UAM

Enrichment task

Kate uses this trick to find out someone's age without asking them.

She says   'Multiply your age by 5, add 4 then subtract your age from
             the answer.
             Now divide your answer by 4.
             What did you get?'

Kate subtracts 1 from the answer she is given. The result is the person's age.

a   Try this on some members of your family.
b   Explain why it works using algebra.
c   Create your own trick to find out someone's age.

4.8 Trial and improvement

Some equations cannot be solved using algebra.
You can find a solution to 1 (or more) decimal places by trying
some values. You can use the result of the first two tries to improve
the accuracy of your next try. This method is called **trial and
improvement**.

Example 13

Use trial and improvement to complete the table to find a solution of the equation

$x^3 - x = 20.$

Give your answer correct to 1 decimal place.

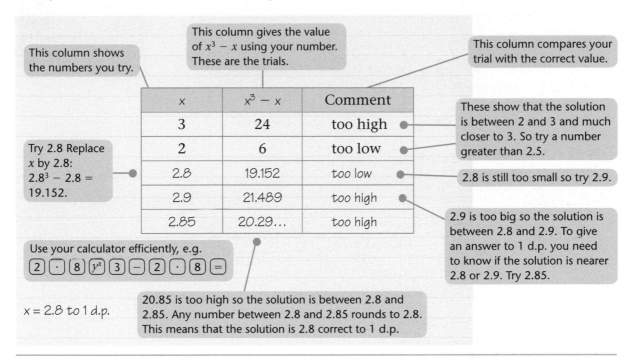

This column shows the numbers you try.

This column gives the value of $x^3 - x$ using your number. These are the trials.

This column compares your trial with the correct value.

x	$x^3 - x$	Comment
3	24	too high
2	6	too low
2.8	19.152	too low
2.9	21.489	too high
2.85	20.29…	too high

These show that the solution is between 2 and 3 and much closer to 3. So try a number greater than 2.5.

Try 2.8 Replace x by 2.8:
$2.8^3 - 2.8 = 19.152.$

2.8 is still too small so try 2.9.

2.9 is too big so the solution is between 2.8 and 2.9. To give an answer to 1 d.p. you need to know if the solution is nearer 2.8 or 2.9. Try 2.85.

Use your calculator efficiently, e.g.

2 . 8 y^x 3 − 2 . 8 =

$x = 2.8$ to 1 d.p.

20.85 is too high so the solution is between 2.8 and 2.85. Any number between 2.8 and 2.85 rounds to 2.8. This means that the solution is 2.8 correct to 1 d.p.

Exam practice 4H

Copy and complete these tables using trial and improvement to find a solution to the equations. Give your answers correct to 1 d.p.

 1 $x^3 + x = 50$

x	$x^3 + x$	Comment
3	30	too low
4	68	too high
3.5		

Start by replacing x with 3.5.
If the value of $x^3 + x$ is bigger than 50, choose a number below 3.5.
If the value is smaller than 50 try a number above 3.5.
You may have to add some rows to the table.

 2 $x^3 + 3x = 40$

x	$x^3 + 3x$	Comment
3	36	too low
4	76	too high

www 3 $x^3 + x = 4$

x	$x^3 + x$	Comment
1	2	too low

www 4 $x^2 - \dfrac{1}{x} = 5$

x	$x^2 - \dfrac{1}{x}$	Comment
2	3.5	too low
3	8.66...	too high

www 5 $x^3 - 5x = 6$

x	$x^3 - 5x$	Comment
3	12	too high

ICT task

You can use a spreadsheet program to do the calculations for trial and improvement. You can find values for $x^3 - x$ like this.

	A	B	C	D
1	x	$x^3 - x$		
2	3	24 ●		
3	2	●		
4				
5				

Enter the formula A2^3−A2 in this cell.

Find out how to use the 'fill' function to work out values in this column.

Decide what value to try here, then use the fill function again.

Use this method to find a solution to these equations. Give your answers correct to 3 d.p.

a $x^3 - x = 5$ **b** $x^3 - x = 1$ **c** $x^3 - x = -30$

4.9 Inequalities

$x > 3$ is called an **inequality**. It means that x can stand for any number greater than 3.

You can use a number line to show this inequality.

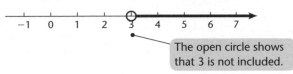

The open circle shows that 3 is not included.

> The symbol $>$ means 'greater than'.
> The symbol $<$ means 'less than'.

$x \leqslant 2$ is a different type of inequality. It means that x can stand for any number less than or equal to 2.

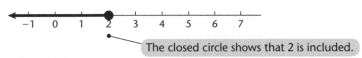

The closed circle shows that 2 is included.

> The symbol $\geqslant$ means 'greater than or equal to.'
> The symbol $\leqslant$ means 'less than or equal to.'

Solving inequalities

Solving an inequality means finding the values of x for which it is true.

You can use these facts to help solve an inequality.

> The solution will look like '$x <$ a number' or '$x >$ a number'.

You can add the same number to both sides or subtract the same number from both sides. $5 > 3$: • adding 4 to both sides gives $9 > 7$ which is true • subtracting 6 from both sides gives $-1 > -3$ which is also true.	You can multiply or divide both sides by the same positive number. $5 > 3$: • multiplying both sides by 2 gives $10 > 6$ which is true. Do not multiply or divide by a negative number. $5 > 3$: multiplying both sides by -2 gives '$-10 > -6$' which is not true.

Example 14

Solve these inequalities and show the solution on a number line.
a $2x < 7$ **b** $3x - 5 \geqslant 7$

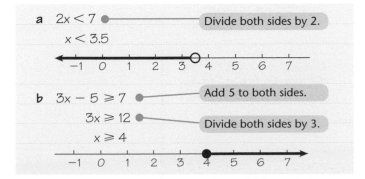

a $2x < 7$ Divide both sides by 2.
$x < 3.5$

b $3x - 5 \geqslant 7$ Add 5 to both sides.
$3x \geqslant 12$ Divide both sides by 3.
$x \geqslant 4$

Sometimes two inequalities are combined.

Example 15

Find the integers that satisfy $6 < 5n \leq 15$.

$6 < 5n \leq 15$ means $6 < 5n$ and $5n \leq 15$. The values of n must make both inequalities true.

$6 < 5n \leq 15$ •————— Divide all three expressions by 5.

$1.2 < n \leq 3$

Show this on a number line. You can now see the integers for which both inequalities are true. The integers are all the positive and negative whole numbers, and zero.

$n = 2$ and 3

Exam practice 4l

1   Solve these inequalities:
   a $2x < 8$
   b $x + 1 < 6$
   c $3x > 9$
   d $x - 4 < 2$
   e $x + 7 > 4$
   f $2x > 5$
   g $2x \geq 10$
   h $x + 2 \geq 5$
   i $x - 4 \leq 10$
   j $3p < -9$
   k $x - 3 > -1$
   l $2s \geq -4$

2   Solve these inequalities:
   a $2x + 3 < 9$
   b $3x - 2 > 6$
   c $6x < x + 10$
   d $x - 2 \leq 6$
   e $x + 4 > 3x$
   f $2y + 5 > 9$
   g $5a - 2 \geq 13$
   h $2x - 3 \leq 7$
   i $7x + 1 > x + 11$
   j $2t + 4 < 18 - t$
   k $3k \geq 2k + 6$
   l $7y - 9 \leq 3y$

   In part **c** start by subtracting x from both sides.

3   Write down the integers that satisfy each inequality.
   a $6 < x < 10$
   b $-3 < x < 2$
   c $4 \leq n < 7$
   d $4 < 2x < 10$
   e $-2 < 2n < 8$
   f $-3 \leq 5n < 15$
   g $4 < 4x \leq 14$
   h $-6 \leq 2n \leq 2$
   i $3 \leq 4n < 8$

   Be careful. Look at the inequality signs.

Summary of key points

- You can solve an equation by reversing the addition, subtraction, multiplication or division.
- You must always do the same thing to both sides of an equation.
- When an equation contains brackets, start by multiplying out the brackets.
- You can find an approximate solution to an equation by trying values and then improving the values you try until you have an answer that is accurate enough.
- You can add the same number to both sides or subtract the same number from both sides of an inequality.
- You can multiply or divide both sides of an inequality by the same positive number.
- Do not multiply or divide an inequality by a negative number.

Most students who get GRADE E or above can:
- write an expression from a problem
- solve equations like $2x - 6 = 3$

Most students who get GRADE C can also:
- solve equations containing brackets
- solve inequalities
- use trial and improvement.

Glossary

Equation	two expressions connected by an equals sign
Expression	a collection of numbers and letters with no equals sign
Identity	two expressions that mean the same but written differently and connected by an equals sign
Inequality	two expressions related by an inequality sign
Integers	all the positive and negative whole numbers, and zero
Solving	finding values that make an equation or inequality true
Trial and improvement	using the result of one trial number to find a more accurate answer

5 Angles and lines

This chapter will show you:
- ✓ what a line segment is
- ✓ how to distinguish between acute, obtuse and reflex angles
- ✓ how to measure an angle
- ✓ what vertically opposite angles are
- ✓ that angles on a straight line add up to 180°
- ✓ the meaning of supplementary and complementary angles
- ✓ the different types of angles obtained when a straight line cuts two or more parallel lines

Before you start you need to know:
- ✓ what an analogue clock face looks like
- ✓ how to add, subtract, multiply and divide whole numbers
- ✓ how to find a fraction of a quantity
- ✓ how to solve equations

5.1 Types of angle

A **point** has position but no size.

An **angle** measures the amount of turning.

One complete turn or **revolution** is divided into 360 **degrees** (360°).

> **Did you know**
> that the Babylonians divided one complete revolution into 360 degrees? Maybe this was because there were 360 days in their year.

A **right angle** is a quarter of a revolution.
A right angle is 90°.

Half a revolution is 2 right angles or 180°.

> The sign for a right angle is ⌐

An **acute angle** is smaller than 1 right angle.

> An acute angle is smaller than 90°.

An **obtuse angle** is larger than 1 right angle but smaller than 2 right angles.

> An obtuse angle is between 90° and 180°.

A **reflex angle** is larger than 2 right angles

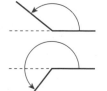

> A reflex angle is larger than 180°.

You can use three letters to name an angle.
B is the **vertex** of the angle. AB and BC are the **arms** of the angle.
You can call this ∠ABC, AB̂C or ∠B.

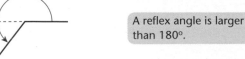 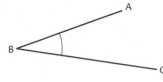

> The symbol ∠ means 'angle'.

Only one straight line can be drawn through two points. This line goes on for ever in both directions.

The straight line joining two points is called a **line segment**. AB is a line segment. AB has a length that can be measured.

When you use a ruler to measure the length of a line, your answer will depend on the subdivisions on your ruler. Usually you can read a length to the nearest subdivision.

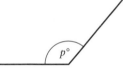

This length is between 5.7 cm and 5.8 cm. It is nearer 5.7 cm so you would give its length as 5.7 cm

---

Example 1

Write down the mathematical name that describes the size of each angle.

 a

b

 c

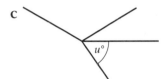

a   obtuse

$p°$ is bigger than 90° but smaller than 180°.

b   reflex

$r°$ is bigger than 180°.

c   acute

$u°$ is smaller than 90°.

Example 2

Use a **protractor** to measure this angle.

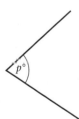

First estimate the size of $p°$. It is acute and a little smaller than 90°, so $p°$ is about 80°.

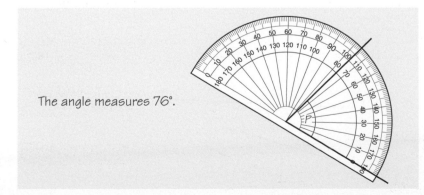

The angle measures 76°.

Place the protractor with the base line on one arm and the centre of the base line on the vertex of the angle.

Make sure that you read the scale that starts at 0 and not the one that starts at 180°. Read the angle to the nearest subdivision.

Exam practice 5A

1   Say whether each of the marked angles is acute, obtuse or reflex.

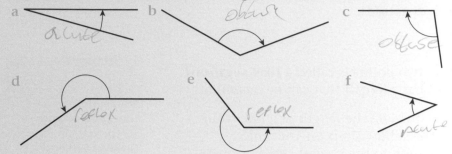

a   *acute*   b   *obtuse*   c   *obtuse*

d   *reflex*   e   *reflex*   f   *acute*

2   Work out the number of degrees in
    a $\frac{3}{4}$ of a turn   b $1\frac{1}{2}$ turns
    c $\frac{1}{3}$ of a right angle   d   0.6 of a right angle.

3   How many degrees does the hour hand of a
    clock turn through when
    a   it starts at 4 and stops at 5
    b   it starts at 3 and stops at 11
    c   it starts at 10 and stops at 3?
    In each case state whether the angle is acute,
    obtuse or reflex.

1 revolution = 360°.
There are 12 hours in
1 revolution so in
1 hour the hand turns
through
360° ÷ 12 = 30°

4   a   The minute hand of a clock is pointing at the 3.
        It turns clockwise through 90°. What number is it pointing at?
    b   The minute hand of a clock is pointing at the 6.
        It turns anticlockwise through 120°. What number is it
        pointing at?
    c   The minute hand of a clock is pointing at the 9.
        It turns clockwise through 270°. What number is it pointing at?
    d   The minute hand of a clock is pointing at the 2.
        It turns anticlockwise through 150°. What number is it pointing at?

Clockwise
means in the
same direction as the
hands of a clock turn.
Anticlockwise
means in the
opposite direction.

5   In this question
    i   state whether the angle is acute, obtuse or reflex
    ii   estimate its size
    iii use a protractor to measure its size.

Remember to use the
scale that starts at
0° on the arm of the
angle where you place
the base line of the
protractor.

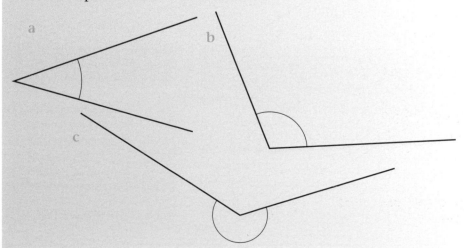

a

b

c

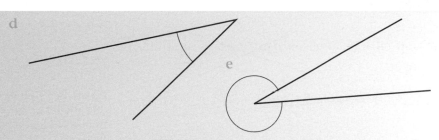

d
e

6 Draw the following angles as accurately as you can without using a protractor.
Now measure each one with a protractor to see how accurate you were.
a 45°   b 150°   c 330°   d 30°
e 60°   f 200°   g 75°   h 275°

7 Use a protractor to draw an angle of
a 30°
b 45°
c 90°
d 110°
e 160°.

Draw one arm of the angle.
Place the base line of the protractor on this line with the centre on one end.
Read from the scale starting at 0 and mark the size. Join this mark to the end of the line.

5.2 Relationships between angles

Angles at a point add up to 360°.
$p + q + r + s = 360$

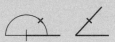

'Angles at a point' means that the angles make a complete turn around a point.

Angles on a straight line add up to 180°.
$c + d + e = 180$

When two lines cross the angles that are opposite each other are called **vertically opposite angles**.
Vertically opposite angles are equal.

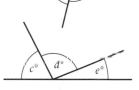

$w°$ and $y°$ are vertically opposite angles, so $w = y$.
$x°$ and $z°$ are vertically opposite angles, so $x = z$.

Complementary angles add up to 90°.
$a°$ and $b°$ are complementary angles because
$a + b = 90$.

Use a letter to name the angle.

$a°$ is the complement of $b°$ and $b°$ is the complement of $a°$.

Two angles that add up to 180° are called **supplementary angles**.
$f + g = 180$

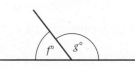

$f°$ is the supplement of $g°$ and $g°$ is the supplement of $f°$.

Example 3

Find the value of **a** *a*   **b** *b*.
Give a reason for your answer.

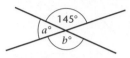

> **a** *a* + 145 = 180 because *a*° and 145° are supplementary angles.
>
>   *a* = 180 − 145 = 35
>
> **b** *b* = 145
>
>   because *b*° and 145° are vertically opposite angles.

Use the fact that *a* and 145 add up to 180 to make an equation, then solve your equation.

Example 4

Work out the value of *d*.
Give a reason for your answer.

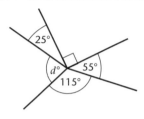

> 25 + 90 + 55 + 115 + *d* = 360 because they are angles at a point.
>
>   285 + *d* = 360
>
>   *d* = 360 − 285 = 75

Use the fact that angles at a point add up to 360° to make an equation.

Example 5

Find the value of *x*.

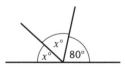

> *x* + *x* + 80 = 180
>
>   2*x* + 80 = 180
>
>   2*x* = 100
>
>   *x* = 50

The three angles add up to 180° because they are on a straight line. Use this fact to form an equation. Solve the equation to find *x*.

Exam practice 5B

1 Find:
   a the complement of 67°   b the complement of 24°
   c the supplement of 45°   d the supplement of 125°

 2 James said that 60° and 30° are supplementary.
   Why is James wrong?

 3 Sally said that 55° is the complement of 45°.
   Why is Sally wrong?

In questions 4 to 13 work out the value of each letter.
Give a reason for your answer.

4
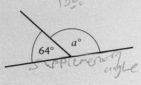

5
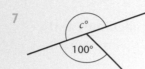

6
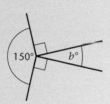

7
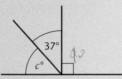

8
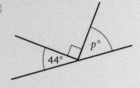

9
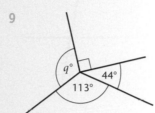

10
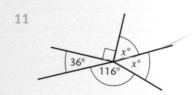

11
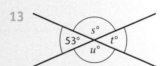

12
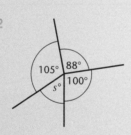

13

14
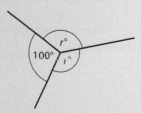

Jade wrote

360 − 100 − 260 = 130
   $r = 130°$

Jade's answer is correct but her working is not.
Write your solution to the problem.

15 Paul said that the supplement of 20° is a reflex angle.
Is Paul correct? Give a reason for your answer.

16 Amy said that the difference between the supplement of 35°
and the complement of 65° is 120°.
Is Amy correct? Give a reason for your answer.

17 Find the sum of the supplement of 145° and the complement
of 84°.

5.3 Angles and parallel lines

Parallel lines are lines that are always the same distance apart however far they are drawn.

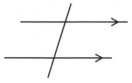

Parallel lines are marked with arrows.

A line crossing parallel lines is called a **transversal**.

A straight line will always cut parallel lines at the same angle.

The angles are called **corresponding angles**. They are equal.

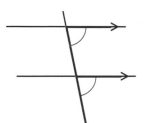

You can draw the letter F round corresponding angles Look for the letter F to help you find a pair of corresponding angles.

These two angles are **alternate angles**. They are equal.

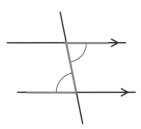

You can draw the letter Z round alternate angles. Look for the letter Z to help you find a pair of alternate angles.

Example 6

Find the value of a.
Give a reason for your answer.

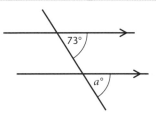

73 because 73° and $a°$ are corresponding angles.

Example 7

Find the value of c.

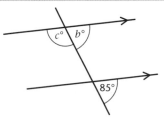

$b = 85$

$b + c = 180$ $b°$ and $c°$ are angles on
so $85 + c = 180$ a straight line.
$c = 180 - 85$
$c = 95$

You need to combine two facts to find c. First look for any two angles that are equal: $b°$ and 85° are corresponding angles so they are equal.

Exam practice 5C

1 Copy and complete these sentences.
   a Angles $a°$ and .... are corresponding angles.
   b Angles $a°$ and .... are alternate angles.

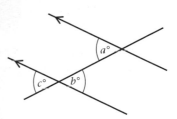

2 Copy and complete these sentences
   a Angle $e°$ = Angle .... because ....
   b Angle $e°$ + Angle $d°$ = ... because ....

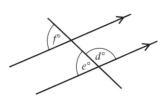

3 a Write down the angle that corresponds to $h°$.
   b Write down the angle that is alternate to $i°$.
   c Write down the angle that is vertically opposite $j°$.

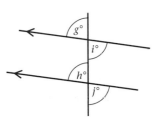

4 a Write down the angle that is alternate to $w°$.
   b Write down the angle that corresponds to $y°$.
   c Write down the angle that is vertically opposite $z°$.

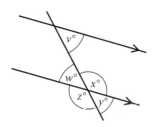

In questions 5 to 18 find the value of each letter.
Give a reason for your answer.

5

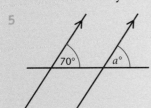

6

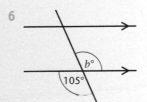

7

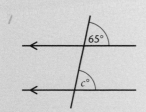

8

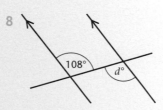

9

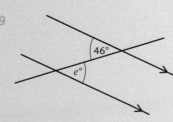

10

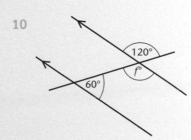

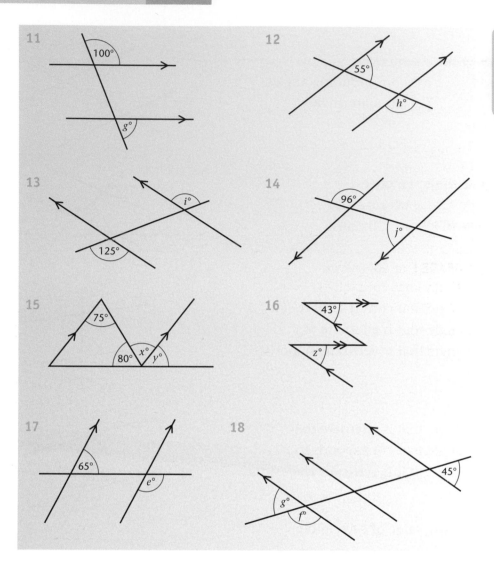

11

12

In questions **11** to **18** you need to find the sizes of some of the unmarked angles first. Mark these on a copy the diagram.

13

14

15

16

17

18

Summary of key points

- A revolution is one complete turn.
  1 revolution = 4 right angles = 360°.
- 1 right angle = 90°.
- Vertically opposite angles are equal.
- Angles on a straight line add up to 180°.
- Angles at a point add up to 360°.
- Corresponding angles are equal.
- Alternate angles are equal.

Most students who get GRADE E or above can:

- recognise and use vertically opposite angles
- know and use angles on a straight line and angles at a point.

Most students who get GRADE C can also:

- use alternate and corresponding angles to solve problems.

Glossary

Acute angle	an angle smaller than 90°
Alternate angles	a pair of angles formed by a straight line crossing a pair of parallel lines; also called Z-angles
Angles at a point	angles making a complete turn around a point
Angles on a straight line	angles making a straight line
Anticlockwise	the opposite of clockwise
Clockwise	the same direction as the hands of a clock turn
Complementary angles	two angles whose sum is 90°
Corresponding angles	a pair of angles formed by a straight line crossing a pair of parallel lines; also called F-angles
Degree	$\frac{1}{360}$ of a complete revolution
Line segment	the straight line joining two points
Obtuse angle	an angle that is bigger than 90° but smaller than 180°
Protractor	an instrument for measuring angles
Reflex angle	an angle that is larger than 180°
Revolution	one complete turn
Right angle	an angle of 90°
Supplementary angles	two angles whose sum is 180°
Transversal	a line that crosses parallel lines
Vertex	the point where the arms of an angle meet
Vertically opposite angles	the angles formed when two straight lines cross

6 Shapes 1

This chapter will show you:
✓ the different types of triangles
✓ what the sum of the angles of any triangle is
✓ the properties of isosceles and equilateral triangles
✓ what the sum of the angles of any quadrilateral is
✓ the names and properties of different quadrilaterals
✓ what a polygon is
✓ what the sum of the interior angles of a polygon is and what the sum of the exterior angles is
✓ the properties of regular polygons
✓ how to decide whether or not two shapes are congruent
✓ the different parts of a circle

Before you start you need to know:
✓ how to work with whole numbers
✓ that angles at a point add up to 360°
✓ the difference between complementary and supplementary angles
✓ how to recognise alternate, corresponding and vertically opposite angles
✓ how to solve equations

6.1 Triangles

A triangle has three sides and three angles.

Capital letters are used to label the corners.
These letters are used to name the triangle.
Each side is named using the letters at its ends.

In a **scalene triangle**, the three sides have different lengths.

In an **acute-angled triangle** all the angles are acute.
In an **obtuse-angled triangle** one of the angles is obtuse.

Angles of a triangle

The three angles of any triangle add up to 180°.

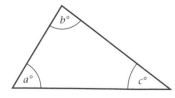

You can prove this for any triangle.

The diagram shows triangle ABC.

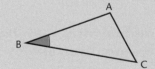

B is the **vertex** of the green angle.
AB and BC are the arms of the angle.
This angle is called ∠ABC or ∠B or B̂.

The plural of vertex is **vertices**.
Every triangle has three vertices.

The difference between a demonstration and a proof.
A demonstration shows that something is true for a particular case.
A proof shows that something is true in all cases.

You can draw a triangle, measure the three angles and add them up. This demonstrates that the three angles of your triangle add up to 180°. It does not prove that the three angles of any triangle add up to 180°.

In this diagram CE is parallel to AB so

$\angle A = \angle ECD$ (corresponding angles)

$\angle B = \angle BCE$ (alternate angles)

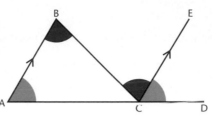

The three angles at C add up to 180°
(angles on a straight line)

so $\angle A + \angle B + \angle C = 180°$

Therefore **the angles of any triangle add up to 180°**.

You can also use this diagram to prove that **an exterior angle of a
triangle is equal to the sum of the two inside opposite angles**.

Exterior angle $\angle BCD = \angle BCE + \angle ECD$

$= \angle B + \angle A$

So the exterior angle $\angle BCD$ = the sum of the two opposite
interior angles.

> An **exterior angle**
> is formed when a side
> is extended in either
> direction.
>
>
>
> An interior angle is an
> angle between two
> sides inside the shape.

> **Class discussion**
>
> Can you find another way of proving
> that the external angle = $\angle A + \angle B$?
> Think of the facts that you know about
> straight lines and then a triangle

Example 1

a Calculate the value of a.

b Give a reason for your answer.

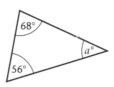

a $68 + 56 + a = 180$

$124 + a = 180$

$a = 180 - 124$

$a = 56$

b The three angles of a triangle add up to 180°.

> The sum of the three
> angles in the triangle is
> $68 + 56 + a$ degrees.
> You know this sum is
> 180 degrees. Use this
> to form an equation.

Example 2

a Work out the value of b

b Give a reason for your answer.

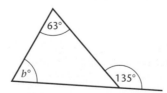

a $b + 63 = 135$

$b = 135 - 63$

$b = 72$

b The exterior angle of a triangle equals the sum of the two interior
opposite angles.

> Use the fact that the
> sum of the two interior
> angles is equal to the
> exterior angle to form
> an equation.

Exam practice 6A

Find the value of each letter. Give reasons for your answers.

1
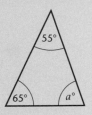

2
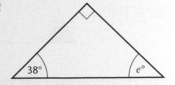

3
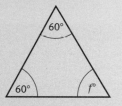

4
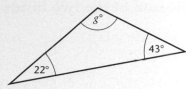

5
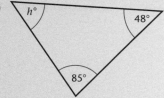

6
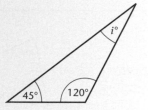

7
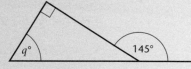

8
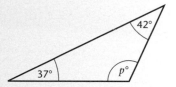

9
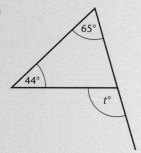

10
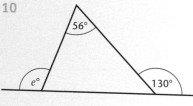

11
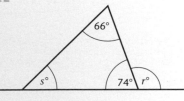

12

13
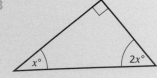

14
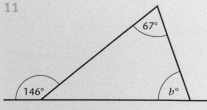

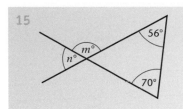

15

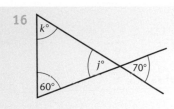

16

You need other facts as well as the facts about angles and triangles.

6.2 Special triangles

An **isosceles** triangle has two equal sides and two equal angles.
The equal angles are called the **base angles** of the triangle.

You know that a triangle is isosceles if you know that two sides are equal or that two angles are equal.

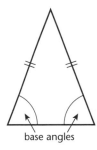

base angles

The equal sides and the **base angles** on this isosceles triangle are marked.
You can see that neither of the base angles is between the equal sides.

An **equilateral triangle** has three equal sides and three equal angles. Each angle is 60°.

You know that a triangle is equilateral if the three sides are equal or if all the angles are 60°.

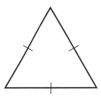

An isosceles triangle has one axis of symmetry.
An equilateral triangle has 3 axes of symmetry.
Lines of symmetry are considered in Chapter 16.

In a **right-angled** triangle one of the angles is 90°.

Example 3

Work out the value of p.
Give reasons for your answer.

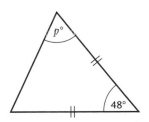

$p + p + 48 = 180$ because the base angles of an isosceles triangle are equal so the unmarked angle is also $p°$ and the angles of a triangle add up to 180°.

$2p = 180 - 48$
$2p = 132$
$p = 66$

Example 4

a Write down the value of q.

b Work out the value of r.
Give reasons for your answers.

a $q = 44$

The triangle is isosceles so the base angles are equal.

b $q + 44 + r = 180$ The angles of a triangle add up to 180°.

   $44 + 44 + r = 180$ Replace q with 44.

      $88 + r = 180$

         $r = 180 - 88$

         $r = 92$

Exam practice 6B

1 Write down the mathematical name of each triangle.

a

b

c

d
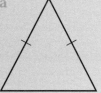

e

2 Anna said that this triangle is equilateral.
Explain why Anna is correct.

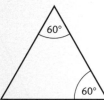

> In an equilateral triangle all the angles are equal.

UAM

3 Joe said that this triangle is isosceles.
Explain why Joe is correct.

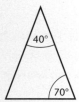

> The base angles of an isosceles triangle are equal.

UAM

4 Freddy said that one of the angles in this triangle is a right angle.
Is Freddy is correct?
Give a reason for your answer.

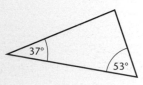

UAM

5 Kay said that two sides of this triangle are
   the same length.
   Is Kay correct?
   Give a reason for your answer.

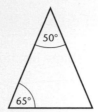

> In an isosceles triangle
> two of the sides are
> equal in length.

In questions 6 to 15 find the value of each letter.
Give reasons for your answers.

6

7

8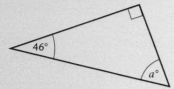

9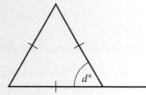

10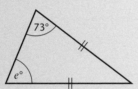

11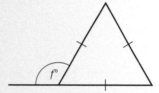

12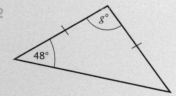

13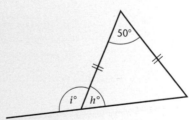

14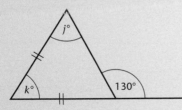

15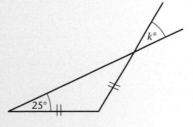

> You need the facts
> about vertically
> opposite angles.

16 Tim had to find $a°$ in this diagram.
    He wrote
        $a = 40 + 40 = 80 - 180 = 100$
    Tim's answer is correct, a is 100,
    but what he has written is wrong.
    a Explain what is wrong.
    b Write your own solution to the problem.

6.3 Quadrilaterals

A **quadrilateral** is a flat shape bounded by four straight lines.

A **diagonal** is a line joining two opposite vertices.

Every quadrilateral has two diagonals.

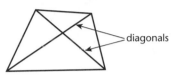

←diagonals

Each diagonal divides a quadrilateral into two triangles.

The sum of the angles in any triangle is 180° so **the sum of the angles of a quadrilateral is 360°.**

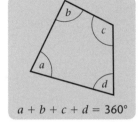

$a + b + c + d = 360°$

Example 5

Find the value of

a x **b** y.

Give a reason for your answer.

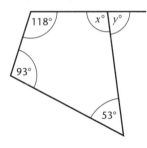

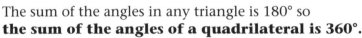

a $118 + 93 + 53 + x = 360$ The angles of a quadrilateral add up to 360°.

$264 + x = 360$

$x = 360 - 264$

$x = 96$

> Use the fact that the angles of a quadrilateral add to 360° to make an equation.

b $x + y = 180$ Angles on a straight line add up to 180°

$96 + y = 180$

$y = 180 - 96$

$y = 84$

> Replace x with 96.

Example 6

Work out the value of p.

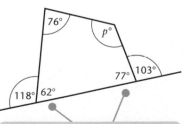

$77 + 76 + p + 62 = 360$

$215 + p = 360$

$p = 360 - 215$

$p = 145$

> Use the fact that angles in a quadrilateral add up to 360°.

> First find the size of the unknown angles inside the quadrilateral. You can use the fact that angles on a straight line add up to 180°.

Exam practice 6C

Work out the value of each letter.

1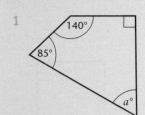

2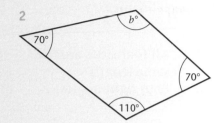

3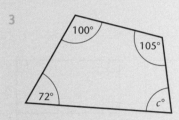

4

5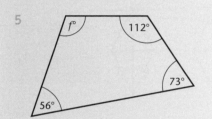

6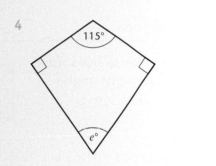

Find the value of the unmarked angle in the quadrilateral first and then mark it in a copy of the diagram.

7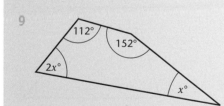

8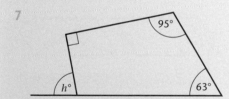

9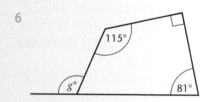

10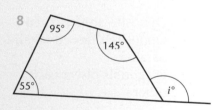

Use the fact that the sum of the four angles in a quadrilateral is 360° to make an equation.

11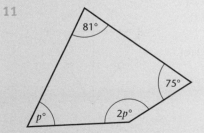

12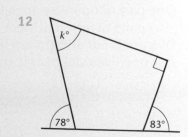

In question 12 you must find the unmarked angles in the quadrilateral first.

6.4 Special quadrilaterals

Some quadrilaterals have special names.

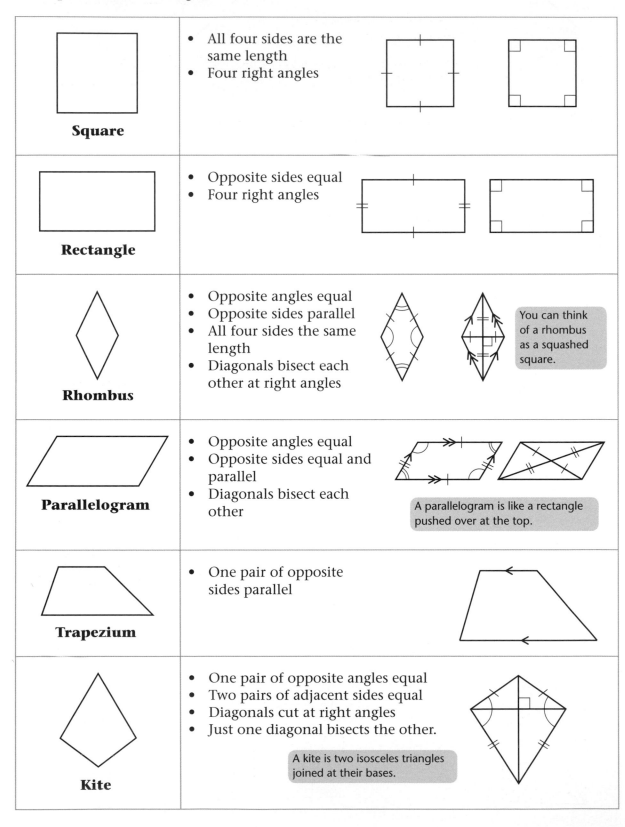

Square	• All four sides are the same length • Four right angles
Rectangle	• Opposite sides equal • Four right angles
Rhombus	• Opposite angles equal • Opposite sides parallel • All four sides the same length • Diagonals bisect each other at right angles
Parallelogram	• Opposite angles equal • Opposite sides equal and parallel • Diagonals bisect each other
Trapezium	• One pair of opposite sides parallel
Kite	• One pair of opposite angles equal • Two pairs of adjacent sides equal • Diagonals cut at right angles • Just one diagonal bisects the other.

You can think of a rhombus as a squashed square.

A parallelogram is like a rectangle pushed over at the top.

A kite is two isosceles triangles joined at their bases.

Example 7

Work out the value of each letter.

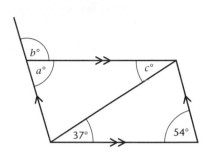

$a = 54$	$a°$ and $54°$ are opposite angles of a parallelogram so they are equal.
$b = 180 - 54$ $b = 126$	$a°$ and $b°$ are angles on a straight line so they add up to $180°$
$c = 37$	$c°$ and $37°$ are alternate angles so they are equal.

In questions **1** to **14** find the value of each letter.

1

2

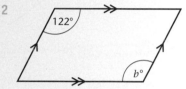

3

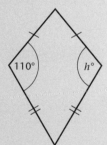

4

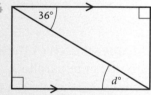

Alternate angles are equal.

5

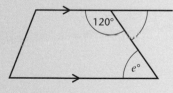

6

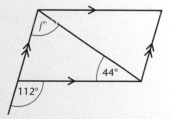

An exterior angle of a triangle equals the sum of the two interior opposite angles.

7

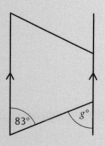

8

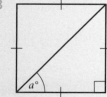

9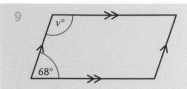

10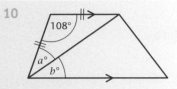

11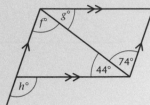

12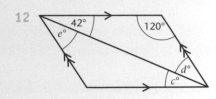

13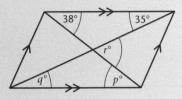

14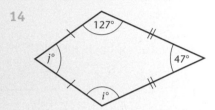

15 Show how two of these triangles can be put together to form
   a an isosceles triangle
   b a rectangle
   c a parallelogram.

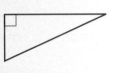

(UAM) 16 What is the mathematical name of each of these quadrilaterals?   Sketch each shape.
   a Both pairs of its opposite sides are parallel.
   b It is a parallelogram in which one angle is a right angle.
   c It is a parallelogram with both its diagonals the same length.
   d Its diagonals are the same length, bisect each other, and cross at right angles.
   e It is a parallelogram with four equal sides.

(UAM) 17 Jamie drew this diagram.

He said that this proved that a quadrilateral with both diagonals the same length must be a rectangle.
   a Is this a demonstration or a proof?
   Give a reason.
   b Is it true that a quadrilateral with both diagonals the same length must be a rectangle?

18 Colleen said that if a parallelogram has one angle equal to 90°, all the angles must be 90°.
(UAM) Is Colleen correct? Give a reason for your answer

6.5 Polygons

A **polygon** is a flat shape bounded by straight lines.

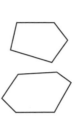

A polygon with 3 sides is a triangle.
A polygon with 4 sides is a quadrilateral.

A polygon with 5 sides is a called a **pentagon**.

A polygon with 6 sides is called a **hexagon**.

Exterior angles

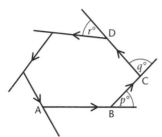

> Think about walking around the polygon in the direction of the arrows, starting at A. At B you turn through an angle $p°$ to walk to C, then an angle $q°$ to walk to D, and so on. By the time you get back to A you have turned through 360°.

The sum of the exterior angles of any polygon is 360°.

> This means that the sum of the exterior angles of any quadrilateral is 360°.

Interior angles

> The sum of the interior and exterior angles is 180° × (number of sides).
> You know that the exterior angles add up to 360°, so the sum of the interior angles is 180° × (number of sides) − 360°.

The sum of the interior angles in any polygon is
   180° × (number of sides) − 360°
or 90° × (2 × number of sides − 4)

> The formula for the sum of the interior angles of a polygon with n sides is 90° × (2n − 4).

Example 8

a Calculate the values of p and q.
b What is the mathematical name of this quadrilateral? Give a reason for your answer.

a $110 + 105 + 70 + p = 360$
$285 + p = 360$
$p = 360 − 285$
$p = 75$
$110 + q = 180$
$q = 70$

> Angles on a straight line add up to 180°.

> The exterior angles of a quadrilateral add to 360°.

b Trapezium because 70° and $q°$ are the same size and are alternate angles so two of the sides are parallel.

Example 9

Find the sum of the interior angles of
a a pentagon   **b** a hexagon.

a In a pentagon
    sum of the interior angles $= 90° \times (2 \times 5 - 4)$
                     $= 90° \times 6$
                     $= 540°$

> A pentagon has 5 sides.
> $(2 \times \text{number of sides} - 4) = 2 \times 5 - 4 = 6$

b In a hexagon
    sum of the interior angles of $= 90° \times (2 \times 6 - 4)$
                     $= 90° \times 8$
                     $= 720°$

> A hexagon has 6 sides.
> $(2 \times \text{number of sides} - 4) = 2 \times 6 - 4 = 8$

Regular polygons

A **regular polygon** has all its sides the same length and all it angles equal.

These polygons are regular.

Equilateral triangle

Square

Regular
Pentagon

Regular
Hexagon

> **Did you know**
> that the United States Defence Department building is called The Pentagon because of its shape?

Example 10

A regular polygon has 10 sides.
Find   **a**   the size of an exterior angle
          b   the size of an interior angle.

a Size of an exterior angle $= 360° \div 10 = 36°$

> The sum of all the exterior angles is 360°. There are 10 of them and they are all equal.

b Size of an interior angle $= 180° - 36° = 144°$

> An exterior angle and the interior angle next to it add up to 180°.

Example 11

Each interior angle of a regular polygon is 156°.
How many sides does it have?

Each exterior angle is $180° - 156° = 24°$

Number of sides $= 360° \div 24° = 15$

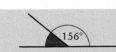

> First find an exterior angle.
> (No. sides) $\times 24 = 360$.
> So (No. sides) $= 360 \div 24$.

Exam practice 6E

In questions 1 to 4 find the value of x.

1
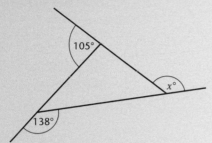

2
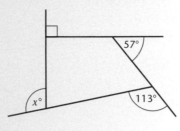

3
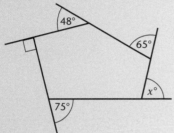

4
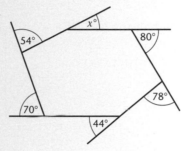

5   Find the size of each exterior angle of a regular polygon with
   a   6 sides   b   8 sides   c   12 sides   d   18 sides.

6   Find the size of each interior angle of a regular polygon with
   a   5 sides   b   8 sides   c   12 sides   d   20 sides.

> First find the size of an external angle.

7   How many sides has a regular polygon if each exterior angle is
   a   20°   b   30°   c   45°?

8   How many sides has a regular polygon if each interior angle is
   a   120°   b   140°   c   135°?

9   Is it possible for the exterior angles of a regular polygon to be
   a   40°   b   50°   c   60°   d   70°?
   Give reasons for your answers.

10   Is it possible for the interior angles of a regular polygon to be
   a   90°   b   130°   c   135°   d   165°?
   Give reasons for your answers.

11   Find the value of x in each of these diagrams:

> First find the sum of the interior angles.

a
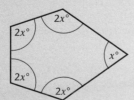

b
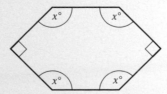

12 a This is a regular polygon.
       What is its mathematical name?
    b O is the centre of the polygon.
       Work out the value of *p*.
    c Find the value of *q*.

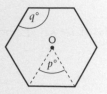

The angle at O is 360°
divided by the number
of sides.

UAM 13 ABCDE is a regular pentagon.
             Find a the value of *x*
                   b the value of *y*.

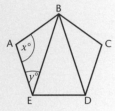

Triangle ABE is
isosceles.

UAM 14 ABCDEF is a regular hexagon.
             Find a the size of ∠BAF
                   b the sizes of the other two
                      angles in △BAF
                   c the size of ∠BFC.

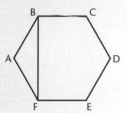

△ is the symbol used
for 'triangle'.

UAM 15 ABCDEF is a regular hexagon.
             a Find the sizes of the angles
                in ABEF.
             b What is the mathematical name
                for ABEF?

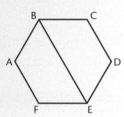

6.6 Congruence

Two shapes are congruent if they are exactly the same shape and size.
Congruent shapes are alike in all respects.

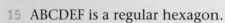

Example 12

These two triangles are
congruent.

Find **a** the length of AC
      b the size of angle C.

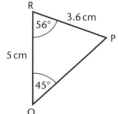

Sides or angles that are
in the same position in
both figures are called
corresponding sides
or angles. They are the
same size.

a AC = 3.6 cm

Look for the side in triangle PQR that
corresponds to AC. AC is opposite the angle 45°
PR is opposite the angle 45° so AC = PR.

b ∠P = 180° − 101° = 79°
    ∠C = 79°.

∠C = ∠P (they are both opposite the 5 cm
side). You can find ∠P using the fact that the
three angles in △PQR add up to 180°.

Exam practice 6F

1   Write down whether or not the two shapes are congruent.

If you are not sure trace one shape and see if it will fit over the other one. You may need to turn the shape over.

a    b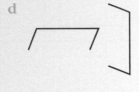

c    d

e    f

g   h

2   Which pair of these shapes are congruent?

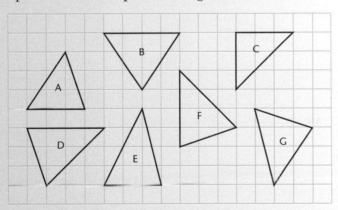

3   Which two pairs of these shapes are congruent?

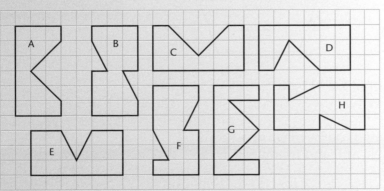

4 Which shapes are congruent with A?

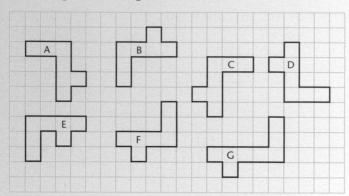

5 These two triangles are congruent.

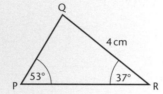

a What is the size of ∠C?
b Write down the length of PR.

6 These two quadrilaterals are congruent.

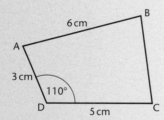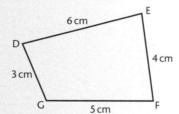

a What is the size of ∠G?
b Write down the length of BC.

7 These two trapeziums are congruent.

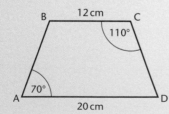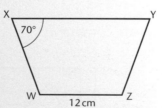

a Write down the length of XY.
b What is the size of ∠WZY?

8 a What is the mathematical name of this polygon?
   b David says that triangle ABE and triangle BCD are
      congruent.
      What assumptions has David made?

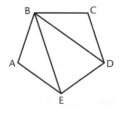

Class discussion

What assumptions do you need
to make about the diagrams for
the statement to be true?

1 •

The other two angles are
70° and 40°.

•

Each angle is 60°.

•

This is a rectangle.

•

These rectangles are
congruent.

2

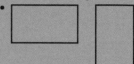

• If you assume that this is
  a square, what can you
  say about the lengths of
  the sides?
• If you assume that this
  is a parallelogram, what
  can you say about the
  lengths of the sides?
• If you assume that this
  is a trapezium, what
  can you say about the
  lengths of the sides?

9 a What is the mathematical name of this regular polygon?
  b Name an isosceles triangle in this diagram.
  c Name a triangle congruent with triangle BCD.

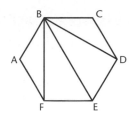

6.7 Circles

You can draw a circle using a pair of compasses.

The line drawn by the pencil is the **circle**. The length of this line is the **circumference**.

A straight line through the centre O joining two points on the circumference is a **diameter**.

A straight line from a point on the circumference to the centre is a **radius**.

Part of the perimeter of a circle is an **arc**.

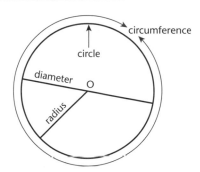

All the points on the circle are the same distance from the centre, O. O is where you put the point of your compasses.

A **chord** is a straight line that joins two points on the circle. It divides the area enclosed by a circle into two parts called **segments**.

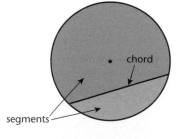

The larger segment is the major segment. The smaller segment is the minor segment.

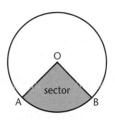 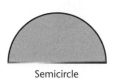

This diagram shows a **sector** of a circle.
When the angle AOB = 90° it is called a **quadrant**.
When the angle is 180° it is called a **semicircle**.

This is where the tangent touches the circle. This point is called the **point of contact**.

This straight line is a **tangent**.
It touches the circle at one point.

Exam practice 6G

1 Write down the word that completes each sentence:
   a A chord of a circle passing through the centre is a ....
   b A straight line from the centre of a circle to a point on the circumference is a ....
   c A straight line joining two points on the circumference of a circle is a ....
   d The part of the circle from A to B is an ....

2 What mathematical word describes the line
   a AB
   b AC?

3 What is the mathematical name of the line
   a OR
   b PQ?

4 What mathematical word describes the line
   a DF
   b EG?
   Give reasons for your answers.

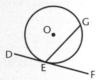

5 What mathematical word describes the line
   a PR   b QR?
   Give reasons for your answers.

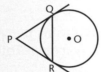

6 Write down the name of each green area.
   a   b   c   d

7 a Draw a circle.
   b Draw and label a radius on your circle.
   c Draw and label a diameter on your circle.
   d Draw and label a tangent to your circle.

8 a On this diagram name
      i   a diameter
      ii   a chord
      iii a tangent
      iv   a radius.
   b Ravi said:
      'There are three lines on the diagram that are radii.'
      Is Ravi correct? Explain your answer.

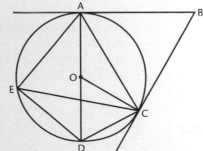

Summary of key points

- The angles of any triangle add up to 180°.
- The angles in a quadrilateral add up to 360°.
- In a square all four sides are the same length and every angle is 90°.
- In a rectangle the opposite sides are equal and all the angles are 90°.
- In a parallelogram the opposite sides are equal and parallel, the opposite angles are equal, and the diagonals bisect each other.
- A kite has one pair of opposite angles equal, two pairs of sides next to each other equal and one diagonal is bisected by the other at right angles.
- In a trapezium one pair of opposite sides are parallel.
- A polygon is a flat shape bounded by straight lines.
- The sum of the exterior angles of any polygon is 360°.
- The sum of the interior angles of any polygon is
  (180° × number of sides) − 360° or 90° × (2 × number of sides − 4).
- The sum of an interior angle and an exterior angle at any vertex is 180°.
- In a regular polygon, all the sides are equal, all the exterior angles are equal and all the interior angles are equal. Each exterior angle is equal to 360° ÷ (number of sides).

Most students who get GRADE E or above can:
- use the facts about angles, triangles and quadrilaterals to calculate the value of an angle.

Most students who get GRADE C can also:
- use the facts about angles and polygons to find the value of an angle.

Glossary

Acute-angled triangle	a triangle in which all the angles are acute
Arc	part of a circle
Base angles	the angles opposite the equal sides of an isosceles triangle
Chord	a straight line joining two points on a circle
Circle	a curve that is everywhere the same distance from a point (this is the centre of the circle)
Circumference	the length of a circle
Diagonal	a line joining two opposite vertices
Diameter	a chord that goes through the centre of a circle
Equilateral triangle	a triangle in which all the sides are equal and all the angles are 60°
Exterior angle	the angle formed by extending the side of a shape
Hexagon	a polygon with six sides
Interior angle	the angle between two sides within a shape
Isosceles triangle	a triangle in which two sides are equal in length and the angles opposite these sides are equal
Kite	a quadrilateral with two pairs of adjacent sides equal
Obtuse-angled triangle	a triangle in which one angle is obtuse

Glossary (continued)

Parallelogram	a quadrilateral with both pairs of opposite sides equal and parallel
Pentagon	a polygon with five sides
Polygon	a flat shape bounded by straight lines
Quadrant	a quarter of a circle
Quadrilateral	a flat shape bounded by four straight lines
Radius	a straight line from the centre of a circle to a point on its circumference
Rectangle	a quadrilateral with all angles equal to 90°
Regular polygon	a polygon with all its sides and angles equal
Rhombus	a parallelogram with all four sides equal
Right-angled triangle	a triangle with one right-angle
Sector	a part of a circle between radii
Segment	a part of a circle between a chord and an arc of the circle
Semicircle	half a circle
Scalene triangle	a triangle with sides of different lengths
Square	a rectangle with four equal sides
Tangent	a straight line that touches a circle at one point
Trapezium	a quadrilateral with just one pair of opposite sides parallel
Vertex	a point where two edges of a plane shape meet

7 Constructions

This chapter will show you:
✓ how to draw a triangle accurately
✓ how to bisect an angle using ruler and compasses only
✓ how to draw some angles using ruler and compasses only
✓ how to construct the perpendicular bisector of a line
✓ how to construct the perpendicular to a line at a point on the line
✓ how to construct the perpendicular from a point to a line
✓ how to draw a regular polygon
✓ how to draw parallel lines

Before you start you need to know:
✓ how to use a pair of compasses
✓ how to use a protractor
✓ the common units of length
✓ the properties of isosceles and equilateral triangles
✓ the properties of the different quadrilaterals
✓ the names and properties of polygons

7.1 Constructing triangles

A triangle has three angles and three sides.
You can **construct** a triangle when you are given three measurements.
You need to know the length of at least one side.

> Construct means 'draw accurately'.

Example 1

This triangle is not drawn to scale.
Construct the triangle using ruler and compasses.

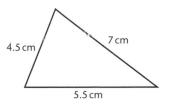

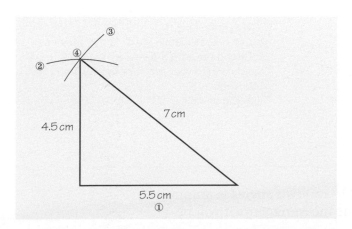

① Draw the side that is 5.5 cm long.
② Use a ruler to open the compasses to 4.5 cm (the length of another side). With the point of the compasses on one end of the first side, draw an arc.
③ Open the compasses to 7 cm (the length of the third side).
With the compass point on the other end of the first side draw an arc to cut the first arc.
④ Join the point where the arcs cross to each end of the first line.

The triangle you draw when given the lengths of three sides is unique.
If you draw another triangle whose sides are the same three lengths,
the two triangles will be **congruent**.

Example 2

This triangle is not drawn to scale.
Construct the triangle using a ruler and protractor.

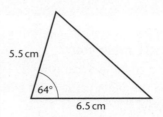

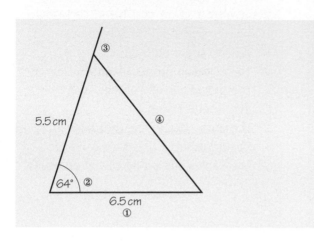

① Draw one of the sides whose length you know.
② Next use a protractor to construct an angle of 64° at one end of the line. Make this arm quite long.
③ Measure 5.5 cm along this line and mark a point.
④ Join this point to the other end of the first line.

The triangle you draw when given the lengths of two sides and the
angle between them is unique.
If you draw another triangle whose sides are the same length with the
same angle between them, the two triangles will be congruent.

Example 3

This triangle is not drawn to scale.
Construct the triangle using a ruler and protractor.

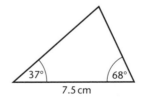

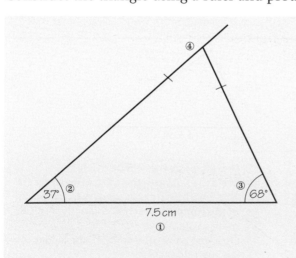

① Draw the side that is 7.5 cm long.
② Now use your protractor to construct an angle of 37° at one end of the side. Make this arm quite long.
③ Construct an angle of 68° at the other end.
④ Extend the arms if necessary until they cross. You can check your accuracy by measuring the third angle.
It should be 180° − 37° − 68° = 75°.

The triangle you draw when given one side and two angles is unique.
If you draw another triangle with the same measurements it will be
congruent with the first triangle.

Example 4

This triangle is not drawn to scale.
a Draw the triangle accurately.
b Can you draw a different triangle with these measurements?

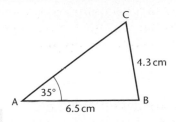

a

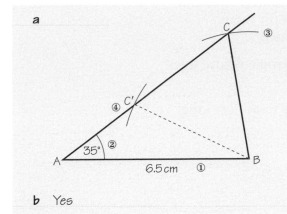

① Draw the side that is 6.5 cm long (AB).
② Construct an angle of 35° one end of the line (A). Make this arm quite long.
③ With the compass point at the other end of the line (B) and your compasses opened to 4.3 cm, draw an arc to cut the arm of the 35° angle. Join this point to the end of the line (B).
④ When you continue the arc it cuts the arm at a second point. When this is joined to B it makes a different triangle with the same measurements.

b Yes

Exam practice 7A

You need a protractor, a ruler and a pair of compasses for these questions.

Make sure you have a sharp pencil.

These triangles are not drawn to scale.
In questions **1** to **8** draw each triangle accurately and make any measurements asked for.

1

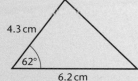

Measure the angle opposite the longest side.

2

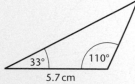

Measure the side opposite the angle of 65°.

3

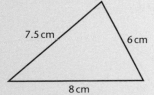

Measure the third side.

4

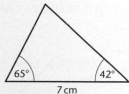

Measure the shortest side.

5

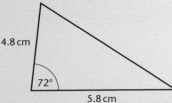

Measure the angle opposite the side of length 5.8 cm.

6

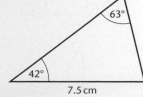

You need to calculate the third angle before you can start.

Measure the side opposite the angle of 42°.

7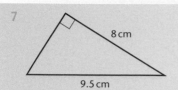

8 cm

9.5 cm

Measure the smallest angle.

8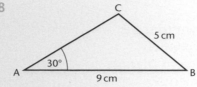

C

5 cm

30°

A   9 cm   B

Can you draw a different triangle with these measurements?

9 Make an accurate drawing of an equilateral triangle whose sides are 8 cm long.

10 a Draw accurately an isosceles triangle with a base 7 cm long and base angles of 68°.
  b How long are the equal sides?

11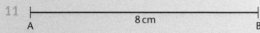

A   8 cm   B

This line is a diagonal of a rhombus.
The sides of the rhombus are 7 cm long.
  a Copy this line leaving at least 6 cm above and below it.
  b Construct the rhombus.
  c Measure the other diagonal.

7.2 Congruent triangles

Constructing triangles shows that two triangles are congruent if they satisfy any one of four conditions.

- The three sides of one triangle are equal to the three sides of the other triangle. (SSS)

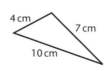

4 cm
7 cm
10 cm

7 cm
10 cm
4 cm

- Two sides and the included angle of one triangle are equal to two sides and the included angle of another triangle. (SAS)

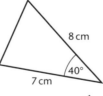

8 cm
40°
7 cm

7 cm
40°
8 cm

- Two angles and one side of one triangle are equal to two angles and the corresponding side of another triangle. (AAS)

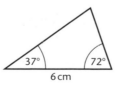

37°   72°
6 cm

37°
6 cm   72°

- Each triangle has a right angle, and the hypotenuse and one side of one triangle are equal to the hypotenuse and one side of the other triangle. (RHS)

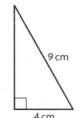

9 cm
4 cm

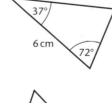

4 cm   9 cm

Example 5

Are these two triangles congruent? Give a reason.

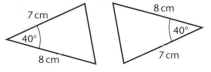
a

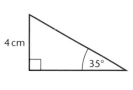

b

a Yes. Two sides of one triangle are equal to two sides of the other triangle and the angle between them is 40°, so the triangles are congruent (SAS).

b Yes. Two angles in one triangle are equal to two angles in the other triangle and the side of length 4 cm is opposite 35° in both triangles, so the triangles are congruent (AAS).

Exam practice 7B

In questions **1** to **8** state whether or not the two triangles are congruent. Say which of the four conditions is satisfied.

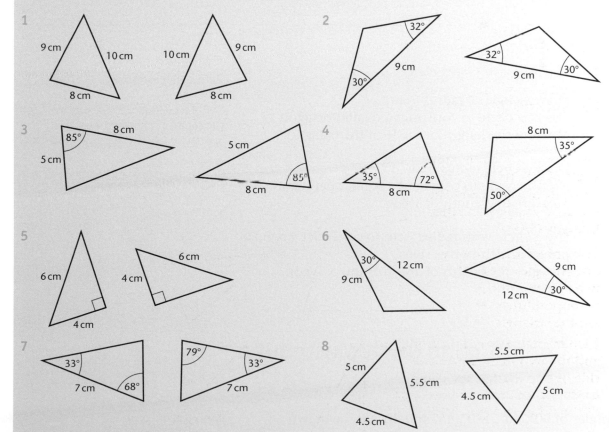

7.3 Drawing regular polygons

You can use a circle to draw a regular polygon.
Divide the angle at the centre of the circle into the same number of
equal parts as there are sides in the polygon.

Example 6

a Draw a regular hexagon using a circle with
   radius 6 cm.
b Measure the length of a side of the hexagon.

When you join each vertex of a
regular **hexagon** to its centre,
you get 6 identical equilatral
triangles: each angle at the
centre is 360° ÷ 6 = 60°.

a

① Draw the circle.
② Draw a diameter.
③ Now draw two more diameters through O at
   60° to the first diameter. (This gives you six
   angles of 60° at the centre.)
④ Join points where the arms of the diameters
   meet the circle.

b The length of a side is 6 cm.

Exam practice 7C

1 a Draw a circle of radius 5 cm.
      Use this circle to construct a regular octagon.
   b Measure the length of a side of the octagon.

An octagon has 8 sides.

Start by calculating the angles at
the centre of the circle, then use a
protractor to draw the angles you need.

2 a Draw a circle radius 6 cm.
      Use the circle to construct a regular pentagon.
   b Measure the length of a side.

A pentagon has 5 sides.

3 a Use a circle with radius 7 cm to construct a regular
      polygon with twelve sides.
   b Measure the length of a side of the polygon.

7.4 Constructing angles without a protractor

Angles of 90°, 60°, 120°, 45° and 30° can be drawn
without using a protractor.

When you use compasses for these
constructions, open them to about 5 cm.

Example 7

Construct an angle of 60° at a point A on a line segment XY.

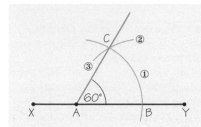

① With the point of the compasses on A draw an arc starting well above XY to cut XY at B.
② Without changing the radius move the point of the compasses to B and draw an arc to cut the first arc at C.
③ Join AC. The angle at A is 60°.
∠A = 60° because the lengths AB, AC and BC are all equal.
If you join CB, △ABC is an equilateral triangle.

This construction also gives an angle of 120° at A.

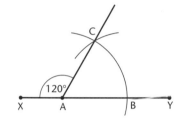

Example 8

Bisect angle A.

Bisect means 'cut exactly in half'.

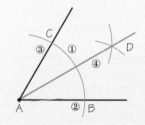

① With the point of your compasses on A, draw an arc to cut both the arms of ∠A, at B and C.
② Put the compass point on B and draw an arc between the arms.
③ Next put the point on C and, keeping the radius the same, draw an arc to cut the other arc, at D.
④ Join AD. AD bisects ∠A.

Example 9

Construct an angle of 30° at A.

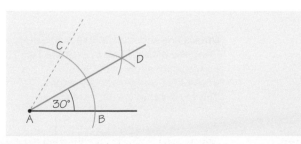

Start by constructing an angle of 60°.
This is labelled ∠CAB on the diagram.
Then bisect this angle.
∠DAB is 30° because $\frac{1}{2} \times 60° = 30°$.

Example 10

Construct the **perpendicular bisector** of the line segment PQ.

> **Perpendicular** means 'at right angles'.
> **Bisector** means 'cut exactly in half'.

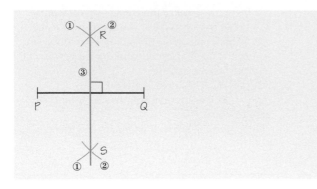

① Open your compasses to a radius more than half PQ. With the point of your compasses on P, draw arcs above and below PQ.
② Move the compass point to Q. With the same radius, draw arcs to cut the first arcs above and below the line, at R and S.
③ Join RS. This is the perpendicular bisector of the line segment PQ.

PQRS is a rhombus and the diagonals of a rhombus intersect at right angles.

You can use this construction to find the midpoint of a line.

Example 11

Construct the line that is perpendicular to the line AB at the point P.

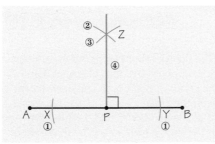

① Open your compasses to about 5 cm. Put the compass point on P. Draw an arc on each side of P to cut the line, at X and Y.
② Open your compasses more, then put the compass point at X and draw an arc above the line.
③ Move the compass point to Y and, with the same radius, draw an arc to cut the first arc at Z.
④ Join PZ.
PZ is perpendicular to AB.

This method can also be used to construct an angle of 90° at a point P on a line.

Example 12

Construct an angle of 45°.

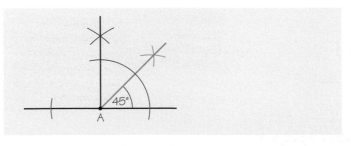

Draw a line and mark a point on it, at A.
Using the construction in Example 10, construct an angle of 90° at A.
Then bisect one of the right angles.
This gives 45° as $\frac{1}{2} \times 90° = 45°$.

Example 13

Draw a perpendicular from the point A to the line BC.

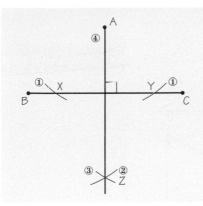

① Open your compasses to a radius more than the distance from A to the line BC.
  With the compass point on A draw arcs to cut the line BC, at X and Y.
② Move the compass point to X and draw an arc below the line.
③ Move the compass point to Y and, with the same radius, draw an arc to cut the last arc, at Z.
④ Join AZ.
AZ is perpendicular to BC.

Example 14

Draw a line through P parallel to the line AB.

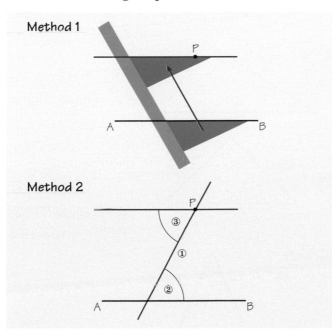

Method 1

This method uses a ruler and set square.
Put the long edge of the set square along AB.
Put the ruler against a short side of the set square.
Slide the set square along the ruler until the long edge passes through P.
Draw a line along this edge.
This line is parallel to AB.

Method 2

① Draw any line through P to cut the line AB.
② Measure the angle between your line and AB.
③ Use a protractor to draw an angle the same size at P.
You have drawn a pair of equal alternate angles so the arm of this angle is parallel to AB.

Exam practice 7D

In questions 1 to 11 only use a ruler and a pair of compasses.

Only use the equipment listed. If you do not show all your construction lines you will not get all the marks available.

1 a Copy this line.   P •————————
   b Draw an angle of 60° at P.
   c Bisect your angle of 60°.
   d What is the size of the two smaller angles at P?

2 a Copy this line.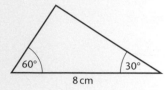
   b Draw an angle of 90° at C.
   c Bisect your angle of 90°.
   d What is the size of the two smaller angles at C?

3 a This triangle is not drawn to scale.
      Construct this triangle accurately.
   b Measure the length of the side
      opposite the angle of 60°.

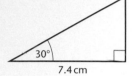

Remember, you must
not use a protector.

4 a Construct this triangle accurately.
   b Measure the length of the side opposite
      the right angle.

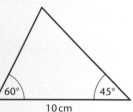

5 a This triangle is not drawn to scale.
      Construct this triangle accurately.
   b Measure the length of the side opposite
      the angle of 45°.

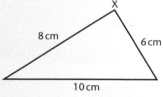

6 a Construct this triangle accurately.
   b Construct the perpendicular from X
      to the longest side.
   c Measure the length of your
      perpendicular line.

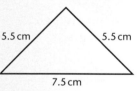

7 a Construct this isosceles triangle
      accurately.
   b Construct the perpendicular bisector
      of the side of length 7.5 cm.
   c Does this bisector pass through the
      opposite vertex of the triangle?

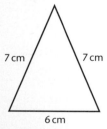

'vertex' means
'corner'.

8 a Construct this isosceles triangle accurately.
   b Construct the perpendicular bisector of one
      of the longer sides.
   c Does this bisector pass through the
      opposite vertex?

9 a Construct this isosceles triangle.
   b Construct the perpendicular from
      P to the base of the triangle.
   c Describe the point where this
      perpendicular cuts the base.

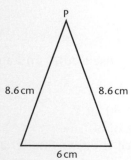

10 a Construct a triangle so that one side is 7.5 cm long and the angles at each end of this side are both 45°.
    b Measure the third angle in the triangle.
    c What special name is given to this triangle?

11 Draw this kite accurately.

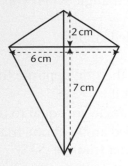

In questions 12 to 15 use either of the methods given in Example 13 to draw parallel lines.

12 a Draw this parallelogram accurately.
    b Measure the shorter diagonal.

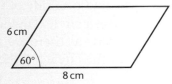

13 a Draw this square accurately.
    b Measure a diagonal.

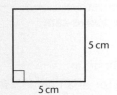

14 a Draw this rhombus accurately.
    b Measure the longer diagonal.

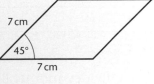

15 Draw this rectangle accurately.

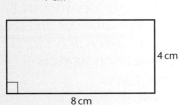

Summary of key points

- You can construct a unique triangle when you are given
  - three sides
  - two sides and the included angle
  - two angles and one side
  - a side, a right angle and the side opposite the right angle.
- Two triangles are congruent if
  - the three sides of one triangle are equal to the three sides of the other triangle (SSS)
  - two sides and the included angle of one triangle are equal to two sides and the included angle of the other triangle (SAS)
  - two angles and one side of one triangle are equal to two angles and the corresponding side of the other angle (AAS)
  - each triangle has a right angle and the hypotenuse and one side of one triangle are equal to the hypotenuse and one side of the other triangle (RHS)
- To draw a regular polygon use a circle. Divide the angle at the centre of the circle into the same number of equal parts as there are sides to the polygon. The points where the arms of these angles cut the circle are the vertices of the polygon.

Most students who get GRADE E or above can:
- draw a triangle accurately.

Most students who get GRADE C can also:
- construct the perpendicular bisector of a line or bisect an angle using ruler and compasses only.

Glossary

Bisector	a line that divides another line or an angle exactly in two
Congruent	exactly the same size and shape
Construct	draw accurately
Hexagon	a polygon with six sides
Perpendicular	at right angles

8 Formulae

This chapter will show you:
✓ what a formula is
✓ how to use a formula
✓ how to make a formula using letters
✓ how to change the subject of a formula

Before you start you need to know:
✓ how to work with negative numbers
✓ how to work with fractions and decimals
✓ how to solve an equation
✓ how to collect like terms
✓ the meaning of t^2

8.1 Formulae

A **formula** is a rule connecting quantities.
The rule for finding the area of a rectangle is a formula.

You can use a formula to find one quantity when you know the size of the other quantities.

> Area of a rectangle
> = length × breadth.

> The plural of formula is formulae.

Example 1

A travel agent works out the price of a holiday using the formula

Price = number of nights × rate per night + cost of flight

a Find the price of a holiday for 10 nights at a hotel whose rate is £35 per night and where the flight costs £200.
b Akosua books a 7 night holiday priced at £450. She chooses a hotel whose rate is £40 a night.
What is the cost of her flight?

---

a Price = number of nights × rate per night + cost of flight

= 10 × £35 + £200

= £350 + £200

= £550

> Substitute the values into the formula.

> Remember: do multiplication before addition.

b Price = number of nights × rate per night + cost of flight

£450 = 7 × £40 + cost of flight

£450 = £280 + cost of flight

cost of the flight = £450 − £280 = £170

> This is an equation. You can solve it to find the cost of the flight.

Exam practice 8A

1 Sally uses this formula to find the number of cans in a pack.

> **Number of cans = number of cans in one layer ×
> number of layers.**

A pack has 30 cans in a layer and 8 layers.
Find the number of cans in the pack.

2 A delivery company uses this rule to work out its charges.

> **10 p per kilogram × distance from depot in miles.**

Find the delivery charge on a package weighing 50 kg to be
delivered to an address 100 miles from the depot.
Give your answer in pounds.

3 Jamie uses this formula for working out the time needed to cook
a fruit cake.

> **Time = 80 minutes per kg + 20 minutes.**

How long does it take to cook a cake weighing $4\frac{1}{2}$ kg?
Give your answer in hours and minutes.

4 This formula gives the capacity of an engine.

> **Capacity = capacity of one cylinder × number of cylinders.**

a Find the capacity of an engine with 6 cylinders, each of
which has a capacity of 400 cubic centimetres.
b A car has a capacity of 1000 cubic centimetres and four cylinders.
Find the capacity of one cylinder.

5 The formula for the perimeter of a rectangle is

> **perimeter = 2 × length + 2 × the width.**

Find the perimeter of a rectangle 20 cm long and 15 cm wide.

6 Sophie uses this formula to find the number of sausages to buy
for a barbeque.

> **Number of sausages = 3 × number of people +
> 12 spare sausages.**

a How many sausages should she buy to feed 20 people?
b How many people can she feed with 36 sausages?

7 This formula gives the number of tins of cat food delivered to a
supermarket.

> **Number of tins = 48 × number of boxes.**

a Find the number of tins in 20 boxes.
b The supermarket orders 240 tins. How many boxes will be
delivered?

8 The rule for working out the cost of hiring a car is

> **£15 per day plus £0.10 per mile.**

a Find the cost of hiring the car for 5 days and driving it 800 miles.
b Gretchen hires the car for 4 days. She is charged £140. How
many miles did she drive?

8.2 Writing a formula

You can make a formula using words or letters. Use the clues in the words of the rule to decide how the letters and numbers are connected.

> A formula always has an equals sign.

Example 2

A shirt manufacturer used this formula to calculate the number of buttons needed.

Number of buttons = 12 × number of shirts.

Using N for the number of buttons and S for the number of shirts, write down the formula the manufacturer uses.

$N = 12 \times S$ Replace 'Number of buttons' with N and 'number of shirts' with S, then simplify the formula.

$N = 12S$ Remember that a formula has an equals sign. Do not write just $12S$ in your examination.

Sometimes you are not told which letters to use.
You must say what your letters stand for.

Example 3

Jenny uses this rule to work out the number of buns to buy for a barbeque.

Two buns per person and ten spare buns.

a Write down a formula in words for the number of buns needed in terms of the number of people coming to the barbeque.

> This means your formula must be written using the words 'the number of buns' on one side and the words 'the number of people' with connecting numbers on the other side of the equals sign.

b Write your formula using letters.

a Number of buns = Two buns per person and ten spare buns.
Number of buns = 2 × number of people + 10

b Let n stand for the number of buns and x stand for the number of people.

> The unknown quantities are the number of people and the number of buns. So choose letters to stand for each of these.

$n = 2 \times x + 10$
$n = 2x + 10$

Exam practice 8B

1 A car hire firm charges £40 a day plus £50 insurance.
Write a formula in words for the charge in terms of the number of days the car is hired.

2 A computer repair shop charges £30 an hour plus the cost of new parts.
Write a formula in words for the charge in terms of the number of hours and the cost of new parts.

3 The number of bottles of water delivered to a shop is twelve times the number of boxes delivered.
a Eight boxes are delivered. How many bottles is this?
b Write down a formula in words giving the number of bottles delivered in terms of the number of boxes delivered.

4 Adam uses this formula to find the number of apples in a box.

   Number of apples = 20 × number of layers.

Using N for the number of apples in the box and n for the number of layers, write down a formula for N in terms of n.

Make sure that you use N and n for the correct quantities.

5 The area of a rectangle is equal to its length multiplied by its width.
Using A for the area, l for the length and w for the width, write down a formula for the area of a rectangle in terms of its length and width.

6 Freda uses this rule for working out the time needed to defrost sausages in her microwave.

   2 minutes per sausage plus 1 minute.

a Write a formula in words for the time in terms of the number of sausages.
b Use t for the time in minutes and n for the number of sausages to write a formula for t in terms of n.

7 This formula gives the capacity of an engine.

   Capacity = capacity of one cylinder × number of cylinders.

Write this formula using C for the capacity of the engine, c for the capacity of one cylinder and n for the number of cylinders.

8 The rule for finding the perimeter of a rectangle is

   add twice the length to twice the width.

Use P for the perimeter, l for the length and w for the width to write a formula giving P in terms of l and w.

9 Ossy uses this rule to find the number of nails needed to put up a fence.

   Three times the number of fence panels plus three.

a How many nails are needed for a fence with 10 panels?
b Write a formula for the number of nails in terms of the number of fence panels i using words ii using letters.

You must say what your letters stand for.

10 The number of chairs put out in a hall for a play is 20 more than the number of tickets sold.
  a 150 tickets are sold for Friday's performance. How many chairs should be put out?
  b Write a formula for the number of chairs to be put out in terms of the number of tickets sold i using words ii using letters.

8.3 Substituting into a formula

You can find the value of one letter when you know the values of the others.

Example 4

You can find the area of a trapezium from the formula $A = \frac{1}{2}h(a + b)$.

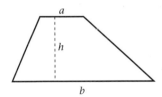

Find the area when $a = 15\,\text{mm}$, $b = 4\,\text{cm}$ and $h = 2.4\,\text{cm}$.

$A = \frac{1}{2}h(a + b)$
$a = 15\,\text{mm} = 1.5\,\text{cm}$

> When you substitute values, make sure they are measured in the same unit. Two of the lengths are in cm and one is in mm, so convert 15 mm to cm.

$A = \frac{1}{2} \times 2.4(1.5 + 4)\,\text{cm}^2$

> Replace the letters with their values. $\frac{1}{2}$ of 2.4 = 1.2

$A = 1.2(1.5 + 4)\,\text{cm}^2$

> Work out the inside of the bracket first.

$= 1.2 \times 5.5\,\text{cm}^2$

$= 6.6\,\text{cm}^2$

> When the lengths are in cm, the area is in cm².

You do not need to know what the letters stand for to substitute into a formula.

Example 5

Use the formula $s = ut - 5t^2$ to work out
a s when $u = 6$ and $t = 1$
b u when $s = 20$ and $t = -4$

a $s = 6 \times 1 - 5 \times 1^2$

$= 6 - 5$

> Do multiplication first.

$= 1$

> Replace u by 6 and t by 1.
> Remember ut means $u \times t$ and t^2 means $t \times t$.

b $20 = u \times (-4) - 5 \times (-4)^2$ •——— $(-4)^2$ means $(-4) \times (-4)$ Replace s by 20 and t by -4.
Put the negative numbers in brackets.

$20 = u \times (-4) - 5 \times (16)$

$20 = u \times (-4) - 80$ This is an equation. Solve it to find u.

$100 = u \times (-4)$

$-25 = u$

or $u = -25$

Exam practice 8C

1 Use the formula $C = 40n$ to find $40n$ means $40 \times n$.
   a C when $n = 4$
   b n when $C = 200$.

2 Use the formula $T = \dfrac{m}{210}$ to find $\dfrac{m}{210}$ means $m \div 210$
   a T when $m = 840$
   b m when $T = 30$.

3 The formula $C = 20t + 50$ is used to work out the charge for a service on a car.   Remember, do multiplication and division before addition and subtraction.
   a   Find C when $t = 2$.
   b   Find t when $C = 120$.

4 The perimeter of a rectangle can be found using the formula
   $P = 2l + 2w$.
   Find P when $l = 10$ and $w = 6$.

5 Use the formula $r = a - b$ to find   Remember subtracting a negative number is the same as adding a positive number.
   a r when $a = 7$ and $b = 5$
   b r when $a = 3$ and $b = -4$
   c a when $r = 2$ and $b = 9$.

6 Use the formula $v = u + at$ to work out   Remember when you multiply two numbers, if the signs are the same, the answer is positive, if the signs are different the answer is negative.
   a v when $u = 10$, $a = -2$ and $t = 4$
   b u when $v = 5$, $a = 2$ and $t = 2$.

7 Use the formula $A = \dfrac{PRT}{100}$ to find
   a A when $P = 100$, $R = 5$ and $T = 2$
   b P when $A = 300$, $R = 4$ and $T = 3$.

8 Use the formula $p = \frac{1}{2}(q + r)$ to work out
   a p when $q = 3$ and $r = 5$
   b p when $q = 8$ and $r = -6$
   c q when $p = 6$ and $r = -8$.

9 Use the formula $N = a + nd$ to find
   a N when $a = 4$, $n = 10$ and $d = 2$
   b N when $a = 3$, $n = 20$ and $d = -2$
   c n when $N = 30$, $a = 5$ and $d = -5$.

10 Use the formula $R = a^2 + b^2$ to find
   a R when $a = 4$ and $b = 6$
   b R when $a = 2$ and $b = -5$.
   c   Will said that R is the same for $a = 2$ and $b = 3$ and for
     $a = -2$ and $b = -3$.
     Is Will correct? Explain your answer.

11 The formula $A = \frac{1}{2}bh$ is used to find
the area of a triangle.
Use the formula to find
   a A when $b = 10\,\text{cm}$ and $h = 8\,\text{cm}$
   b A when $b = 25\,\text{mm}$ and $h = 2\,\text{cm}$
   c h when $A = 10\,\text{cm}^2$ and $b = 5\,\text{cm}$.

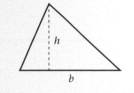

> $\frac{1}{2}bh$ means $\frac{1}{2} \times b \times h$

> h and b must be measured in the same unit. Convert 25 mm to cm.

12 The formula $V = \pi r^2 h$ is used to find the volume
of a cylinder.
Use the formula to find V in terms of π when
   a $r = 2\,\text{cm}$ and $h = 6\,\text{cm}$
   b $r = 2\,\text{mm}$ and $h = 2\,\text{cm}$.

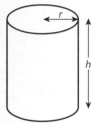

> 'In terms of π' means do not substitute the value of π but leave π in your answer.

8.4 Changing the subject of a formula

When a letter is on its own on one side of the equals sign and is not on the other side, it is called the **subject** of the formula.

Changing the subject of a formula means rearranging the formula so that another letter is the subject.

You can change the subject of a formula by thinking of it as an equation and solving it for the letter you want as the subject.

> t is the subject of
> $t = u + v$.
> A is not the subject of
> $A = 2t - \dfrac{1}{A}$ because A
> is on both sides.

Example 6

Make a the subject of the formula $t = a + b$.

      $t = a + b$
    $t - b = a$
so $a = t - b$

> To change the subject of $t = a + b$ to a you need to solve the equation for a. Subtract b from both sides.

Sometimes you need two steps to change the subject.

Example 7

Make *l* the subject of the formula $P = 2l + 2w$.

$P = 2l + 2w$

$P - 2w = 2l$

$\dfrac{P - 2w}{2} = l$

Subtract 2w from both sides.

Divide both sides by 2.

Exam practice 8D

1 Make the letter in the bracket the subject of the formula.

a $T = n + 6$ (*n*)
b $N = b - 3$ (*b*)
c $d = 2r$ (*r*)
d $A = lb$ (*b*)
e $C = \pi d$ (*d*)
f $d = st$ (*s*)
g $x = \dfrac{y}{2}$ (*y*)
h $w = \dfrac{s}{t}$ (*t*)
i $y = 3x + 2$ (*x*)
j $t = 5p - 40$ (*p*)
k $r = 3p - 4$ (*p*)
l $c = x + 2y$ (*y*)
m $y = mx + c$ (*x*)
n $V = \frac{1}{3}Ah$ (*A*)
p $a = 2(b - 4)$ (*b*)
q $w = 3(a - 2b)$ (*a*)

Multiply out the brackets first.

2 A hairdresser dries his towels in a dryer. He uses this rule to find the time needed.

Number of minutes = number of towels plus 20 minutes.

a Using *t* for the number of minutes and *n* for the number of towels, write a formula for *t* in terms of *n*.
b Make *n* the subject of your formula.

3 Square stones of side 1 foot are used to surround square flower beds.
The number of stones needed, *N*, to surround a bed whose sides are *w* feet is given by the formula

$N = 4w + 4.$

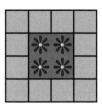

a Make *w* the subject of this formula.
b Petra uses 36 stones to go round a square flower bed. How wide is the bed?
c Petra has 18 stones left. Explain why she cannot use all these stones to surround a square bed.

4 This formula can be used to find the area, *A*, of a trapezium.

$2A = h(b + c)$

a Make *b* the subject of this formula.
b Find *b* when $A = 20$, $h = 4$ and $c = 4$.

Summary of key points

- You can use a formula to find one quantity when you know the sizes of the other quantities.
- When you write a formula you must include an equals sign.
- A formula that gives one quantity in terms of others has that quantity on its own on one side of the equals sign.
- To change the subject of a formula, rearrange it so that the new subject is in terms of the other quantities.

Most students who get GRADE E or above can:
- use a formula to find one value when the other values are known
- write a formula using given letters from a rule in words.

Most students who get GRADE C can also:
- change the subject of a formula.

Glossary

Formula   a rule connecting quantities
Subject   the quantity on its own on one side of the equals sign and not on the other side

Perimeter and area

This chapter will show you:
- ✓ how to find the perimeter of a shape
- ✓ how to find the area of a square, rectangle, triangle, parallelogram and trapezium
- ✓ how to convert different units of length
- ✓ how to convert different units of area
- ✓ how to find the circumference and area of a circle

Before you start you need to know:
- ✓ how to calculate with a mixture of +, −, × and ÷
- ✓ the properties of different triangles
- ✓ the properties of different quadrilaterals
- ✓ the different parts of a circle
- ✓ how to square a number
- ✓ how to solve equations

9.1 Length

There are two systems for measuring length.

Metric units

The metric units of length in everyday use are the kilometre (km), the metre (m), the centimetre (cm) and the millimetre (mm).

The relationship between these units are:

  1 km = 1000 m
  1 m = 100 cm = 1000 mm
  1 cm = 10 mm

Imperial units

The mile is the only Imperial unit of length in everyday use in the U.K.
Yards, feet and inches are other Imperial units of length that are used occasionally.
The relationships between these units are:

  1 foot = 12 inches
  1 yard = 3 feet

> You need to know these relationships.

You can use the relationships between different units to convert a measurement in one unit to another unit.
To convert to a smaller unit, you multiply.
To convert to a larger unit, you divide.

You can convert between Imperial and metric units of length using

  5 miles ≈ 8 km
  2 inches ≈ 5 cm
  1 foot ≈ 30 cm.

> You need to know these conversions.

Example 1

Convert
a   5.5 km to metres
b   154 cm to metres
c   7843 mm to centimetres.

a 5.5 km = 5.5 × 1000 m = 5500 m	A metre is smaller than a kilometre, so multiply by 1000. (1 km = 1000 m)
b 154 cm = 154 ÷ 100 m = 1.54 m	You are changing to a larger unit so divide. (1 m = 100 cm)
c 7843 mm = 7843 ÷ 10 cm = 784.3 cm	A mm is smaller than a cm so divide by 10. (1 cm = 10 mm)

Example 2

Convert   **a**   60 miles into kilometres   **b**   120 kilometres into miles.

a 60 × 8 ÷ 5 = 96 60 miles ≈ 96 km	5 miles ≈ 8 km so 1 mile ≈ 8 ÷ 5 km and 60 miles ≈ 60 × 8 ÷ 5 km
b 120 × 5 ÷ 8 = 75 120 km ≈ 75 miles	8 km ≈ 5 miles so 1 km ≈ 5 ÷ 8 miles and 120 km ≈ 120 × 5 ÷ 8 miles

Exam practice 9A

1 Measure the length of each line in centimetres.
   Give your answer to the nearest centimetre.

   a _____

   b _____

   c _____

   d _____

2 Measure the length of each line in millimetres.
   Give your answer to the nearest millimetre.

   a _____

   b _____

   c _____

   d _____

3 Bev said that her father was 6 ft 2 in tall.
   If you assume that this height is rounded to the nearest inch,
   what is the shortest height that her father could be?

4 Convert   a   6 km into m   b   10 cm into mm
            c   10 000 m into km   d   7600 m into km.

5 Convert   a   70 mm into cm   b   4500 mm into m
            c   800 cm into m   d   0.056 km into m.

6 Convert   a   2 m into mm   b   178 mm into cm
            c   3.5 km into m   d   0.0073 km into cm.

7 Convert   a   36 inches into feet   b   9 feet into yards.

> **Class discussion**
>
> You cannot give a measurement as an exact number of units.
> - Claire measured her table. She gave its length as 182 cm. What is the longest that the table can be if you assume the measurement is rounded to the nearest cm?
> - Andy said he was 152 cm tall. What is the shortest height he could be if you assumed he has rounded his height to the nearest cm? What other assumptions can you make? How will these affect your answer?

8 Convert into kilometres
  a 40 miles   b 65 miles   c 200 miles.

9 Convert into miles
  a 400 km   b 64 km   c 160 km.

10 The man is 180 cm tall.
   Estimate the height of the door he is standing near.

11 Convert approximately
  a 12 inches into centimetres   b 60 centimetres into inches
  c 30 inches into centimetres   d 50 centimetres into inches.

> You can do this without converting them into the same unit if you know that 1 metre is slightly longer than 1 yard.

12 Arrange these lengths in order of size, longest first.

    30 inches,   2 feet,   1 metre,   120 cm

13 Ed said that 120 kilometres is more than 80 miles.
   Is Ed correct? Give a reason for your answer.

> 1 yard = 36 inches,
> 1 inch ≈ 2.5 cm

14 Bev said that 2 metres is longer than 6 feet.
   Is Bev correct? Give a reason for your answer.

15 The box of cereal is 40 cm high.
   Estimate the height of
  a the jar   b the mug   c the cupboard

9.2 Perimeter

The **perimeter** of a shape is the total distance around it.

Example 3

Find the perimeter of this square.

3 cm

> All four sides of a square are the same length, so the perimeter is 4 × length of a side.

Perimeter = 4 × 3 cm = 12 cm.

Example 4

Find the perimeter of this rectangle.

3 cm

5 cm

5 + 3 + 5 + 3 = 16
Perimeter = 16 cm.

Example 5

Find the perimeter of this shape.

This side is 4 + 4 cm

This side is 8 + 4 cm

Go around clockwise. Start at A, writing down the lengths of the sides in order, until you get back to A.

$8 + 4 + 4 + 4 + 12 + 8 = 40$

Perimeter = 40 cm.

Example 6

The perimeter of this rectangle is 54 cm. How long is it?

12 cm

a cm

Use the fact that the perimeter is 54 cm to form an equation.

$a + a + 12 + 12 = 54$

$2a + 24 = 54$

$2a = 30$

$a = 15$

Length = 15 cm.

Exam practice 9B

1 These shapes are drawn on 1 centimetre square paper.
   Find the perimeter of each shape.

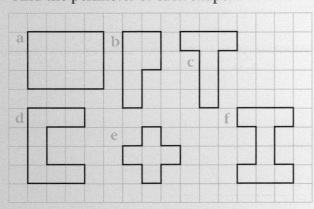

2 Find the perimeter of each square.

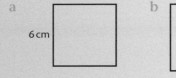

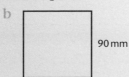

a   6 cm

b   90 mm

c   0.4 km

3 Find the perimeter of each shape.

a
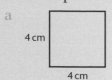
4 cm
4 cm

b
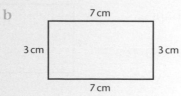
7 cm
3 cm   3 cm
7 cm

c
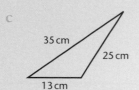
35 cm
25 cm
13 cm

d
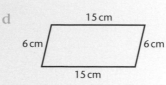
15 cm
6 cm   6 cm
15 cm

4 Find the perimeter of an equilateral triangle with side
  a 4 cm   b 6.3 mm   c 0.45 km.

> All three sides of an equilateral triangle are the same length.

5 a What is the mathematical name of this triangle?
  b What is the length of the unmarked side?
  c Work out the perimeter.

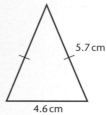
5.7 cm
4.6 cm

6 The perimeter of a square is 60 cm.
  Work out the length of a side.

7 The perimeter of this rectangle is 80 cm.
  How wide is it?

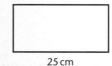
25 cm

8 The perimeter of this triangle is 45 cm.
  Work out the length of the third side.

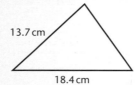
13.7 cm
18.4 cm

9 The perimeter of this triangle is $3x$ cm.
  All the sides are equal.
  a Write down an expression for the length of one side.
  b What is the mathematical name of this shape?

10 a What is the mathematical name of this special quadrilateral?
   b Work out its perimeter.

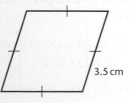
3.5 cm

11 Find the perimeter of each shape.

a

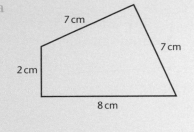

7 cm
7 cm
2 cm
8 cm

b

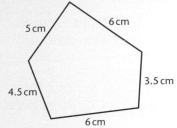

5 cm
6 cm
3.5 cm
4.5 cm
6 cm

c

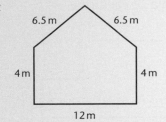

6.5 m   6.5 m
4 m   4 m
12 m

d

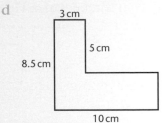

3 cm
5 cm
8.5 cm
10 cm

e

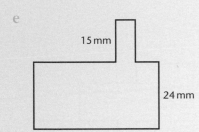

15 mm
24 mm
45 mm

f

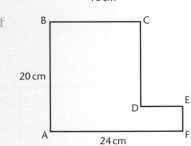

B   C
20 cm
D   E
A   24 cm   F

CD + EF = AB and
BC + DE = AF

9.3 Units of area

The area of a shape is the amount of space inside it.
Area is measured in squares.

This square has a side of 1 cm.
The area covered by this square is called
1 square centimetre ($1\,cm^2$).

The dark square has a side of 1 mm.
The area covered by this square is
called **1 square millimetre** ($1\,mm^2$).

The relationships between metric units of area are:
$$1\,cm^2 = 10 \times 10\,mm^2 = 100\,mm^2$$
$$1\,m^2 = 100 \times 100\,cm^2 = 10\,000\,cm^2$$
$$1\,km^2 = 1000 \times 1000\,m^2 = 1\,000\,000\,m^2$$

Areas of land are measured in **hectares** (ha)
where 1 ha = $10\,000\,m^2$.

In the Imperial system areas of land are measured in **acres**
where 1 acre = 4840 square yards.

To convert between hectares and acres use
1 hectare = 2.47 acres.

Class discussion

The unit used to describe
an area depends on what
is being measured.
Which unit would you use
for measuring the area of
• an oak leaf
• a bedroom window
• the bedroom floor
• a field
• a county
• a fingernail
• a carpet
• a postcard
• a playing field
• an ocean
• a supermarket receipt
• a stick-on price tag?

To convert from hectares into
acres multiply by 2.47.
To convert from acres into hectares
divide by 2.47.

Exam practice 9C

1   Convert
   a   1.2 cm² into mm²   b   450 mm² into cm²   c   0.5 km² into m²
   d   5600 m² into km²   e   0.4 km² into m²   f   564 mm² into cm².

2   Convert
   a   100 hectares into acres   b   24.7 acres into hectares
   c   123.5 acres into hectares   d   30 hectares into acres.

3   These shapes are drawn on 1 cm square paper. Find the area of each one.

   a   b
   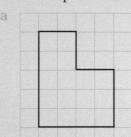   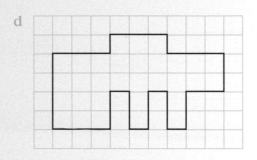

   c   d
   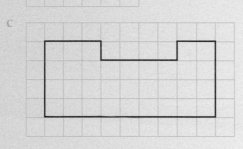   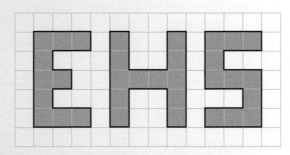

4   Ashley said 'The area of this square is 10 mm²
    Explain why Ashley is wrong.

5   These letters are drawn on
    1 centimetre square paper.
    Which letter has
    a   the largest area
    b   the smallest area?

    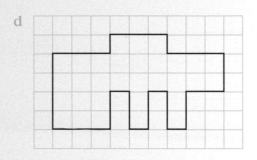

6   These numbers are drawn on 1 centimetre square paper.

    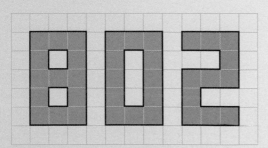

    Which number has   a   the largest area   b   the smallest area?

9.4 Areas of squares and rectangles

Area of a square = (length of a side)^2.
Area of a rectangle = length × breadth.

Example 7

Find the area of the following shapes.

a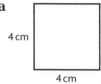

4 cm

4 cm

b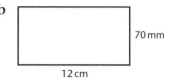

70 mm

12 cm

a 4 × 4 = 16
Area of square = 16 cm^2

b 70 mm = 7 cm
12 × 7 = 84
Area of rectangle = 84 cm^2

> Both lengths must be in the same units. Convert 70 mm into cm by dividing by 10.

Example 8

Find the area of this workshop floor.

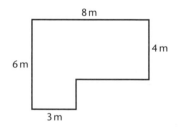

8 m

4 m

6 m

3 m

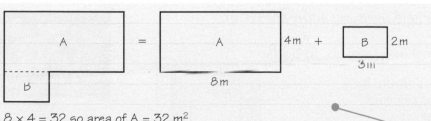

A = A 4 m + B 2 m

3 m

8 m

B

8 × 4 = 32 so area of A = 32 m^2.
3 × 2 = 6 so area of B = 6 m^2.
Area of floor = (32 + 6) m^2 = 38 m^2.

> Divide the area into two rectangles. Label each area. Make a shape equation and write the measurements on each rectangle.

> This is a shape equation.

Exam practice 9D

1   Find the area of each square.

   a

   6 cm

   b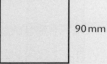

   90 mm

   c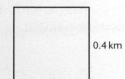

   0.4 km

2 Find the area of each rectangle.

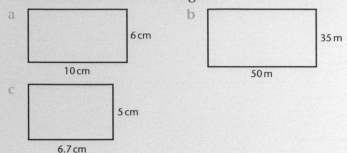

a   6 cm   10 cm

b   35 m   50 m

c   5 cm   6.7 cm

3 Find the area of this rectangle.

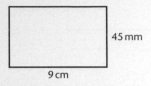

45 mm

9 cm

Both lengths must be measured in the same unit. Convert 45 mm into cm.

4 All measurements on each shape are in centimetres.
   Draw a shape equation and use it to find the area of each shape.

Assume that all the corners are right angles.

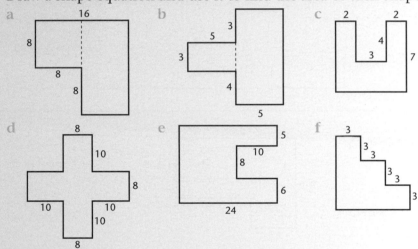

a   16   8   8   8

b   3   5   3   4   5

c   2   2   4   3   7

These shapes can be divided into two or more rectangles.

d   8   10   8   10   10   10   8

e   5   10   8   6   24

f   3   3   3   3   3   3

5 A rectangular sports field measures 400 m by 320 m.
   Find its area
   a   in square metres   b   in hectares.

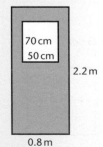

6 This diagram shows a frame for a
   photograph made out of card.
   Work out the area of
   a   the card
   b   the space available for a photograph
   c   the card showing when the photograph
       is on it.

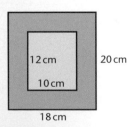

12 cm   20 cm
10 cm
18 cm

7 A wooden door has a glass panel.
   a   Find the area of the glass panel
   b   The door is to be painted on both sides.
       Work out the area to be painted.

70 cm
50 cm   2.2 m

0.8 m

9.5 Areas of other shapes

Triangle

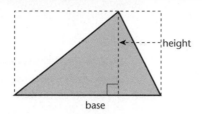

> The area of the shaded triangle is equal to half the area of the rectangle that surrounds it.

Area of a triangle $= \frac{1}{2} \times$ base $\times$ height

Parallelogram

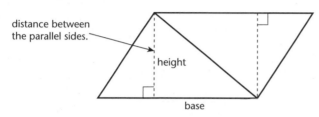

> A diagonal of a parallelogram divides it into two identical triangles.
> Area of one triangle $= \frac{1}{2} \times$ base $\times$ height
> So the area of the parallelogram is twice this.

> Height means perpendicular height.
> For a triangle this is the perpendicular distance between the base and the vertex opposite it.
> For a parallelogram this is the distance between one set of parallel sides.

Area of a parallelogram = base $\times$ height

Trapezium

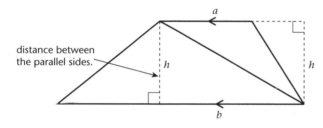

> The diagonal divides the trapezium into two triangles.
> The area of one is $\frac{1}{2}bh$ and the area of the other (which is upside down) is $\frac{1}{2}ah$.
> So the area of trapezium $= \frac{1}{2}ah + \frac{1}{2}bh$
> $= \frac{1}{2}(a + b) \times h$

Area of a trapezium
$= \frac{1}{2}$(sum of parallel sides) $\times$ distance between them

---

Example 9

Find the area of each triangle.

a

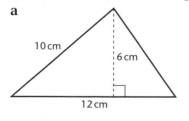

b

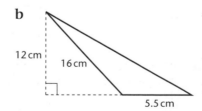

a Area of triangle $= \frac{1}{2} \times 12 \times 6$ cm^2
$= 36$ cm^2

> The base is 12 cm and the perpendicular height 6 cm. The length marked 10 cm is not needed.

b Area of triangle $= \frac{1}{2} \times 5.5 \times 12$ cm^2
$= 33$ cm^2

> The base is 5.5 cm and the perpendicular height 12 cm. The length marked 16 cm is not needed.

Example 10

Find the area of this parallelogram.

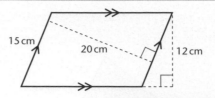

Area = 15 × 20 cm²
     = 300 cm²

One side of the parallelogram is 15 cm. The distance between this side and the side opposite it is 20 cm. It is these two measurements you need to find the area. The measurement of 12 cm is not needed to answer the question.

Exam practice 9E

1   These shapes are drawn on centimetre squared paper. Find the area of each one.

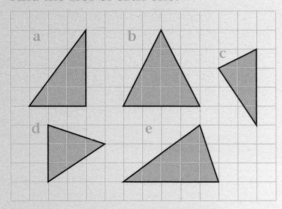

2   Find the area of each shape.

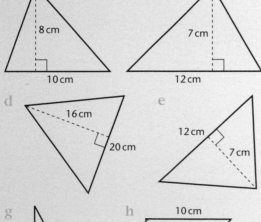

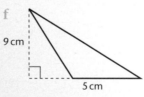

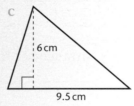

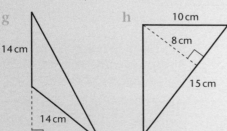

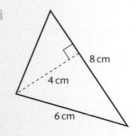

Sometimes it helps if you turn the page around.

When three measurements are given in a question and you only need two make sure that you choose the right two. You need the base and the perpendicular height from this base.

3 These shapes are drawn on 1 centimetre square paper.
Find the area of each.

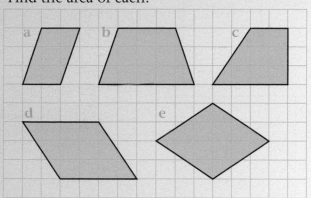

4 Find the area of each parallelogram.

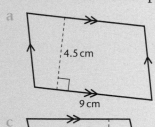

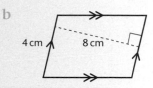

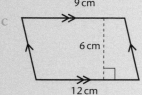

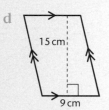

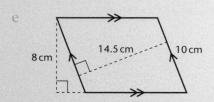

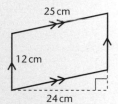

Take care. You are given three measurements but you only need two.

5 Find the area of the pink shape.

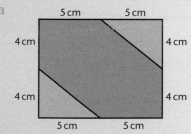

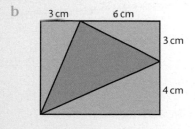

Find the area of the rectangle, then the areas of the triangles that are shaded. Subtract the sum of their areas from the area of the rectangle to give the area coloured pink.

6 Find the area of each shape.

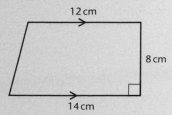

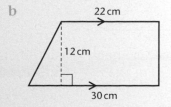

Area of trapezium
= ½ sum of parallel sides × distance between them.

c
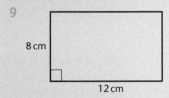
19 cm
10 cm
15cm

d
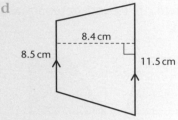
8.4 cm
8.5 cm
11.5 cm

e
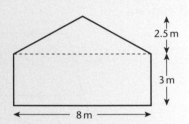
7 cm
12 cm
7 cm

f
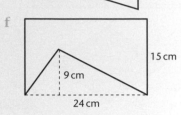
15 cm
9 cm
24 cm

First find the area of the rectangle around the shape.

7 The diagram shows the end wall of a bungalow. Find its area.

2.5 m
3 m
8 m

8 The sketch shows a white rectangular flag which has a shaded diagonal band across it. Using the measurements on the diagram, find
   a the length and width of the rectangle
   b the area of the rectangle
   c the area of the flag that is white
   d the area of the shaded band.

6 cm ← 54 cm →
6 cm
34 cm
6 cm
6 cm

9
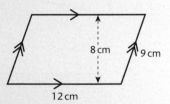
8 cm
12 cm

8 cm 9 cm
12 cm

Lee says that the area of the parallelogram is greater than the area of the rectangle.
Is Lee correct?
 Give a reason for your answer.

10

4 cm
5 cm
8 cm

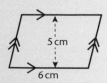
5 cm
6 cm

   a What is the mathematical name of each shape?
   b Ian says that the areas of the two shapes are the same.
      Is Ian correct?
 Give a reason for your answer.

11

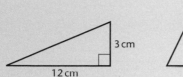
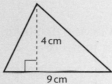

Kay says that the areas of these two triangles are the same.
Is Kay correct?
Give a reason for your answer.

UAM

12 Two-fifths of this area is shaded.
Work out the area that is
a shaded   b not shaded.

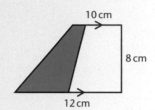

9.6 Circles

In a circle:
Diameter = 2 × radius.

Circumference = 2 × π × radius
= π × diameter.

Area = π × (radius)².

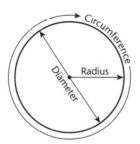

The **circumference** of a circle is the perimeter of the circle.

The formula for the circumference of a circle is $C = 2\pi r$ or $C = \pi d$.
The formula for the area of a circle is $A = \pi r^2$

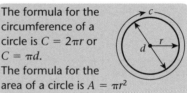

You can show where the formula for the area of a circle comes from by cutting a circle into small slices and then arranging them as a 'rectangle'. (You have to cut one slice in half to do this.)

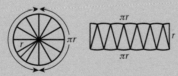

The area of the circle = the area of the rectangle
= length × width = $\pi r \times r = \pi r^2$

Example 11

The diameter of a wheel is 60 cm.
Find   **a** an estimate for the circumference
      b the circumference to the nearest centimetre.

For estimates use 3 as the value of π.

a Estimate of circumference = 3 × 60 cm = 180 cm

Circumference = π × diameter.

b Circumference = π × 60 cm
= 188.4... cm
= 188 cm to the nearest cm.

Use your calculator.
Press
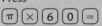

π is a number – it is the ratio of the circumference of a circle to its diameter.

π cannot be written exactly either as a fraction or as a decimal. Sometimes you are asked to give your answer in terms of π.

Example 12

Find the area of this semicircle.
Give your answer in terms of π.

This means leave π in your answer.

Radius = 5 cm
Area of circle = π × (radius)²
$\pi \times (5)^2 = \pi \times 25 = 25\pi$
Area of semicircle = $\frac{1}{2} \times 25\pi$ cm² = 12.5π cm².

radius = $\frac{1}{2}$ diameter

Work out the value of 5² but leave π as a symbol.

Example 13

The distance round a circular running track is 400 m.
Work out the diameter of the track to the nearest metre.

Circumference = π × diameter
Use D for the diameter and replace 'circumference' by 400.

$400 = \pi \times D$
$D = \dfrac{400}{\pi} = 127.3\ldots$
Diameter of track is 127 m to the nearest metre.

Press

Example 14

The diameter of the circular top of a tin is 8 cm.
Find its area to the nearest cm² .

Area = π × (radius)²
    = $\pi \times 4 \times 4$ cm²
    = 50.2… cm²
Area of top = 50 cm² to the nearest whole number.

You are given the diameter. You need to find the value of the radius.
Radius = $\frac{1}{2}$ diameter. $\frac{1}{2}$ of 8 = 4.

Exam practice 9F

1 Use $\pi = 3$ to estimate the circumference of these circles.

To find an estimate use 3 as the value of π.

a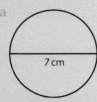
7 cm

b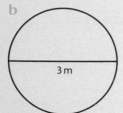
3 m

c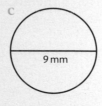
9 mm

2 Use $\pi = 3$ to estimate the circumference of a circle with radius
   a 10 cm   b 8 m   c 30 mm.

3 Estimate the circumference of this wheel.

←—75 cm—→

4 The radius of a circular clock face is 12 cm.
   a What is its diameter?
   b Estimate its circumference.

5 Use π = 3 to estimate the diameter of a circle with a circumference of
   a 180 cm   b 7.5 m   c 96 mm.

6 Find, in terms of π,
   a the circumference of a circle of radius 4 cm
   b the area of a circle of radius 3 m
   c the diameter of a circle with a circumference of 60 cm.

 In questions 7 to 15 give your answers correct to 1 decimal place.

7 Find the circumference of a circle when
   a the diameter is   i 7 cm   ii 3.5 cm   iii 734 mm
   b the radius is   i 9 cm   ii 8.3 cm   iii 75 m.

8 This circular kitchen table top has a plastic strip around the edge.
   How long is the strip?

90 cm

9 The diameters of three different sized plates are 16 cm, 21 cm and 27 cm.
   Find the circumference of each.

10 This is a semicircle.   ←—10 cm—→
    Work out
    a the perimeter
    b the area.

A semicircle is half a circle.

11 a The radius of a circular flower bed is 22 metres. Find its area.
    b The diameter of a circular brooch is 38 mm. Find its area.

12 a The diameter of a plate is 17 cm. Find its area.
    b Flo said that the area of another plate which had a diameter of 25 cm was more than twice as much. Was Flo correct? Give a reason for your answer.

UAM

13 The diagram shows a mount for a photo
    frame. A circle, diameter 14 cm, has been
    removed from a square of side 20 cm.
    Find
    a   the area of the original square card
    b   the circular area cut out
    c   the area of the mount.

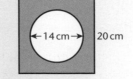

14 This is a Pembroke table.
    It has two semicircular leaves that
    hang vertically when the table is
    not wholly opened out.
    Find
    a   the area of the rectangular top
    b   the area of one semicircular leaf
    c   the total surface area of the table
        when it is opened out.

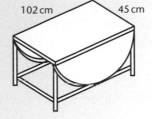

15 Sam makes a telephone shelf that
    fits into a corner in the hall.
    The top and bottom are two
    quadrants of plywood and the
    sides are two rectangles.
    Use the measurements on the
    diagram to find
    a   the area of one quadrant
    b   the total area of plywood used to make the shelf.
        (neglect the thickness of the plywood)

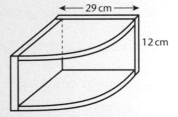

Summary of key points

- You need to know these relationships between units:
  1 km = 1000 m, 1 m = 100 cm, 1 cm = 10 mm
  1 yard = 3 feet, 1 foot = 12 inches,
  5 miles ≈ 8 km, 2 inches ≈ 5 cm
  1 foot ≈ 30 cm
- To change a larger unit to a smaller unit multiply.
- To change a smaller unit to a larger unit divide.
- The perimeter of a shape is the distance around it.
- Area of a rectangle = length × breadth.
- Area of a triangle = $\frac{1}{2}$ base × perpendicular height.
- Area of a parallelogram = length of one side × distance between that side and the side opposite it.
- Area of a trapezium = $\frac{1}{2}$ (sum of the parallel sides) × distance between them.
- The area of a compound shape can often be found by dividing it into smaller simple shapes e.g. rectangles.
- Circumference of a circle = 2π × radius or π × diameter.
- Area of a circle = π × (radius)^2.

Most students who get GRADE E or above can:
- convert between metric and imperial units
- find the perimeter and area of a rectangle.

Most students who get GRADE C can also:
- find the perimeter and area of a semicircle.

Glossary

Acre	an Imperial unit for measuring area
Circumference	the length of a circle
Hectare	a metric unit of area
Perimeter	the distance all round a shape
Square centimetre	the area covered by a square with side 1 cm
Square millimetre	the area covered by a square with side 1 mm

10 Shapes 2

This chapter will show you:
- ✓ what a cube, cuboid, prism and cylinder are
- ✓ how to draw the net for a cuboid, prism, pyramid and cylinder
- ✓ how to draw the plan, front elevation and side elevation for different solids
- ✓ how to find the surface area of a cube, cuboid, right prism and cylinder

Before you start you need to know:
- ✓ how to draw shapes accurately
- ✓ how to find the area of a square, a rectangle, a triangle, a parallelogram and a trapezium
- ✓ how to find the circumference and area of a circle

10.1 Cubes, cuboids and prisms

This is a **cube**. It has:
- 6 faces (top, bottom and 4 sides),
- 12 edges (an **edge** is where two faces join)
- 8 vertices or corners (a **vertex** is where 3 or more faces meet).

The faces are all squares and the edges are all the same length.

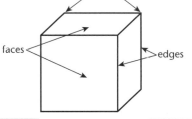

This is a **cuboid**.
It has the same number of faces, edges and vertices as a cube.
The edges are not all the same length.
The faces are rectangles, but not all the same size.
Each pair of opposite faces are identical rectangles.

A cuboid is a rectangular block like a brick.

A cube is a special type of cuboid.

These are **prisms**. The two ends of a prism are the same and can be any shape. The other faces are rectangles.

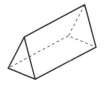 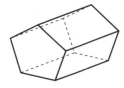 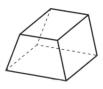

When a prism is cut parallel to its ends the shape of its cut face is called its **cross-section**.

A cuboid is a rectangular prism. Its cross-section is a rectangle.

In this example the cross-section is a triangle.

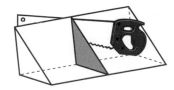 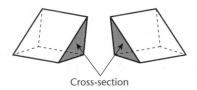

Cross-section

The cross-section of a prism is **uniform**.
This means it is exactly the same throughout.

The cross-section of this prism is a circle.
It is called a **cylinder**.

> This solid is not a prism because the cross-section changes as you go along its length.

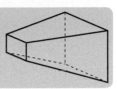

Exam practice 10A

1   This is a cuboid.
    a   How many of its edges are 4 cm long?
    b   How many of its edges are 2 cm long?
    c   How many faces measure 3 cm by 2 cm?
    d   What are the measurements of the smallest faces?

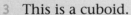

2   This is a cuboid.
    a   How many edges are 5 cm long?
    b   How many edges are 2 cm long?
    c   How many corners does the solid have?
    d   How many edges meet at each corner?

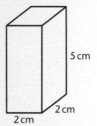

3   This is a cuboid.
    a   How many faces does it have?
    b   How many faces are rectangles
        measuring 6 cm by 3 cm?
    c   How many edges are 5 cm long?
    d   What is the length of one of the shortest edges?

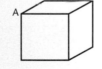

4   This is a cube.
    a   How many square faces does it have?
    b   How many edges of equal length does it have?
    c   How many faces meet at A?
    d   How many edges meet at A?

5   This cube rests on a table.
    a   How many edges lie on the table?
    b   How many edges are vertical?
    c   How many edges are horizontal?
    d   How many edges are neither horizontal nor vertical?

 6   This cuboid rests on a table.
    a   Audrey said that all the vertical faces are
        the same size and shape. Is Audrey correct?
        Give a reason for your answer.
    b   Hugh said that the largest faces are squares. Is Hugh correct?
        Give a reason for your answer.
    c   Nikki said that the sum of the lengths of all the edges is 44 cm.
        Is Nikki correct? Give a reason for your answer.

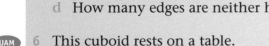
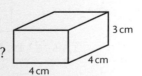

7 Write down the mathematical name for each solid.

a

b

c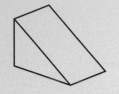

d

e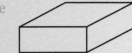

f

8 The cross-section of this prism is a trapezium.
   Write down the number of
   a faces   b edges   c vertices.

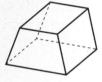

9 The cross-section of this prism is a regular hexagon.
   Write down the number of
   a faces   b edges   c vertices.

10.2 Nets

You can make some solids from a flat piece of card.
The shape you need is called a **net**.

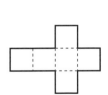

This net makes a cube.

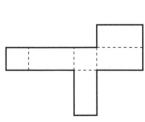

This net makes a cuboid

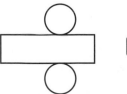

This net makes a cylinder

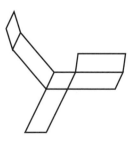

Exam practice 10B

www   1 This net will make a cube.
         a   Cut out a copy of this net along the solid line.
             Fold it up to make a cube.
         b   Write down the letters that meet with A.

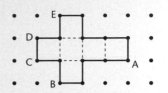

www   2 This net will make a cuboid.
         a   Cut out a copy the net along the solid line.
             Fold it up to make the cuboid.
         b   Write down the letter that meets with A.

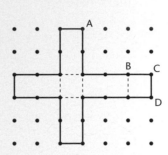

3 This net will make a cuboid.

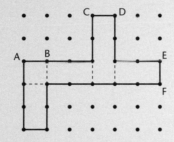

   a   Write down the letters that meet with A when the
       cube is constructed.
   b   Which edge meets with the edge CD?

4 Draw a net for each cuboid on 1 cm dotted paper.

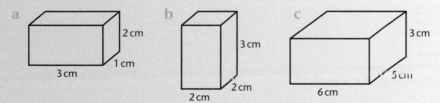

a   2 cm 1 cm 3 cm

b   3 cm 2 cm 2 cm

c   3 cm 5 cm 6 cm

5 This is the net for a cuboid drawn on 1 cm squared paper.

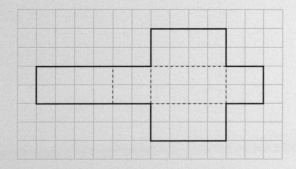

What are the measurements of this cuboid?

6 This is a net for a triangular prism.
   a Copy it on to 1 cm squared
      paper.
      Cut it out and fold it up to
      make the prism.
   b Write down the letters that
      meet with C.

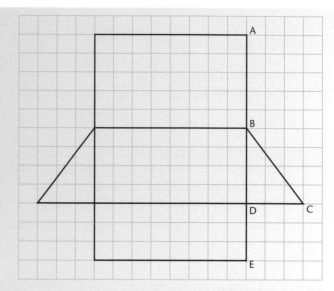

7 Draw a net for this prism.

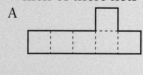

Use 1 cm squared paper.

8 Which of these nets will make a cuboid?

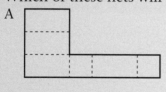

A   B   C

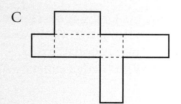

D

9 Which of these nets will make a cube?

A   B

C   D

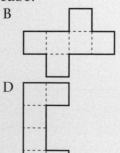

10 Jarvinder said 'This net will make a cube'.
    Is he right?
    Explain your answer.

10.3 Plans and elevations

When you look at a solid from different directions, you see different shapes.

This beaker looks different depending on which way you look at it.

When you look directly from above you see a circle (the top) with another circle (the bottom) in the middle.

This is called a **plan**.

When you look from the side you see this shape.

This is called an **elevation**.

Example 1

This solid is made from 10 cubes.
Draw the view
a from direction A   b from direction B.

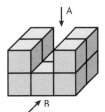

a

Looking from direction A (above) you can see the tops of 6 cubes. This is the plan.

b

Looking from direction B, (the front) you can see the sides of 5 cubes. This is the front elevation.

Example 2

a Draw the plan of this solid.
b Draw the elevation of this solid from direction A.

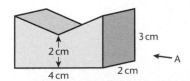

a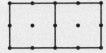

When you look from above you can see the edges shown in red. The sloping edges shown in green look shorter than they are. They look flat.

b

> The broken line shows that there is an edge that you cannot see.

Exam practice 10C

Use 1 cm squared or dotted paper for this exercise.

1 This solid is made from 5 cubes.
   Draw the view
   a from direction A
   b from direction B.

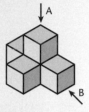

2 This solid is made from 7 cubes.
   Draw the view
   a from direction A
   b from direction B.

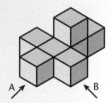

3 This solid is made from cubes.
   Draw the view
   a from direction A
   b from direction B.

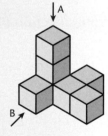

4 This shape is made from 11 cubes.
   Draw the elevation from the direction
   of the arrow.

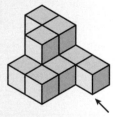

5 This shape is made from 10 cubes.
   a Draw the elevation
      i   from direction A
      ii from direction B.
   b Draw the plan.

> The plan is the view of a solid from above.

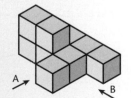

6 This shape is made from 10 cubes.
   a Draw the elevation
      i   from direction A
      ii from direction B.
   b Draw the plan.

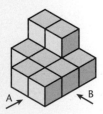

7 Draw the views in the directions of the arrows.
   All measurements are given in centimetres.

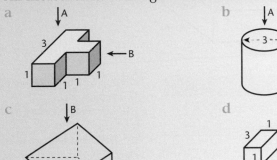

8 Draw the elevation of each solid from the direction shown by
   the arrow.

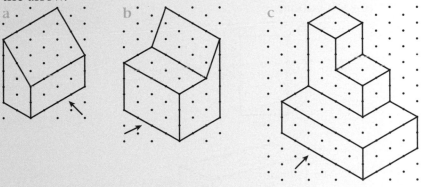

These solids are drawn
on an isometric grid.
The dots are 5 mm
apart in all directions.

9 Sketch a solid with this plan and elevations.

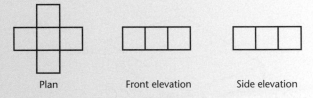

Plan   Front elevation   Side elevation

10 Sketch a solid with this plan and elevations.

Plan   Front elevation   Side elevation

10.4 Surface area of a cuboid

A cuboid has three pairs of identical opposite faces. You can find the
total surface area by adding together the areas of the six rectangular
faces.

Example 3

Find the total surface area of this cuboid.

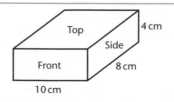

	Top	Bottom	Side	Side	Front	Back
Area (cm²)	10 × 8 = 80	10 × 8 = 80	4 × 8 = 32	4 × 8 = 32	10 × 4 = 40	10 × 4 = 40

80 + 80 + 32 + 32 + 40 + 40 = 304

Total surface area = 304 cm².

The top and bottom measure 10 cm by 8 cm.
The two sides measure 4 cm by 8 cm
The front and back measure 10 cm by 4 cm.
You can use a table to make sure you do not miss any faces.

Exam practice 10D

1 Find the total surface area of each cuboid.

The area of a rectangle = length × breadth

a
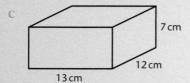
10 cm
15 cm
30 cm

b
5 cm
15 cm
6 cm

c
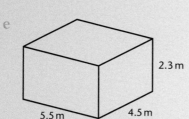
7 cm
12 cm
13 cm

d
8 cm
25 cm
12.5 cm

e
2.3 m
5.5 m   4.5 m

f
30 mm
240 mm
185 mm

2 This is a box for sending wedding cake through the post .
Work out its total surface area.

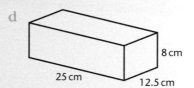
18 mm
5 cm
7 cm

The lengths must be in the same units. Change 18 mm to cm.

3 This is a child's building block.
The blocks are to be painted yellow.
One can of paint will cover an area of 1 m².
Eli says that the paint in one can is enough to paint more than 100 blocks.
Is Eli correct? Give a reason for your answer.

1 m² = 10 000cm²

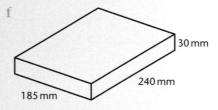
3 cm
4 cm
8 cm

UAM

10.5 Surface area of a prism

Example 4

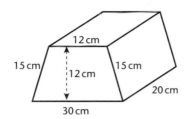

The cross-section of this prism is a trapezium.
Find the total surface area of this prism.

	Front	Back	Top	Bottom	Side	Side
Area (cm²)	$\frac{1}{2}(12 + 30) \times 12$ = 252	$\frac{1}{2}(12 + 30) \times 12$ = 252	12×20 = 240	30×20 = 600	15×20 = 300	15×20 = 300

The area of a trapezium
= $\frac{1}{2}$(sum of the parallel sides) × (distance between them)

252 + 252 + 240 + 600 + 300 + 300 = 1944
Total surface area = 1944 cm².

> The front and back are trapeziums.
> The other sides are rectangles.
> The sides measure 15 cm by 20 cm.
> The top measures 12 cm by 20 cm.
> The bottom measures 30 cm by 20 cm.
> You can use a table to make sure you do not miss any faces.

Cylinder

This cylinder has radius r and height h.

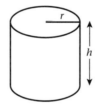

The ends are circles so the area of each end is πr^2.

The curved part opens out into a rectangle measuring $2\pi r$ by h.
So area of curved surface area = $2\pi rh$

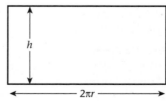

Example 5

A cylindrical water tank is 1.24 m high and has a radius of 54 cm.
Find   **a**   the curved surface area of the tank
      b   its total surface area.
Give your answer in square metres to 1 decimal place.

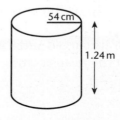

a Height of cylinder = 1.24 m

Radius of cylinder = 0.54 m

Curved surface area = $2\pi rh$

$= 2 \times \pi \times 0.54 \times 1.24\,m^2$

$= 4.207...\,m^2$

$= 4.2\,m^2$ to 1 d.p.

Both dimensions must be in the same units. The answer is asked for in square metres, so convert 54 cm to metres.

b Area of one end = πr^2

$= \pi \times (0.54)^2\,m^2$

$= 0.916...\,m^2$

Total surface area = $(0.916... + 0.916... + 4.207...)\,m^2$

$= 6.03...\,m^2$

$= 6.0\,m^2$ to 1 d.p.

Do not use rounded answers in calculations.

Exam practice 10E

1 Find the total surface area of each shape.

a

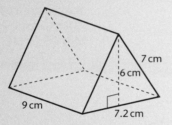

b

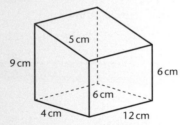

2 This is a ridge tent.
Work out the total surface area of the tent.
Give your answer in square metres correct to 1 decimal place.

This DOES include the ground area.
Take care with units.

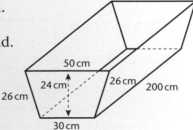

3 This diagram shows a water trough.
It is made from three rectangular planks with a trapezium at each end.
Find
a the area of each end piece
b the total area of the outside of the trough.

It does not have a top.

4 The circumference of this cylinder is 6 cm.
It is 10 cm high.
Work out the area of its curved surface.
Give your answer to the nearest cm².

5   The curved surface of a cylindrical can is covered by a label.
    The diameter of the tin is 7.4 cm and it is 10 cm high.
    Work out   a   the circumference of the tin
                b   the area of the label.
    Give your answer to the nearest cm².

6   The radius of a cylinder is 4 cm.
    It is 12 cm long.
    Work out   a   the area of one end
                b   its curved surface area
                c   the percentage of the total surface area that is
                    curved.
    Give your answers to 1 d.p.

7   A coin is 1.5 mm thick and has a diameter of 2.5 cm.
    Find the total surface area of the coin giving your answer
    in cm² to 1 d.p.

Take care with units.

8   A garden roller has a radius of 35 cm and is 60 cm wide.
    a   Find, in square metres, the area rolled by
        i   one complete turn of the roller
        ii 100 complete turns of the roller.
    b   How many revolutions are needed to roll an area of
        800 square metres? Give your answer correct to the nearest
        whole number.

9

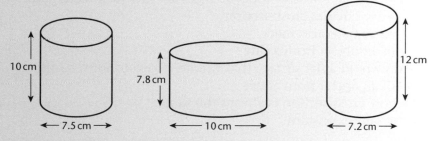

Kobi has three cylinders. Which cylinder has
a   the largest curved surface area
b   the smallest curved surface area
c   the smallest total surface area?
Give reasons for your answers.

Summary of key points

- The plan of an object is what you see by looking from above.
- The front and side elevation gives views from the sides.
- The surface area of a cuboid is the sum of the areas of three identical pairs of rectangles.
- The surface area of a cube is six times the area of one of its square faces.
- When the cross-section of a prism is a shape made of straight lines all the sides are rectangles.
- The curved surface area of a cylinder with radius r and height h is $2\pi rh$.

Most students who get GRADE E or above can:

- recognise and name cubes, cuboids, prisms and cylinders.

Most students who get GRADE C can also:

- calculate the surface area of a prism and a cylinder.

Glossary

Cross-section	a slice through a solid
Cube	a solid whose faces are squares
Cuboid	a solid with six faces whose opposite faces are identical rectangles
Cylinder	a prism with a circular cross-section
Edge	the line where two faces meet
Elevation	the view of an object from a side
Net	a shape drawn on a flat surface that can be folded to form a solid
Plan	the view of an object from above
Prism	a solid whose cross-section is always the same
Uniform	always the same, constant
Vertex	a corner

11 Sequences

<table>
<tr><td>

This chapter will show you:
- ✓ what a sequence is
- ✓ how to continue a sequence
- ✓ how to make a sequence from a formula
- ✓ how to find a particular term in a sequence
- ✓ how to find a formula for the nth term of a sequence

</td><td>

Before you start you need to know:
- ✓ what even, odd and square numbers are
- ✓ how to recognise powers of 2 and powers of 10
- ✓ how to substitute values in an expression
- ✓ the meaning of n^2
- ✓ how to solve equations

</td></tr>
</table>

11.1 Sequences

A **sequence** is a list with a first member, a second member, a third member, and so on.

The members are called the **terms** of the sequence.

The terms can be any objects, such as numbers or expressions or shapes.

> These are sequences:
> 2, 4, 6, 8, ...
> $x + 1, 2x + 2, 3x + 3, ...$
> $\square, \square\square, \square\square\square, ...$

Continuing a sequence of numbers

There is usually a pattern or rule that you can use to continue the sequence. You can spot this rule in simple cases.

Example 1

A sequence starts 2, 4, 6, 8, ...
a Write down the next two terms.
b What is the tenth term of this sequence?

a 10, 12	2, 4, 6, 8, ... are the even numbers starting with 2, so the next two terms are the next two even numbers.
b 20	You can find the tenth term by listing the terms until you get to the tenth. You can also find the tenth term by spotting that each term is a multiple of 2. The 3rd term is 3 × 2, the fifth term is 5 × 2, so the tenth term is 10 × 2 = 20

Sometimes you are given a rule for continuing a sequence.

Example 2

A sequence starts 3, 6, 9, ...
The rule for continuing this sequence is
    'add the last two terms together'.
Write down the next term in the sequence.

15

> The last two terms are 6 and 9. 6 + 9 = 15.

You need to be able to spot these patterns

- even numbers   8, 10, 12, 14, ... is a sequence of even numbers

- odd numbers   7, 9, 11, 13, ... is a sequence of odd numbers

- square numbers   4, 9, 16, 25, ... is a sequence of square numbers

- powers of 2   2, 4, 8, 16, 32, ... are powers of 2

- powers of 10   10, 100, 1000, 10 000, ... are powers of 10

- numbers that increase by the same amount   Each number in 2, 5, 8, 11, ... is 3 more than the number before it.

Exam practice 11A

1 Write down the next two numbers in each sequence.
   a 6, 8, 10, 12, ...   b 16, 25, 36, 49, ...   c 16, 32, 64, ...
   d 1, 4, 7, 10, ...   e 5, 4, 3, 2, ...   f 10, 100, 1000, ...
   g 3, 7, 11, 15, ...   h 9, 11, 13, 15, ...   i 80, 40, 20, ...
   j 10, 6, 2, −2, ...

2 Write down the value of a and b in each sequence.
   a 2, 4, 8, a, 32, b, ...   b 12, 15, a, 21, 24, 27, b, ...
   c 100, 81, 64, a, 36, 25, b, ...   d 10, 7, 4, a, −2, −5, b, ...
   e a, 8, 10, 12, 14, 16, b, ...   f a, 2, 5, 8, 11, b, ...

3 The first three numbers in a sequence are 1, 3, 9, ...
   The rule for continuing the sequence is
       'multiply the last term by 3'.
   Write down the next two numbers.

4 A sequence begins 1, 8, 15, ...
   The rule for continuing the sequence is
       'add 7 to the last term'.
   Find the next two numbers.

5 The first three numbers in a sequence are 9, 4, −1, ...
   The rule for continuing the sequence is
       'subtract 5 from the last term'.
   What are the next two numbers?

6 A sequence starts 128, 64, 32, ...
   The rule for continuing the sequence is
       'divide the last term by 2'.
   Write down the next two numbers.

7 A sequence begins 1, 4, 10, …
   The rule for continuing the sequence is
   'add 1 to the last term then multiply by 2'.
   Write down the next two numbers.

8 The first three numbers in a sequence are 1, 2, 5, …
   The rule for continuing the sequence is
   'square the last number then add 1'.
   What are the next two numbers?

9 A sequence starts 1, 3, 7, …
   The rule for continuing the sequence is
   'multiply the last term by 2 and add 1'.
   Write down the next three numbers.

10 A sequence starts 5, 10, 15, …
   The rule for continuing the sequence is
   'add 5 to the last term'.

   UAM   Explain why 52 is not a number in this sequence.

11 A sequence starts 4, 6, 12, …
   The rule for continuing the sequence is
   'subtract 2 from the last term then multiply by 3'.
   a   Work out the next three numbers.

   UAM   b   Explain why 200 is not a number in this sequence.

12 A sequence starts 10, 14, 22, …
   The rule for continuing the sequence is
   'subtract 3 from the last term then multiply by 2'.
   a   Work out the next three numbers.
   b   Is 88 a number in this sequence?

   UAM   Explain your answer.

11.2 Patterns

You can continue a sequence of patterns by spotting how the
patterns change.

Example 3

Here is a sequence of patterns.

Pattern 1   Pattern 2   Pattern 3   Pattern 4

> The number of dots in the patterns
> makes this sequence of numbers:
>   1, 3, 6, 10, …
> These are called **triangular numbers**.

a   Draw the next pattern in the sequence.
b   How many dots are needed for the seventh pattern?
     Explain your answer.

a

> The sequence of patterns continues by adding a row of dots with one more dot than the row above. The last row of pattern 4 has 4 dots so the last row of pattern 5 has 5 dots.

b 28

Pattern 5 has 15 dots, pattern 6 has 6 more dots and

pattern 7 has 7 more dots.

Pattern 7 has 15 + 6 + 7 = 28 dots.

A sequence can also be a list of expressions or equations.

Example 4

This is a sequence of expressions.

   $x + 10, 2x + 9, 3x + 8, \ldots$

Write down the next two expressions.

   $4x + 7, 5x + 6$

> The number multiplied by x goes up by 1 each time and the number on its own goes down by 1 each time.

Exam practice 11B

1 This is a sequence of patterns made with matchsticks.

Pattern 1   Pattern 2   Pattern 3

 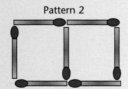 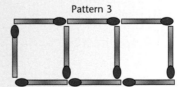

a Sketch pattern 4.

b Copy and complete this table.

Pattern number	1	2	3	4	5	6
Number of matchsticks	4	7	10			

c The rule for working out the number of matchsticks is

   'three times the pattern number plus 1'.

How many matchstick are there in pattern 40?

2 This is a sequence of expressions.

   $x + 4, x + 6, x + 8, \ldots$

Write down the next two expressions.

3 This is the start of a sequence of patterns.

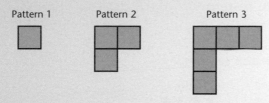

Pattern 1   Pattern 2   Pattern 3

a Sketch pattern 4.
b Copy and complete this table.

Pattern number	1	2	3	4	5	6
Number of squares	1	3	5			

c The rule for working out the number of squares is

   'multiply the pattern number by 2 then subtract 1'.

   How many squares will be in pattern 50?

4 This is the start of a sequence of equations.
   $x + 20 = 40, 2x + 18 = 38, 3x + 16 = 36, ...$
   Write down the next two equations in this sequence.

5 These are first few equations in a sequence.
   $x + 4 = 3, x + 3 = 2, x + 2 = 1$
   a Write down the next two equations in this sequence.
   b Explain why x has the same value in every term.

6 These are the first three patterns in a sequence.

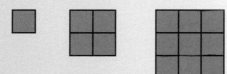

   a Write down the number of squares in the fourth pattern.
   b Explain why there is no pattern with 30 squares in this
      sequence.

7 This is the start of a sequence of blocks.

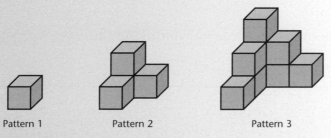

Pattern 1   Pattern 2   Pattern 3

a Copy and complete this table.

Pattern number	1	2	3	4	5
Number of blocks	1	4	9		

UAM

  b How many blocks are added to pattern 6 to make pattern 7?
  c How many blocks are there in pattern 9?
      Explain your answer.

8 These are the first three patterns in a sequence.

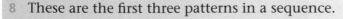

    Pattern 1   Pattern 2   Pattern 3

  a Copy and complete this table.

Pattern number	1	2	3	4	5
Number of dots	4	8	12		

  b How many dots are there in pattern 8?
  c The rule for finding the number of dots is

      'multiply the pattern number by 4'.

      How many dots are in pattern 20?
  d The numbers of dots makes a sequence.
      Grace said that 50 is a number in this sequence.
      Explain why Grace is wrong.

UAM

9 Write down the next two terms in each of these sequences.
  a $3x, 5x, 7x, \ldots$
  b $x + 1, x + 4, x + 9, \ldots$
  c $x + 20, 2x + 19, 3x + 18, \ldots$
  d $2x = 4, 4x = 8, 8x = 16, \ldots$
  e $2(x + 5), 3(x + 3), 4(x + 1), \ldots$
  f $x + 1 = 5, x = 4, x - 1 = 3, \ldots$
  g $(2, 5), (3, 7), (4, 9), (5, 11), \ldots$

11.3 Writing the rule for continuing a sequence

When you spot the pattern you can write a rule for continuing the
sequence.

Example 5

A sequence starts 7, 5, 3, 1, −1, …
Write down a rule for continuing the sequence.

Subtract 2 from the last term.

You need to subtract 2 to get the next term.

$$7 \xrightarrow{-2} 5 \xrightarrow{-2} 3 \xrightarrow{-2} 1 \xrightarrow{-2} -1$$

Exam practice 11C

1   A sequence starts 7, 9, 11, …
    Write a rule for continuing the sequence.

> You must explain how to get the next term from the one before. The rule to continue the sequence 3, 4, 5, … can be written as 'Add 1 to the last term.'
> Do not write just '+ 1'.

2   Write a rule for continuing each sequence.
    a   1, 4, 7, 10, …   b   15, 13, 11, 9, …
    c   64, 32, 16, 8, …   d   100, 10, 1, 0.1, …
    e   12, 18, 24, 30, 36, …   f   100, 90, 80, 70, …

3   These are the first three patterns in a sequence.

    Pattern 1   Pattern 2   Pattern 3

    a   Copy and complete this table.

Pattern number	1	2	3	4	5
Number of dots	3	5			

    b   The numbers of dots make a sequence.
        Write down a rule for continuing this sequence.
    c   Which pattern number has 11 dots?

4   This is the start of a sequence of patterns.

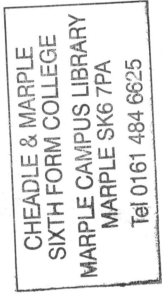

    a   Copy and complete this table

Pattern number	1	2	3	4	5
Number of stars	1	4			

    b   Copy this sentence and add the missing word.

        **The number of stars in a pattern is equal to
        the pattern number …**

    c   How many stars are there in pattern 9?

5   These are the first three patterns in a sequence.

    pattern 1   pattern 2   pattern 3

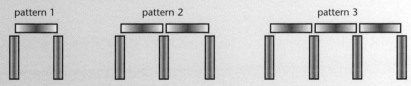

    a   A sequence is made from the number of sticks in each pattern.
        Write down the first four numbers in the sequence.

b Write a rule for getting the next number in this sequence.
c Maryan said that all the numbers in this sequence are odd
   numbers.
   Is Maryan right?

   Explain your answer.

11.4 The nth term

Each term in a sequence has a term number. The first term is term
number 1, the second term is term number 2, and so on.

The **nth term** is term number n where n stands for any number.

The nth term can be given in words.
The nth term can also be given as an expression with n in it.

You can use the nth term to find any term in a sequence.

> In words:
> 'the terms are equal
> to the term number
> plus 4'
> Using n:
> 'nth term $= n + 4$'

Example 6

The rule for finding the terms of a sequence is

'twice the term number plus one'.

a Write down the first three terms of the sequence.
b Which term is equal to 15?

a Term 1 $= 2 \times 1 + 1 = 3$
   Term 2 $= 2 \times 2 + 1 = 5$
   Term 3 $= 2 \times 3 + 1 = 7$

b $2 \times$ (term number) $+ 1 = 15$
   $2 \times$ (term number) $= 14$
   Term number is 7.

> The rule is $2 \times$ (term number) $+ 1$.
> So term 1 is $2 \times (1) + 1$.
> Remember to do the multiplication first.

Example 7

The nth term of a sequence is $n^2 + 3$.
a Write down the first three terms of the sequence.
b Will the number 50 be in this sequence? Explain your answer.

a 1st term $= 1^2 + 3 = 4$
   2nd term $= 2^2 + 3 = 4 + 3 = 7$
   3rd term $= 3^2 + 3 = 9 + 3 = 12$

> The 1st term is the value of $n^2 + 3$ when $n = 1$.

b When $n = 7$, $n^2 + 3 = 52$ so the 7th term is 52.
   When $n = 6$, $n^2 + 3 = 39$ so the 6th term is 39.
   50 is between 39 and 52, so it is not a term in this sequence.

> Find a few terms. If 50 is a term it is probably
> the 6th or 7th.

You can use a list of the terms to find the rule for the nth term.

Example 8

These are the first three patterns of a sequence.

 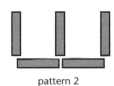 

pattern 1   pattern 2   pattern 3

a Copy and complete this table.

Pattern number	1	2	3	4	5	6
Number of sticks	3	5	7			

b Find a rule that gives the number of sticks in terms of the pattern number.

c Carly has 50 sticks.

  i What is the largest pattern number she can make?

  ii Can she use all her sticks? Explain your answer.

a

Pattern number	1	2	3	4	5	6
Number of sticks	3	5	7	9	11	13

> The numbers increase by 2 each time.

b

Pattern number	1	2	3	4	5	6
Number of sticks	3	5	7	9	11	13
Pattern number × 2	2	4	6	8	10	12

> The number of sticks increases by 2 each time.
> Try multiplying the pattern number by 2. Add another row to the table to show these numbers.

Number of sticks = 2 × (pattern number) + 1

Check: number of sticks in pattern 6 = 2 × 6 + 1 = 13 ✓

> You can see that you get these numbers by adding 1 to the numbers below.

c i All the patterns use an odd number of sticks, so 49 is the largest number of sticks that Carly can use.

49 = 2 × (pattern number) + 1

48 = 2 × (pattern number)

So the pattern number is 24.

> You can use the rule from part **b** to form an equation.
> You could use n instead of the unknown pattern number:
> $49 = 2n + 1$.

  ii Carly cannot use all her sticks. Pattern 24 uses 49 of her sticks so there is 1 left.

Exam practice 11D

1 Write down the first three terms of the sequence whose nth term is

  a $3n - 1$ b $4n + 5$ c $8 - 2n$

  d $4 - 3n$ e $n + n^2$ f $n^2 - 1$.

2 a   Write down the first two terms of the sequence whose nth term is $5n + 1$.

  b   What is the 10th term in this sequence?

  c   Is 37 a term in this sequence? Give a reason for your answer.

3   The *n*th term of a sequence is $n^2 + 1$.
    a   Write down the first three terms of this sequence.
    b   Work out the 12th term of this sequence.

UAM

    c   Explain why 100 cannot be a term in this series.

4   The *n*th term of a sequence is $50 - n$.
    a   Write down the first three terms of this sequence.
    b   Find the 20th term of this sequence.

UAM

    c   Explain why 60 cannot be a term in this series.

5   These are the first three patterns in a sequence.

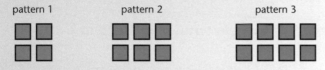

        pattern 1   pattern 2   pattern 3

    a   Copy and complete this table.

Pattern number	1	2	3	4	5	6
Number of squares	4	6				

    b   Find a rule that gives the number of squares in terms of the
        pattern number.

6   Patterns are made with sticks.
    These are the first three patterns in a sequence.

     pattern 1   pattern 2   pattern 3

    a   Copy and complete this table.

Pattern number	1	2	3	4	5	6
Number of sticks	6	8				

    b   Find a rule that gives the number of sticks in terms of the
        pattern number.
    c   How many sticks are in pattern 10?
    d   Which pattern number can you make with 40 sticks?

7   These are the first three patterns in a sequence.

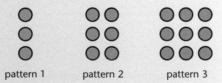

     pattern 1   pattern 2   pattern 3

    a   Copy and complete this table.

Pattern number	1	2	3	4	5	6
Number of circles	3					

    b   Find a rule in words that gives the number of circles in a
        pattern number.
    c   Write your rule using *n* to stand for the pattern number.

d Chas has 100 circles.
   i   Which is the largest pattern number he can make?
   ii Does he have any circles left?
   Explain your answers.

8 These are the first three arrangements in a sequence of tables and chairs.

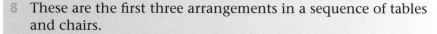
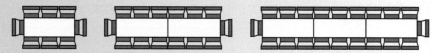

a Copy and complete this table.

Number of tables	1	2	3	4	5	6
Number of chairs	8					

b Find a rule that gives the number of chairs that can be placed round n tables.
c How many tables are needed to seat 78 people?

Enrichment task

This is a sequence of calculations.

$3 \times 9 = 27$
$33 \times 9 = 297$
$333 \times 9 = 2997$

a Write down the next three calculations.
b Write down the value of $3\,333\,333 \times 9$.
c Find the sequence of calculations starting with $4 \times 9 = 36$,
   $44 \times 9 = \ldots$
d What do you think is the value of $777\,777 \times 9$?

Summary of key points

- A sequence has a first member, a second member and so on.
- The rule for continuing a sequence tells you what to do to the last term to get the next term.
- The rule for finding the nth term in a sequence can be used to find any term.

Most students who get GRADE E or above can:
- give the next two numbers or patterns in a sequence.

Most students who get GRADE C can also:
- write down the nth term of a sequence.

Glossary

nth term	any term in a sequence
Sequence	numbers or patterns arranged in order
Term of a sequence	one of the numbers or patterns in the sequence
Triangular numbers	numbers that can be shown as a triangle of dots, for example

6:    15:

12 Volumes

12.1 Volume

Volume measures the space occupied by a solid.
Volume is measured in standard sized cubes.

A cube of side 1 cm has a volume of 1 cubic centimetre (1 cm^3).
A cube of side 1 mm has a volume of 1 cubic millimetre (1 mm^3).
A cube of side 1 m has a volume of 1 cubic metre (1 m^3).

1 cm^3 means 1 cubic centimetre.

The relationships between these units are
$$1 \text{ cm}^3 = 10 \times 10 \times 10 \text{ mm}^3 = 1000 \text{ mm}^3$$
$$1 \text{ m}^3 = 100 \times 100 \times 100 \text{ cm}^3 = 1\,000\,000 \text{ cm}^3$$

Example 1

This cuboid is made from these cubes.
Find its volume.

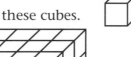

1 cm

There are 3 layers of cubes and 12 cubes in each layer.
So there are 36 cubes each with a volume of 1 cm^3.

Volume = 36 cm^3.

Example 2

Convert   **a** $0.0073\,\text{cm}^3$ into mm^3 **b** $6540\,\text{cm}^3$ into m^3.

a $1\,\text{cm}^3 = 1000\,\text{mm}^3$

So $0.0073\,\text{cm}^3 = 0.0073 \times 1000\,\text{mm}^3$

$= 7.3\,\text{mm}^3$.

> You are converting to a smaller unit, so multiply.

b $1\,\text{m}^3 = 1\,000\,000\,\text{cm}^3$

So $6540\,\text{cm}^3 = \dfrac{6540}{1\,000\,000}\,\text{m}^3 = 0.006\,54\,\text{m}^3$.

> You are converting to a larger unit, so divide.

Exam practice 12A

1   These solids are made from cubes of side 1 centimetre.
   Find their volumes.

a   b    c

d   e 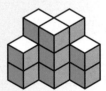   f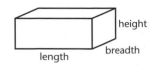

2   Convert
   a $2.5\,\text{m}^3$ into cm^3
   b $6\,\text{cm}^3$ into mm^3
   c $5000\,\text{m}^3$ into cm^3
   d $7500\,\text{cm}^3$ into mm^3
   e $0.079\,\text{cm}^3$ into mm^3
   f $8500\,\text{mm}^3$ into cm^3.

> **Class discussion**
>
> Which unit would you use to measure the volume of
> - the room you are in
> - a brick
> - a teaspoonful of water
> - a 10p coin
> - a paving slab
> - a garden shed?

12.2 Volume of a cuboid

height

length   breadth

Volume of cuboid = length × breadth × height.

Example 3

Find the volume of   **a**   the cube   **b**   the cuboid.

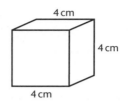

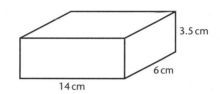

a   Volume of cube = 4 × 4 × 4 cm³ = 64 cm³

> The length, breadth and height of a cube are all the same.

b   Volume of cuboid = 14 × 6 × 3.5 cm³ = 294 cm³

> Press
> ① ④ ⊗ ⑥ ⊗ ③ ⦿ ⑤ ⊜

Example 4

The cross-section of this piece of wood is a T.
Find its volume.

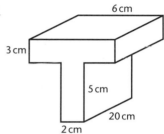

Volume of A is 6 × 3 × 20 cm³ = 360 cm³

Volume of B is 5 × 2 × 20 cm³ = 200 cm³

360 + 200 = 560
Volume of wood = 560 cm³

> This solid can be divided into two cuboids.
>
>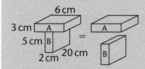
>
> Cuboid A measures 6 cm × 3 cm × 20 cm.
> Cuboid B measures 5 cm × 2 cm × 20 cm.

Exam practice 12B

1   Work out the volume of each cuboid.

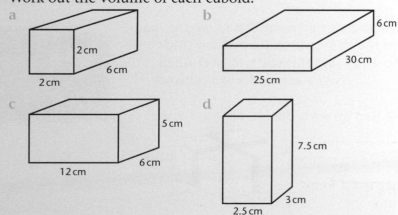

2   Each solid can be made from two cubes or cuboids.
    Find the volume of each solid.

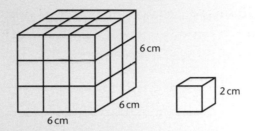

a   2 cm

8 cm   4 cm   2 cm   2 cm   6 cm

b   3 cm 3 cm   4 cm   12 cm   9 cm

c   3 cm   3 cm   3 cm   4.2 cm   4.5 cm   6 cm

Divide each solid into two cuboids.

3   The large cube is made
    from smaller cubes with
    side 2 cm.

6 cm   6 cm   6 cm   2 cm

a   How many small cubes are needed to make the large cube?
b   Work out the volume of   i   the small cube
                             ii the large cube.

4   Find the volume of this concrete
    block in cubic centimetres.

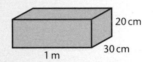

20 cm   30 cm   1 m

The lengths must all be in the same units. As the answer is asked for in cm³, convert 1 m to centimetres.

5   A flat-pack for a wardrobe measures 15 cm by 1.5 m by 2 m.
    Maryse said that its volume was 45 cubic metres.
    a   Was Maryse correct?   b   Give a reason for your answer.

Be careful with the units.

6   A cube has a side of length 1 m. Huw said that this cube takes
    up the same amount of space as 100 cubes of side 10 cm.
    a   Is Huw correct?   b   Give a reason for your answer.

7   The volume of a rectangular box is 360 cm³.
    The base of the box measures 12 cm by 6 cm.
    Mark said that the depth of the box was 8 cm.
    a   Is Mark correct?   b   Give a reason for your answer.

The volume of box = $12 \times 6 \times d$ cm³ where d cm is the depth. Now form an equation using the fact that the volume is 360 cm³.

8   Bob digs a rectangular hole measuring 5 m by 3 m to lay the base
    for a new garage. He wants the base to be at least 30 cm thick.
    He orders 5 m³ of concrete. Tony says this will not be enough.
    a   Is Tony correct?   b   Give a reason for your answer.

9   This rectangular gift box is tied up with ribbon.
    Find
    a   its volume
    b   the total surface area of the box
    c   the length of ribbon needed if 5 cm
        extra is allowed for tying.

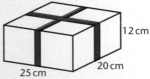

12 cm   25 cm   20 cm

UAM

12.3 Prisms, cylinders and compound shapes

   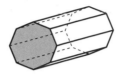

All four shapes have uniform cross-sections. They are all prisms.

Volume of a prism = area of cross-section × length.

Example 5

The cross-section of this prism is a trapezium. Find its volume.

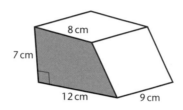

Area of cross-section = $\frac{1}{2}(8 + 12) \times 7\,cm^2$

　　　　　　　　　　　= $10 \times 7\,cm^2$

　　　　　　　　　　　= $70\,cm^2$

> The area of a trapezium
> = $\frac{1}{2}$(sum of parallel sides) × (distance between them).

Volume of prism = area of cross-section × length

　　　　　　　= $70 \times 9\,cm^3$

　　　　　　　= $630\,cm^3$

> Use this method to rework Example 4 on page 155.

Cylinders

A cylinder is a prism with a circular cross-section.

Volume of cylinder = area of cross-section × height.
The formula for the volume, V, is $V = \pi r^2 h$.

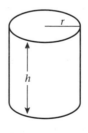

> When a prism is standing on one end the length becomes the height.

> The cross-section is a circle.
> Its area is πr^2.
> The volume is $\pi r^2 \times h$.

Exam practice 12C

1 Find the volume of each prism.

a

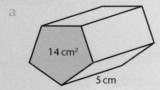

14 cm²

5 cm

b

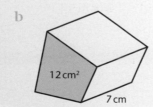

12 cm²

7 cm

> You are given the areas of the cross-sections.

c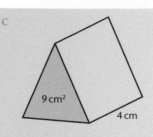

d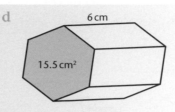

2 Find the volume of each prism.

First work out the area of cross-section.

a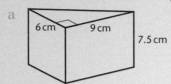

b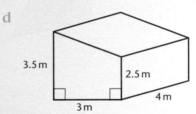

c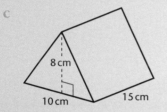

d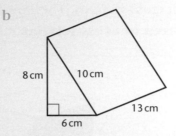

e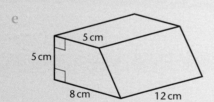

f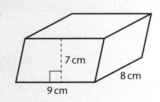

3 Find the volume of each cylinder. Give your answer to 1 d.p.

a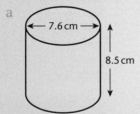

b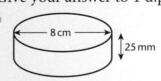

c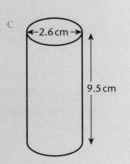

d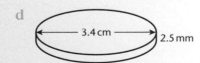

Remember that the volume
$= \pi \times$ (radius)$^2 \times$ height
and that the radius is half
the diameter.

4   Find the volume of each solid. Give your answers to 1 d.p.

a

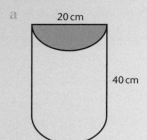

20 cm

40 cm

b

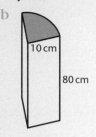

10 cm

80 cm

The cross-section of this solid is a semicircle.

The cross-section of this solid is a quadrant.

A quadrant is a quarter of a circle.

5   The cross-section of this shape is made up of three rectangles.
Find
a   the area of cross-section
b   the volume of the solid.

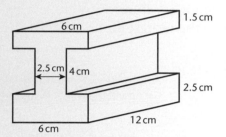

6 cm

1.5 cm

2.5 cm   4 cm

2.5 cm

6 cm   12 cm

You can find the area of the cross-section by dividing it into three rectangles.

12.4 Capacity

The **capacity** of a container is the amount it can hold.
The units of capacity in everyday use are the litre, the centilitre (cl) and the millilitre (ml).
The relationships between them are:

   1 litre = 1000 ml
      1 cl = 10 ml

Petrol is sold in litres. The capacity of a teaspoon is about 5 ml.

Capacity is a measure of volume.
The relationships between units of capacity and units of volume are

      1 litre = 1000 cm^3

   1 millilitre = 1 cm^3

The Imperial units of capacity still used are pints and gallons.

   1 gallon = 8 pints

You can convert between metric and Imperial units of capacity using

      1 litre ≈ 1.75 pints
   1 gallon ≈ 4.56 litres.

≈ means 'approximately equal to'.

Example 6

a   Convert 1.3 litres to ml.
b   Jane needs 1 pint of water.
   How far should she fill this jug?
   Explain your answer.

1000
900
800
700
600
500   ml
400
300
200
100
0

a 1.3 litres = 1.3 × 1000 ml = 1300 ml

> 1 litre = 1000 ml. You are changing to a smaller unit so multiply by 1000.

b 1 pint = 1000 ÷ 1.75 ml = 571.4… ml

> 1.75 pints = 1000 ml so 1 pint = 1000 ÷ 1.75 ml.

She should fill the jug to between 560 and 580 ml.

The subdivisions on the jug are 20 ml apart.
She cannot measure more accurately than between two subdivisions.

Example 7

Find the capacity of this cylindrical drum.
Give your answer in litres to the nearest litre.

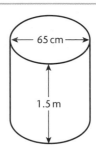

Radius = 65 ÷ 2 = 32.5 cm
Height = 1.5 × 100 cm = 150 cm

> First find the volume. You need the radius and the height in the same units.

Volume = π × (radius)² × height
π × 32.5² × 150 = 497 745.6…

> This is a number of cm³. To change this to litres, divide by 1000.

497 745.6… ÷ 1000 = 497.7…
Capacity = 498 litres to the nearest litre.

Exam practice 12D

1 **a** A carton holds 4 litres of milk. How many millilitres is this?

> 1 litre = 1000 ml

  b Sam buys a $2\frac{1}{2}$ litre can of oil. How many cubic centimetres is this?

  c A carton contains 250 ml of soup. What fraction of a litre is this?

> 1 litre = 1000 cm³

  d Cherie buys $1\frac{1}{2}$ litres of cola. How many millilitres is this?

2 The volume inside a jug is 2000 cm³. How many litres is this?

3 A bag contains 0.02 cubic metres of bulb fibre.
   How many cubic centimetres is this?

4 A bottle holds 75 centilitres of wine.
   What fraction of a litre is this?

> 1 litre = 100 cl

5 A petrol can holds 5 litres. How many cubic centimetres is this?

6 A medicine bottle holds 0.2 litres and a medicine spoon holds 5 ml.
   Peter must take 10 ml of this medicine twice a day.
   a How many spoonfuls must Peter take each day?
   b How many days will the medicine last?

7 This is rectangular water tank.
   a What is the volume of the tank?
   b How many litres will it hold?

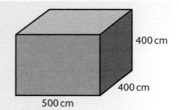

400 cm
400 cm
500 cm

8 Helen wants 8 gallons of diesel but the pump shows litres.
   Jo says that if she buys 40 litres she will have more than 8 gallons.
   a Is Jo correct?   b Give a reason for your answer.

1 gallon ≈ 4.56 litres

9 Some drinks are still sold by the pint.
   Harry says that 2 litres is more than 3 pints.
   a Is Harry correct?   b Give a reason for your answer.

1 litre ≈ 1.75 pints

10

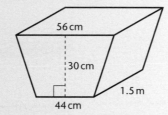

56 cm
30 cm
1.5 m
44 cm

   The cross-section of a water trough is a trapezium whose
   parallel sides are 56 cm and 44 cm and which are 30 cm apart.
   The trough is 1.5 m long.
   a Work out the volume of the trough giving your answer in
      cubic metres.
   b What is the capacity in litres?

1 cubic metre
= 1000 litres.

11 The capacity of the tank on a milk tanker is 5000 litres.
    It is 300 cm long.
    Work out the area of its cross-section.

12.5 Mass

Mass is the scientific name for the amount of matter in an object.
In everyday language we usually talk about the weight of something
rather than its mass.

In science, weight is a
force. It is measured in
newtons.

The units of mass in common use are the kilogram (kg), the gram (g),
the milligram (mg) and the tonne (t).
The relationships between them are:

   1 kg = 1000 g
   1 g = 1000 mg
   1 t = 1000 kg

The pound is an imperial unit still used.
You can convert between pounds (lb) and kilograms using

   1 kg ≈ 2.2 lb.

Example 8

Convert **a** 6780 g into kilograms   **b** 0.06 t into kilograms.

a 1000 g = 1 kg

So 6780 g = $\frac{6780}{1000}$ kg = 6.78 kg.

> You are converting to a larger unit so divide by 1000.

b 1 t = 1000 kg

So 0.06 t = 0.06 × 1000 kg = 60 kg.

> You are converting to a smaller unit so multiply by 1000.

Example 9

a Convert 1.5 kg into pounds.
b Convert 6 lb into kilograms.

a 1.5 × 2.2 = 3.3

1.5 kg ≈ 3.3 lb.

> To convert kg into pounds, multiply by 2.2.

b 6 ÷ 2.2 = 2.73 correct to 2 decimal places.

6 lb ≈ 2.73 kg.

> To convert pounds into kg, divide by 2.2.

Exam practice 12E

1 Convert
   a 2 kg into grams
   b 3.2 t into kilograms
   c 7460 g into kilograms
   d 2450 kg into tonnes
   e 500 g into kilograms
   f 583 kg into tonnes
   g 0.05 kg into grams
   h 1400 g into kilograms
   i 3000 mg into grams
   j 0.06 g into milligrams
   k 0.008 kg into grams
   l 0.0075 t into kilograms

2 A bag of cement weighs 50 kg. A lorry is loaded with 150 bags.
   How many tonnes of cement is this?

> 1 tonne = 1000 kg.

3 Louis buys a 1 kg bag of weedkiller. The instructions say 'Use
   25 g with 5 litres of water'. How many litres of weedkiller can
   Louis mix?

4 Which is heavier, 8 kg or 15 pounds?

> Convert 8 kg into pounds (this is easier than changing pounds to kilograms).

5 Bill buys a 5 kg bag of rice.
   Work out its weight in pounds.

6 Rajiv needs 3 pounds of sugar to make fudge.
   Will a 2 kg bag of sugar be enough?
   Give a reason for your answer.

UAM

12.6 Density

Density measures the mass of 1 unit of volume of a material.
The unit of volume usually used for density is the cubic centimetre
(cm^3).

The density of gold is $19.3 \, g/cm^3$.
This means that $1 \, cm^3$ of gold has a mass of $19.3 \, g$.

You can work out density using $\text{Density} = \dfrac{\text{mass}}{\text{volume}}$.

> g/cm^3 means 'grams per cubic centimetre'.

Example 10

A block of wood has a mass of 200 grams and a volume of $250 \, cm^3$.
Find the density of the wood.

> $250 \, cm^3$ weighs $200 \, g$
>
> $1 \, cm^3$ weighs $\dfrac{200}{250} \, g = 0.8 \, g$
>
> The density of the wood is $0.8 \, g/cm^3$.

> The density of the wood is the mass of 1 cubic centimetre.

When you know the volume of an object and the density of the
material from which it is made, you can work out its mass.

Example 11

The density of copper is $8.9 \, g/cm^3$.
The volume of a block of copper is $400 \, cm^3$. What does the block weigh?

> $400 \times 8.9 = 3560$
>
> So $400 \, cm^3$ weighs $3560 \, g = 3.56 \, kg$.

> The density tells you that $1 \, cm^3$ weighs 8.9 grams. $400 \, cm^3$ weighs 400 times as much.

Exam practice 12F

1 The volume of a silver ingot is $56 \, cm^3$.
   The density of silver is $10.5 \, g/cm^3$. What is the mass of the ingot?

2 A jug holds 35 cubic centimetres of mercury.
   The density of mercury is $13.6 \, g/cm^3$.
   What is the mass of the mercury in the jug?

3 $1 \, cm^3$ of platinum has a mass of $21.5 \, g$.
   Work out the mass of a cuboid of platinum measuring 15 cm by
   5 cm by 2.2 cm.

4 The density of milk is 0.98 grams per cubic centimetre.
   Connie said that 2 litres of milk weighs more than 1 kilogram.
   a Is Connie correct?
   b Give a reason for your answer.

> 1 litre $= 1000 \, cm^3$

5   The density of platinum is 21.5 g/cm³ and the density of gold is
    19.3 g/cm³.
    Lewis said this meant that 20 grams of platinum was heavier
    than 22 grams of gold.
    a   Is Lewis correct?
    b   Give a reason for your answer.

UAM

6   This is a square sheet of glass.
    The glass is 3 mm thick.
    The density of glass is 2.5 g/cm³.
    Work out the mass of the sheet.

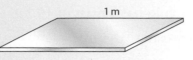

1 m

7   This triangular prism is made of wood.
    a   Work out the volume of the block.
    b   The prism weighs 800 grams.
        Find the density of the wood.

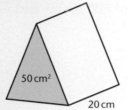

50 cm²

20 cm

8

12 cm²

1 m

This piece of metal weighs 3240 grams.
It has a uniform cross-section of area 12 cm².
Find the density of the metal.

12.7 Formulae and dimensions

Formulae for finding the areas and volumes of shapes contain letters
that represent length, area or volume. Some formulae also contain
numbers or symbols that stand for numbers, such as π.

A length is **one-dimensional**.
An expression with single letters representing
lengths must give a length.

> The letters a and b stand for lengths.
> The expressions $a + b$ and $2\pi a$ give lengths.

An area is **two-dimensional**.
You find an area by multiplying two lengths together.
An expression with two letters representing lengths multiplied
together must give an area.

> The letters a and b
> stand for lengths.
> The expressions ab and
> πa^2 give areas.

A volume is **three-dimensional**.
You find a volume by multiplying three lengths together.
An expression with three letters representing lengths multiplied
together must give a volume.

> The letters a, b and c
> stand for lengths.
> The expressions abc
> and a^2b give volumes.

Example 12

b and c represent lengths, and A represents an area.
State whether each expression represents a length, an area or a volume.

a bc **b** Ab **c** $2\pi b^2 c$

    a bc represents an area.

    b Ab represents a volume.

    c $2\pi b^2 c$ represents a volume.

> length × length is 2-dimensional.

> area × length is 3-dimensional.

> $b \times b \times c$ is three-dimensional.
> 2 and π are numbers.

Exam practice 12G

1 Write true or false for each of these.
  a 5 km is a length
  b 15 cm is an area
  c 4 cm^3 is a volume
  d 2π cm^2 is an area
  e 3 km^2 is a length
  f 54 mm^2 is a volume

2 Write down whether each of these is a length, an area or a volume.
  a the region inside a square
  b the distance around a pond
  c the space inside a box
  d the diameter of a circle
  e the region within a circle
  f the space inside an egg
  g the surface of a cube
  h a perimeter

3 The letters p, q and r each represent a number of centimetres.
  Write down the unit (cm, cm^2 or cm^3) for the capital letter in each formula.
  a $A = pq$
  b $P = p + q + r$
  c $B = \pi q^2$
  d $X = pqr$
  e $P = \pi q^2 r$
  f $D = 2p + 3r$
  g $T = p^2 + q^2$
  h $W = pq + qr$

4 a, b and c represent lengths.
  Which two of these formulae give a volume?
  $E = 4\pi a^2$ $F = 2\pi^2 abc$ $G = \pi a^2 b$ $H = 3(a^3 + b^2)$

5 Nia said that the area of a circle was given by the formula
  $A = 2\pi r$.
  Sheena said that this was definitely wrong.
  Was Sheena correct? Justify your answer.

6 Mike said that the formula for the volume of a solid was
  $V = \pi(r^3 + h^2)$.
  Kim said that it could not be.
  Is Kim correct? Give a reason for your answer.

Summary of key points

- Volume of a cuboid = length × breadth × height.
- The common metric units of volume are mm³, cm³ and m³ where $1\,m^3 = 1\,000\,000\,cm^3$ and $1\,cm^3 = 1000\,mm^3$.
- Volume of a prism = area of cross-section × length.
- Volume of a cylinder = $\pi \times (radius)^2 \times$ height.
- The metric units of capacity are the litre and the millilitre where 1 litre = 1000 ml.
- The Imperial units of capacity still in use are the gallon and the pint where 1 gallon = 8 pints.
- 1 gallon ≈ 4.56 litres and 1 litre ≈ 1.75 pints.
- The relationship between units of volume and units of capacity are 1 litre = 1000 cm³ and 1 ml = 1 cm³.
- The metric units of mass are the gram (g), kilogram (kg), tonne (t) and the milligram (mg) where 1 kg = 1000 g, 1 g = 1000 mg and 1 t = 1000 kg.
- The Imperial unit of mass still in use is the pound where 1 kg ≈ 2.2 lb
- Density of a substance = mass ÷ volume and is measured in grams per cubic centimetre (g/cm³).
- A length has 1 dimension, an area 2 dimensions and a volume 3 dimensions.

Most students who get GRADE E or above can:
- convert between metric and Imperial units
- find the volume of a cuboid.

Most students who get GRADE C can also:
- find the volume of a prism
- convert between units of volume and capacity
- distinguish between formulae for length, area and volume.

Glossary

Capacity	a measure of volume
Cross-section	a slice through a solid
Density	the mass of one unit of volume of a material
Mass	the amount of matter in an object; called weight in everyday language
Volume	the space occupied by a solid

13 Pythagoras' theorem

This chapter will show you:
✓ how to work out the hypotenuse of a right-angled triangle when the other two sides are known
✓ how to work out a side of a right-angled triangle when one side and the hypotenuse are known
✓ how to solve problems involving right-angled triangles

Before you start you need to know:
✓ how to find the square and square root of a number
✓ how to round numbers
✓ the meaning of north, east, south and west.

13.1 Pythagoras' theorem

Pythagoras' theorem connects the lengths of the sides in a right-angled triangle. The side opposite the right angle is called the **hypotenuse**.

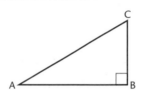

The side AC is opposite the right angle in this triangle, so AC is the hypotenuse.

Pythagoras' theorem states that

> **In a right-angled triangle the square of the hypotenuse is equal to the sum of the squares on the other two sides.**

For this triangle $AC^2 = AB^2 + BC^2$.

Example 1

Triangle LMN has a right angle at M.
Find the length of LN.

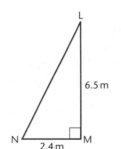

LN is the hypotenuse. Pythagoras' theorem gives $LN^2 = NM^2 + LM^2$. So substitute 2.4 for NM and 6.5 for LM.

$LN^2 = 2.4^2 + 6.5^2$

$\quad\ = 48.01$

$LN\ = \sqrt{48.01}$

$\quad\ = 6.928... = 6.9$ m to 1 d.p.

Press

2 . 4 x^2 + 6 . 5 x^2 =

Press

√ 4 8 . 0 1 =

Exam practice 13A

In questions 1 to 14 find the length of the hypotenuse.
Give answers that are not exact correct to 1 decimal place.

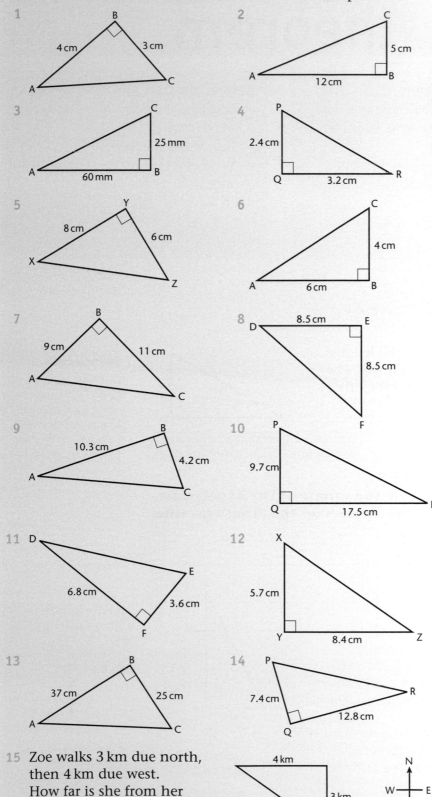

15 Zoe walks 3 km due north, then 4 km due west. How far is she from her starting point?

16 Alan walks 5 km due south, then 3 km due east. How far is Alan from his starting point?

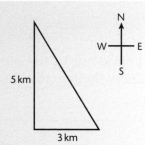

17 A, B and C are three houses.
   a   Work out ∠BAC.
   b   Find the distance from B to C.

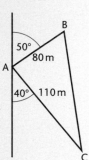

18 Find the length of the longest straight line that can be drawn on this square block of wood.

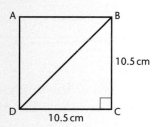

The longest line is one of the diagonals.

19 A door is 2.1 m high and 0.9 m wide. Work out the length of the diagonal.

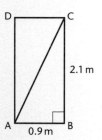

20 Pete had to find the length of a diagonal in this rectangle. He wrote

$3^2 + 5^2 = 9 + 25 = 34 = 5.8$

Answer 5.8

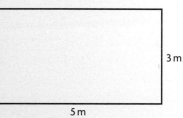

UAM
   a   There are two things wrong with this. Explain what they are.
   b   Write out your solution to this problem.

UAM
21 a   What is the mathematical name of this quadrilateral? Give a reason for your answer.
   b   One diagonal is 6 cm long and the other is 4.5 cm. Work out
      i   the length of AB
      ii   the perimeter of the quadrilateral.

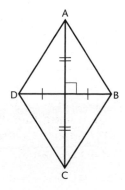

13.2 Finding a shorter side

You can use Pythagoras' theorem to find one of the shorter sides of a right-angled triangle when you know the lengths of the other two sides.

Example 2

Triangle XYZ has a right angle at X.
Find the length of XY.

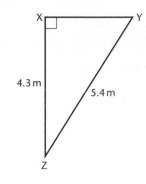

> YZ is the hypotenuse so
> $YZ^2 = XY^2 + XZ^2$ from Pythagoras' theorem.
> Substitute 4.3 for XZ and 5.4 for YZ.

$$5.4^2 = 4.3^2 + XY^2$$
$$5.4^2 - 4.3^2 = XY^2$$
$$10.67 = XY^2$$
$$XY = \sqrt{10.67}$$
$$= 3.266\ldots$$
$$XY = 3.3 \text{ m to 1 d.p.}$$

Exam practice 13B

In questions **1** to **10** find the length of the unknown side.
Give answers that are not exact correct to 1 decimal place.

1
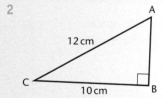

2
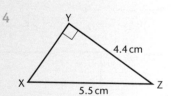

3
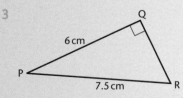

4
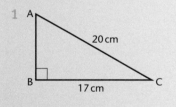

5
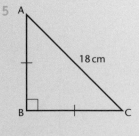

6
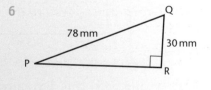

7
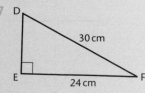

8
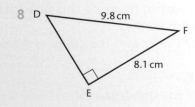

9
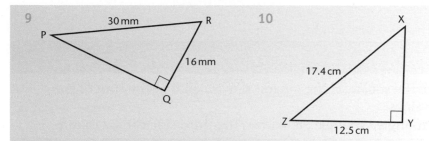

10

11 This is a rectangular football pitch.
Find, to the nearest metre, the length of a short side.

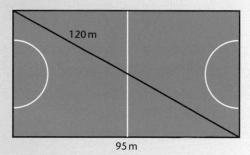

12 This ladder is leaning against
a vertical wall.
How far up the wall does the
ladder reach?

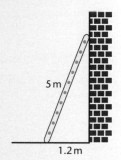

13 This is a sketch of the cross-section of a skip.

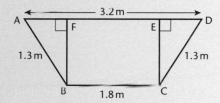

a What is the mathematical name of the shape?
b Find the length of AF.
c Work out the depth (EC) of the skip.
d Find the area of the cross-section of the skip.
e The skip is 1.6 m wide.
Find its capacity in cubic metres.

Summary of key points

- In a right-angled triangle the square of the longest side is equal to the sum of the squares of the other two sides.
- If any two sides in a right-angled triangle are known the third side can be found.

Most students who get GRADE C can:
- use Pythagoras' theorem to find the third side in a right-angled triangle when the lengths of two sides are known.

Glossary

Hypotenuse   the longest side in a right-angled triangle

14 Coordinates and graphs

This chapter will show you:
- ✓ the meaning of coordinates
- ✓ how to find the coordinates of the midpoint of a line segment
- ✓ how to find the length of a line segment
- ✓ what the equation of a straight line looks like and how to plot its graph
- ✓ how to find the gradient of a line and how to recognise parallel lines
- ✓ how to find the equation of a line
- ✓ what a quadratic equation looks like and how to plot its graph

Before you start you need to know:
- ✓ the names and properties of the special triangles and quadrilaterals
- ✓ how to work with fractions
- ✓ Pythagoras' theorem and how to use it
- ✓ how to find the areas of rectangles, triangles, parallelograms and trapeziums
- ✓ how to change the subject of a formula
- ✓ how to work with negative numbers
- ✓ how to substitute numbers into an equation
- ✓ how to solve equations

14.1 Coordinates

You need one number to give the position of a point on a line.
You need two numbers to give the position of a point on a flat surface.
You need three numbers to give the position of a point in space.
These numbers are called **coordinates**.

The coordinates that give of the position of the point on a grid are written as a pair of numbers in brackets.

The point A is at 2 on this number line.

The point A on this surface is 1 along and 2 up.

The point A inside this cuboid is 2 along, 1 across and 2 up.

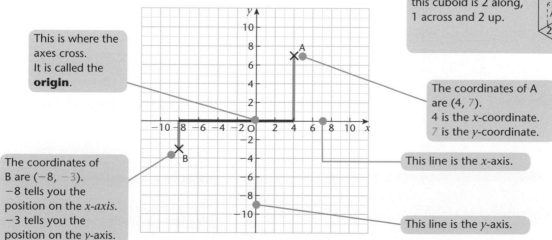

This is where the axes cross. It is called the **origin**.

The coordinates of A are (4, 7).
4 is the x-coordinate.
7 is the y-coordinate.

This line is the x-axis.

The coordinates of B are (−8, −3).
−8 tells you the position on the x-axis.
−3 tells you the position on the y-axis.

This line is the y-axis.

Example 1

Two sides of a rectangle are drawn on this grid.
a   Write down the coordinates of A.
b   Write down the coordinates of C.
c   What are the coordinates of the
    missing vertex?

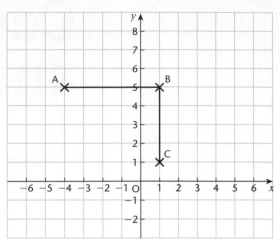

a $(-4, 5)$

You always write the x value first.

b $(1, 1)$

The missing vertex has the same x-coordinate as A and the same y-coordinate as C.

c $(-4, 1)$

The midpoint of a line segment

A **line segment** is the line between two points. The **midpoint** of the line segment is the point halfway between these points.

You can find the coordinates of the midpoint from a graph or by calculation.

Example 2

Find the coordinates of the midpoint, M, of the line AB.

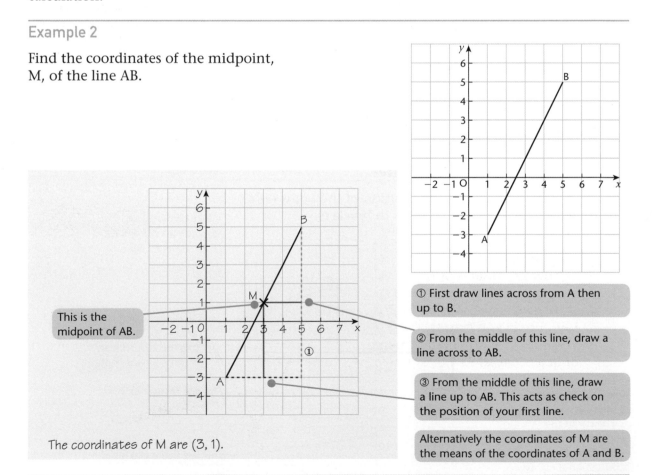

This is the midpoint of AB.

① First draw lines across from A then up to B.

② From the middle of this line, draw a line across to AB.

③ From the middle of this line, draw a line up to AB. This acts as check on the position of your first line.

Alternatively the coordinates of M are the means of the coordinates of A and B.

The coordinates of M are (3, 1).

The length of a line segment

You can find the length of a line that is parallel to the x-axis or to the y-axis by counting grid lines.
You can use Pythagoras' theorem to find the length of a sloping line.

Example 3

Find the length of AB. Give your answer to 1 decimal place.

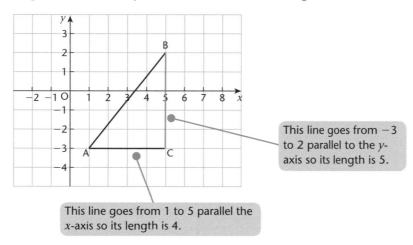

Draw lines across from A then up to B to make a right-angled triangle.

This line goes from -3 to 2 parallel to the y-axis so its length is 5.

This line goes from 1 to 5 parallel the x-axis so its length is 4.

AC $= 4$ and BC $= 5$

$AB^2 = AC^2 + BC^2$ Pythagoras' theorem

$AB^2 = 4^2 + 5^2$
$\quad = 16 + 25 = 41$

$AB = \sqrt{41} = 6.40\ldots = 6.4$ to 1 d.p.

Triangle ABC has a right angle at C, so you can use Pythagoras' theorem to find AB.

Exam practice 14A

Remember that the x-coordinate is first.

1 Copy this diagram.
   a Write down
      i   the coordinates of A
      ii the coordinates of B.
   b Plot the point D at (0, 4).
   c Join A to D and C to D.
   d What is the mathematical name
      of quadrilateral ABCD?

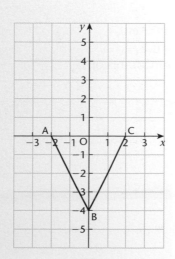

2 Copy this diagram.
  a Write down
    i   the coordinates of A
    ii the coordinates of C.
  b Plot the point D at (4, 2).
  c Join A to D and C to D.
  d What is the mathematical
     name of quadrilateral ABCD?

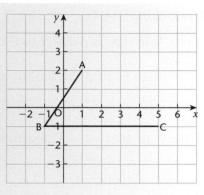

3 ABCD is a rectangle.
  On a copy of the diagram,
  complete the rectangle and
  write down the coordinates of D.

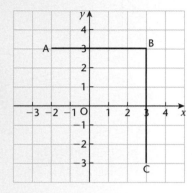

4 ABCD is a parallelogram.
  On a copy of the diagram,
  complete the parallelogram and
  write down the coordinates of D.

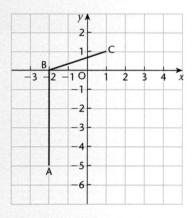

5 ABCD is a kite.
  On a copy of the diagram,
  complete the kite and
  write down the coordinates of D.

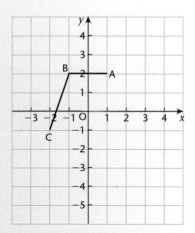

The diagonal AC is a
line of symmetry.

6 a What is the mathematical name
   of the triangle ABC?
  b Write down the length of AB.
  c Write down the coordinates
    of the midpoint of AB.

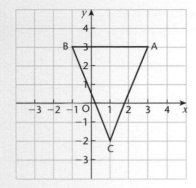

7 a What is the mathematical
    name of the quadrilateral
    ABCD?
  b On a copy of the diagram:
    i   join AC
    ii mark the midpoint of AC
        and label it M.
  c Write down the length of AC
  d What are the coordinates of M.

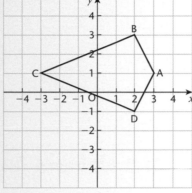

8 a Write down the coordinates
    of the midpoint of
    i   PS
    ii QR.
  b Kwame said 'the length of
    the line joining the
    midpoints of PS and QR is
    the height of the
    quadrilateral PQRS'.
    Explain why Kwame is
    wrong.

UAM

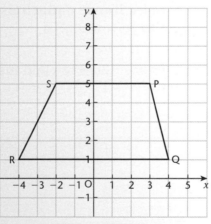

The coordinates of a
point can be decimals
or fractions.

9 a What is the mathematical name of triangle LMN?
  b On a copy of the diagram, mark the midpoint of LM and
    label it P.
  c Write down
    i   the coordinates of P
    ii the length of ML
    iii the length of NP.
  d Calculate the area of
    triangle LMN.
  e Calculate the length
    of LN.

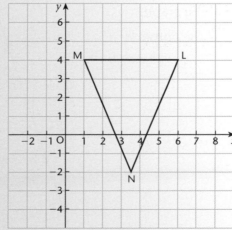

The area of a triangle
$= \frac{1}{2}$ the base × height.

10 a What is the mathematical
       name of the quadrilateral
       PQRS?
    b Write down the length of
       i   PS   ii   QR.
    c Write down the distance
       that P is above the line QR.
    d Find the area of PQRS.
    e Find the length of PQ.
       Give your answer to 1 d.p.
    f Nikki said 'I can use the
       length of PQ as the
       distance between the sides
       PS and QR'.
       Explain why Nikki cannot
       do this.

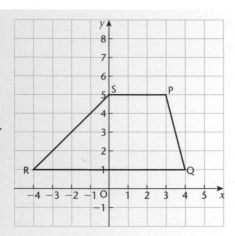

> The area of a trapezium
> $= \frac{1}{2}$ (sum of parallel
> sides) × distance
> between them.

14.2 The graph of a straight line

Equations like $y = 3x + 1$ are called **linear equations**.
When you substitute any number for x you get a
corresponding value for y.

> When $x = 2$,
> $y = 3 \times 2 + 1 = 6 + 1 = 7$.

You can make a table showing some values of x and the
corresponding values of y for $y = 3x + 1$.

x	-1	0	1	2	3
y	-2	1	4	7	10

> This is called a **table of values**.

This is the value of y corresponding to $x = -1$.
It comes from replacing x by -1 in the equation:
$y = 3 \times (-1) + 1 = -3 + 1 = -2$.

You can use the pairs of values as
coordinates to plot points on a graph.

The straight line through these points is
called the graph of $y = 3x + 1$.

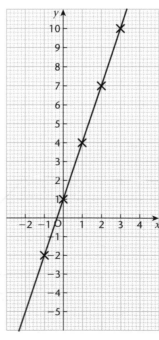

Example 4

a Complete this table of values for $y + 2x = 3$.

x	-1	0	1	2	3
y	5	3			-3

b Draw the graph of $y + 2x = 3$.

a

x	−1	0	1	2	3
y	5	3	1	−1	−3

Substitute $x = 1$ into $y + 2x = 3$:
$y + 2 = 3$. Solve this equation to find y: $y = 3 - 2 = 1$.

Substitute $x = 2$ into $y + 2x = 3$:
$y + 4 = 3$ so $y = 3 - 4 = -1$.

b

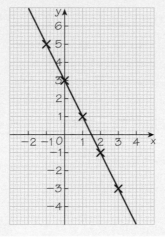

Use the pairs of values as coordinates: $(-1, 5)$, $(0, 3)$, $(1, 1)$, $(2, -1)$, $(3, -3)$.

Draw a straight line through your points and continue it to the edges of the grid. You have made a mistake if one or more points is not on the line so check your working and where you have put the points.

Example 5

This is the graph of $y + x = 6$.

a i Add the graph of $y = 1$.

   ii P is the point where the lines cross.
Mark the point P and write down the coordinates of P.

b i Add the line $x = 4$.

   ii Q is the point where the lines $y + x = 6$ and $x = 4$ cross.
Mark the point Q and write down its coordinates.

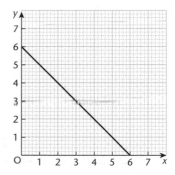

a i This is the graph of $y = 1$ because $y = 1$ everywhere on this line.

   ii The coordinates of P are $(5, 1)$.

b i This is the line $x = 4$ because $x = 4$ everywhere on this line.

   ii The coordinates of Q are $(4, 2)$.

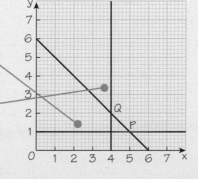

Lines parallel to the axes

An equation of the form $y = c$, where c is a constant, is a line parallel to the x-axis.

An equation of the form $x = k$, where k is a constant is a line parallel to the y-axis.

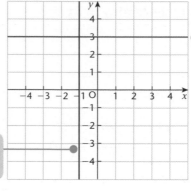

The y-coordinate of every point on this line is 3. The equation of the line is $y = 3$.

The equation of the x-axis is $y = 0$.

The x-coordinate of every point on this line is -1.
The equation of the line is $x = -1$.

The equation of the y-axis is $x = 0$.

Exam practice 14B

1 a Copy and complete this table of values for $y = x + 1$.

x	0	1	2	3	4
y	1	2			5

Use a grid like this for the questions in this exercise.

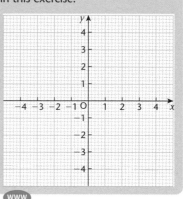

b Draw the graph of $y = x + 1$.

2 a Copy and complete this table of values for $y = 4 - x$.

x	0	1	2	3	4
y	4	3			0

b Draw the graph of $y = 4 - x$.

3 a Copy and complete this table of values for $y = x - 2$.

x	0	1	2	3	4
y	-2	-1			

b Draw the graph of $y = x - 2$.
c On the same set of axes draw the graph of $y = 1$. Write down the coordinates of the point of intersection with $y = x - 2$.

Remember to extend your lines in both directions to the edge of the grid.

4 a Copy and complete this table of values for $y + x = 3$.

x	-1	0	1	2	3
y	4	3			

b Draw the graph of $y + x = 3$.
c Draw the graph of $x = 2$. Write down the coordinates of the points where the two graphs cross.

5 a Copy and complete this table of values for $y = 2x - 1$.

x	-1	0	1	2
y	-3	-1		

b Draw the graph of $y = 2x - 1$.
c Draw the line $x = 3$ on your graph.
d P is the point where the two lines cross.
Mark the point P and write down its coordinates.

6   a   Draw the graph of $y = 2x - 4$.
     b   Draw the line $y = 2$ on your graph.
     c   Write down the coordinates of the point where the two lines cross.

> You need to make a table of values. Choose three different values of x between -4 and 4.

7   a   Draw the graph of $y + 2x = 1$.
     b   There is a point on the line where the x and y coordinates are equal.
       Write down the coordinates of this point.

> Choose three values of x between -1 and 3 to make your table of values.

8   a   Draw the graph of $y = \frac{1}{2}x + 1$.
     b   There is a point on this line where the x-coordinate is 1 more than the y-coordinate.
       Write down the coordinates of this point.

> Choose three values of x between -4 and 4 to make your table of values.

14.3 Gradient

The **gradient** of a line is a measurement of its slope. It is the amount by which y changes when x increases by 1 unit.

The gradient is positive when the line slopes up.

The equation of this line is $y = 2x - 1$. Its gradient is 2. This is positive because the line slopes up.

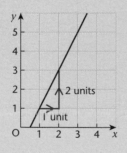

The gradient is negative when the line slopes down.

The equation of this line is $y = 6 - 3x$. Its gradient is -3. This is negative because the line slopes down.

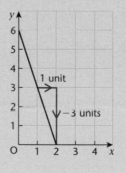

> You can find the gradient of a line by taking two points on it and calculating $\dfrac{\text{vertical change}}{\text{horizontal change}}$.

Example 6

Find the gradient of this line.

> Choose a point on the line whose x-coordinate is a whole number. Go across to the next whole number then down to the line. The amount by which y changes is the gradient of the line.

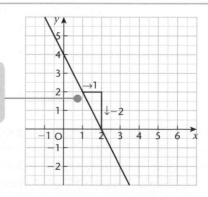

The gradient is -2.

You can find the gradient of a line from its equation.
First make sure that the equation is in the form $y = \ldots$
The gradient of the line is then the number that is multiplied by x.

> You must include the sign.
> $y = -4x + 1$: gradient $= -4$.
> $y = -3 + 2x$: gradient $= 2$.

Example 7

What is the gradient of the line
a $y = 4x - 2$ **b** $y = 7 - x$ **c** $y - \frac{1}{2}x = 5$?

a $y = 4x - 2$
The gradient is 4.

> x is multiplied by 4 so the gradient is 4.

b $y = 7 - x$
The gradient is -1.

> x is multiplied by 1 and the sign is negative, so the gradient is -1.

c $y - \frac{1}{2}x = 5$
$y = 5 + \frac{1}{2}x$
The gradient is $\frac{1}{2}$.

> Write the equation in the from $y = \ldots$

> x is multiplied by $\frac{1}{2}$ and the sign is $+$.

Parallel lines have the same gradient.

> The lines $y = 2x - 1$ and $y = 2x + 3$ are parallel because they both have a gradient of 2.

Exam practice 14C

1   Write down the gradient of
    a $y = 3x + 9$ b $y = 2x - 4$
    c $y = 5 - x$ d $y + 2x = 4$
    e $y = \frac{1}{2}x - 3$ f $y = \frac{1}{2} - \frac{2}{3}x.$

2   Which of these of lines are parallel?
    $y = 3x - 1$, $y = 4x - 3$, $y = 4 + 3x$, $y = 6 - 3x$.

3   Imran said that the lines $y = 5x - 2$ and $y = 2 - 5x$ are parallel.
    Is Imran correct?
    Explain your answer.

4   Find the gradient of each of these lines.

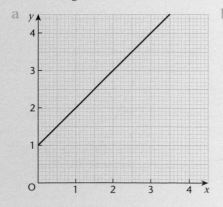

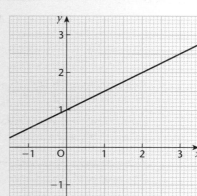

14.4 Finding the equation of a line

You can write the equation of a line in the form $y = mx + c$, where m is the gradient of the line and c is a number.
When $x = 0$, $y = c$. This is the value of y where the line crosses the y-axis.

You can use this to find the equation of a line from its graph.

Example 8

Find the equation of the line through these points.

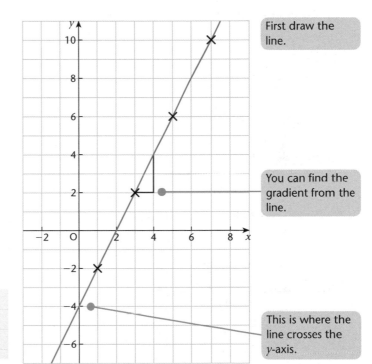

First draw the line.

You can find the gradient from the line.

Now you know the equation is $y = 2x + c$ where c is the value of y where the line crosses the y-axis.

Gradient = 2
The line crosses the y-axis where $y = -4$.
The equation of the line is $y = 2x - 4$.

This is where the line crosses the y-axis.

Sometimes you can write down the equation of a line without having to do any calculations.

Example 9

Write down the equation of each line.

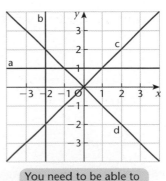

a $y = 1$

Every point on this line has a y-coordinate of 1.

b $x = -2$

Every point on this line has an x-coordinate of -2.

c $y = x$

y-coordinate = x-coordinate for every point on this line.

d $y = -x$

y-coordinate = $- x$-coordinate for every point on this line.

You need to be able to recognise the lines $y = x$ and $y = -x$.

Exam practice 14D

1   Write down the equation of each line.

a
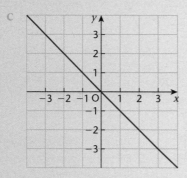

b
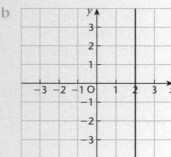

c

 2   a   Write down the coordinates of A and B.
    b   On a copy of the graph, draw the line
        through A and B.
    c   Work out the gradient of the line.
    d   Find the equation of the line.

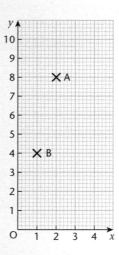

 3

    a   Write down the coordinates of A and B.
    b   On a copy of the graph, draw the line through all the points.
    c   Work out the gradient of the line.
    d   Find the equation of the line.

4 a Plot the points A (1, 5) and B (3, 1).
  b Draw the line through A and B.
  c Work out the gradient of the line.
  d Find the equation of the line.

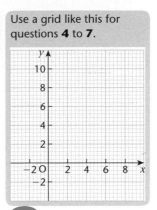

Use a grid like this for questions **4** to **7**.

www

5 a Plot the points A (0, 2) and B (4, 4).
  b Draw the line through A and B.
  c Work out the gradient of the line.
  d Find the equation of the line.
  e Plot the point C (1, 5).
  f Find the equation of the line through C that is parallel to the line through A and B. ●

This line will have the same gradient as the line through A and B, but it goes through C.

6 a Plot the points P (−2, −2) and Q (6, 2).
  b Draw the line through P and Q.
  c Work out the gradient of the line.
  d Find the equation of the line.

7 a Plot the points S (0, 8) and T (2, 0).
  b Find the equation of the line through S and T.
  c Find the equation of the line through the point R (−2, 0) that is parallel to the line through S and T.

8 The cost of a visit by an engineer to repair a washing machine is made up of two parts, a fixed call-out charge and a charge for each hour spent on the job.
The graph shows the bill (£P) for call-outs lasting up to 3 hours.

The equation is in the form
$P = \text{(gradient)} \times t + c$.

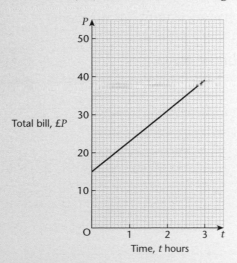

Total bill, £P

Time, t hours

  a Find the equation of the line.
  b Write down the fixed call-out charge.
  c Work out how much the engineer charges for a visit that includes 1 hour's work.

9 The cost of hiring a digger is made up of a fixed charge and a charge for each day it is hired.

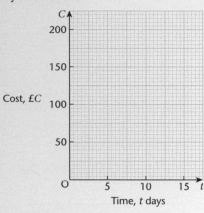

The table shows the cost of hiring the digger for 5, 10 and 15 days.

No. of days (t)	5	10	15
Cost £C	100	150	200

a Plot these points on a copy of the grid and draw a line through them.
b Write down the fixed charge.
c Work out the additional charge for each day the digger is hired.
d Find the equation of the line.
e What is the cost of hiring this digger for 1 week?

14.5 Graphs of quadratics

The equation of a **quadratic graph** has an x^2 term but no higher power of x. It may also have an x term and a number.

You can make a table of values and plot the graph.

> These are equations of quadratic graphs:
> $y = x^2 - 9$,
> $y = x^2 + 3x + 4$

> A quadratic graph looks like
> this $\bigvee$ or this $\bigcap$.

Example 10

a Complete this table of values for $y = x^2 - 9$

x	−4	−3	−2	−1	0	1	2	3	4
y	7	0		−8	−9	−8		0	

b Draw the graph of $y = x^2 - 9$.

a
x	−4	−3	−2	−1	0	1	2	3	4
y	7	0	−5	−8	−9	−8	−5	0	7

Substitute −2 for x in $y = x^2 - 9$.
$y = (-2)^2 - 9 = 4 - 9 = -5$.

Substitute 2 for x in $y = x^2 - 9$.
$y = (2)^2 - 9 = 4 - 9 = -5$.

Substitute 4 for x in $y = x^2 - 9$.
$y = (4)^2 - 9 = 16 - 9 = 7$.

b

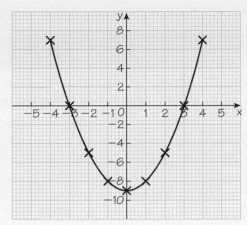

> Plot the points given by the pairs of values of x and y.
> Draw a smooth curve through the points.
> It is not easy to draw a smooth curve. You might find it helps to turn the paper so that your hand is inside the curve.

Exam practice 14E

1 a Copy and complete this table of values for $y = x^2 - 2$.

x	-3	-2	-1	0	1	2	3
y	7		-1	-2	-1		7

> ● Remember that $2^2 = 2 \times 2$ and that $(-2)^2 = (-2) \times (-2) = 4$

  b Draw the graph of $y = x^2 - 2$.

> Use a grid like this for questions in this exercise.
>
>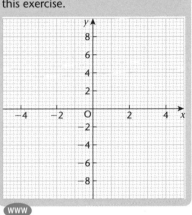
>
> www

2 a Copy and complete this table of values for $y = x^2 + 1$.

x	-2	-1	0	1	2
y	5		1	2	

  b Draw the graph of $y = x^2 + 1$.

3 a Copy and complete this table of values for $y = x^2 - 2x$.

x	-2	-1	0	1	2	3	4
y	8		0			3	

  b Draw the graph of $y = x^2 - 2x$.

4 a Copy and complete this table of values for $y = x^2 + x - 5$.

x	-4	-3	-2	-1	0	1	2	3
y	7		-3			-3		

> You can add rows to the table to find y:
>
> | x | | -4 | -3 | |
> |---|---|---|---|---|
> | x^2 | | | 9 | |
> | $x^2 + x$ | | | 6 | |
> | $y = x^2 + x - 5$ | | 7 | 1 | |

  b Draw the graph of $y = x^2 + x - 5$.

5 a Copy and complete this table of values for $y = 5 - x^2$.

x	-3	-2	-1	0	1	2	3
y	-4		4	5	4		

  b Draw the graph of $y = 5 - x^2$.

Summary of key points

- The coordinates of a point are always given with the distance along the x-axis first.
- You can use Pythagoras' theorem to find the length of a sloping line segment when you know the coordinates of its ends.
- You need to make a table of values to draw the graph of an equation.
- The equation of a straight line is $y = mx + c$ where m is the gradient and c is the value of y where the line crosses the y-axis.
- The equation of a quadratic graph has an x^2 term but no higher power of x.
- You can calculate the gradient of a line by finding how much y changes when the value of x increases by 1 unit.
- When a line slopes up the gradient is positive.
- When a line slopes down the gradient is negative.
- Two lines are parallel when they have the same gradient.
- You can find the equation of a line by working out its gradient, then using the value of y when the line crosses the y-axis to give the value of c.

Most students who get GRADE E or above can:
- complete a table of values and draw the graph of a straight line.

Most students who get GRADE C can also:
- find the gradient and the equation of a straight line.

Glossary

Coordinates	give the position of a point on a grid
Gradient	measures the slope of a line
Line segment	a line between two points
Linear equation	an equation like $y = 2x + 4$
Midpoint	the point halfway between the ends of a line segment
Origin	the point where the axes cross
Quadratic graph	the graph of an equation like $y = 2x^2 - 3x + 4$
Table of values	a table giving values of x and corresponding values of y

15 Using graphs

This chapter will show you:
- ✓ what 'simultaneous equations' means
- ✓ how to use graphs to solve simultaneous equations and quadratic equations
- ✓ how to draw and use conversion graphs
- ✓ the relationship between distance, time and speed
- ✓ how to draw and use distance–time graphs

Before you start you need to know:
- ✓ how to draw the graph of a straight line
- ✓ how to draw the graph of a quadratic
- ✓ the units used for length and how to convert between them
- ✓ the units used for time and how to convert between them

15.1 Simultaneous equations

Solving an equation means finding the value or values of the letters that make both sides of the equation equal.

There is often one solution that satisfies two linear equations. You can find this solution by drawing graphs.

When two equations have solutions in common, they are called **simultaneous equations**. Simultaneous means occurring at the same time.

> The solution of the equation $x + 4 = 6$ is $x = 2$.
> The equation $y = 3x - 2$ has two unknowns. It has many solutions: $x = 1$ and $y = 1$ is just one of them.

Example 1

This diagram shows the graphs of $y = 2x - 3$ and $y = 6x - 4$. Use the graph to find the solution of the simultaneous equations $y = 2x - 3$ and $y = 6x - 4$.

> Each subdivision on this axis represents 0.2.

> Each subdivision on this axis represents 0.1.

> The value of x and y that satisfy both equations will be the coordinates of the point that is on both lines. This is where the lines cross or **intersect**.

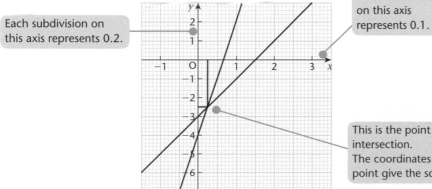

> This is the point of intersection. The coordinates of this point give the solution.

The point of intersection is $(0.25, -2.5)$.
The solution is $x = 0.25$ and $y = -2.5$.

> You can usually read values from a graph to at most 2 decimal places.

Exam practice 15A

1 a Copy and complete the table of values for $y + x = 5$.

x	-1	0	1	2	3	4	5	6
y	6			3		1		-1

www

b This is the graph of $y = 3x - 4$.
On a copy of the graph,
draw the graph of $y + x = 5$.

c Use your graphs to find the solution
of the simultaneous equations $y = 3x - 4$
and $y + x = 5$.

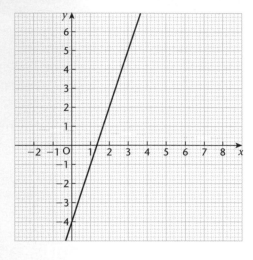

2 a Copy and complete this table of values
for $2y + x = 5$.

x	-1	1	3	5	7
y	3		1	0	

www

b This is the graph of $y = x - 3$.
Draw the graph of $2y + x = 5$ on a copy of
this graph.

c Use your graphs to find the solution of the
simultaneous equations $2y + x = 5$ and
$y = x - 3$.

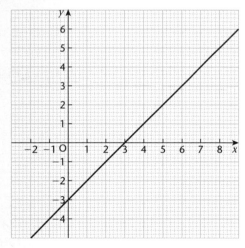

3 a Copy and complete this table of values for $y = x + 1$.

x	-2	0	2	3
y	-1		3	4

b Copy and complete this table of values for $y = 3x - 2$.

x	0	1	2
y	-2	1	

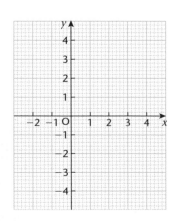

www

c Draw the graphs of $y = x + 1$ and $y = 3x - 2$ on a copy of
this grid.

d Find the solution of the simultaneous equations
$y = x + 1$ and $y = 3x - 2$.

15.2 Quadratic equations

The equation $y = 2x^2 - 3x - 4$ is a **quadratic equation** in two unknowns.

The equation $2x^2 - 3x - 4 = 0$ is an example of a quadratic equation in one unknown. Equations like this usually have two solutions. You can find these solutions from a graph.

Example 2

This is the graph of $y = x^2 - 3x - 1$.
Use the graph to find the solutions
of $x^2 - 3x - 1 = 0$.

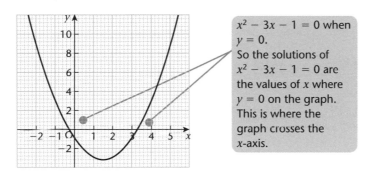

$x^2 - 3x - 1 = 0$ when $y = 0$.
So the solutions of $x^2 - 3x - 1 = 0$ are the values of x where $y = 0$ on the graph. This is where the graph crosses the x-axis.

$x = -0.3$ and $x = 3.3$

Exam practice 15B

1   This is the graph of $y = x^2 - 3x$.
    Use the graph to find the solutions
    of the equation $x^2 - 3x = 0$.

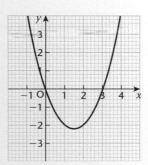

2   This is the graph of $y = x^2 + x - 5$
    Use the graph to find the solutions
    of the equation $x^2 + x - 5 = 0$.

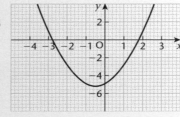

3 a Copy and complete this table of values for $y = x^2 - 2$.

x	-2	-1	0	1	2
y	2		-2		2

> Use copies of this grid for questions **3**, **4** and **5**.
>
> www

  b Draw the graph of $y = x^2 - 2$.
  c Use the graph to solve the equation $x^2 - 2 = 0$.

4 a Copy and complete this table of values for
      $y = 2x^2 - 4x + 1$.

x	-0.5	0	0.5	1	2
y	3.5	1			1

  b Draw the graph of $y = 2x^2 - 4x + 1$.
  c Use the graph to solve the equation $2x^2 - 4x + 1 = 0$.

5 a Make a table of values for $y = 3 - x^2$ for values of x from -2 to 2.
  b Draw the graph of $y = 3 - x^2$.
  c Use the graph to solve the equation $3 - x^2 = 0$.

15.3 Conversion graphs

You can use a **conversion graph** to convert a quantity given in one unit to another unit.

Example 3

Use this graph to convert   **a** €50 to pounds   **b** £45 to euros.

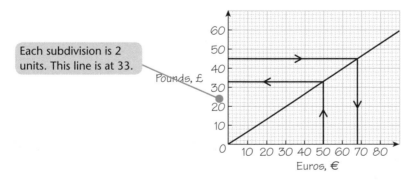

Each subdivision is 2 units. This line is at 33.

> Euros are on the horizontal axis and pounds are on the vertical axis.

  a €50 = £33

  b £45 = €68

You answers will only be as accurate as the scales allow and will always be an estimate.

> Currency conversion can be given more accurately when worked out using arithmetic methods.

You can draw a conversion graph.

Example 4

a Use 2 inches = 5 cm and 20 inches = 50 cm to draw a conversion graph.

b Use your graph to convert 60 cm to inches.

a
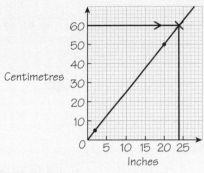

> Plot the point 2 units along the inches axis and 5 units up the cm axis. Then plot the point 20 units along the inches axis and 50 units up the cm axis. Draw a straight line through the points.

b 60 cm = 24 inches

Exam practice 15C

1 Use the conversion graph in example 3 to convert
   a £20 to euros   b €58 to pounds   c £52 to euros.

> Make sure you start from the right axis.

2 Use the conversion graph in example 4 to convert
   a 15 inches to cm   b 36 cm to inches   c 75 cm to inches.

> Make sure you know what each subdivision on the axes represents.

www 3 a Plot the values 10 kg = 22 lb
                            40 kg = 88 lb
          on a copy of this grid.
          Draw a straight line through the points.
       b Use your graph to convert
          i   25 kg to lb
          ii 50 lb to kg.

www 4 a Plot the values
          £10 = US$18 and £50 = US$90
          on a copy of this grid and draw a straight line through them.
       b Use your graph to convert
          i   £8 to dollars
          ii $45 to pounds.

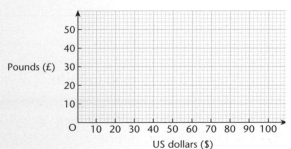

5 a Use the values 0°C = 32°F and 20°C = 68°F to draw a
       conversion graph on a copy of this grid.
   b Use your graph to convert
       i   41° Fahrenheit (°F) to degrees Celsius (°C)
       ii   24°F to °C
       iii −10°C to °F
       iv   50°C to °F.

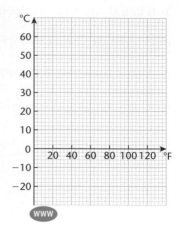

15.4 Distance, time and speed

When something moves it covers distance.

Speed measures the distance covered per unit of time.

Speed is a **compound measure** because it combines distance and time.

$$\text{average speed} = \frac{\text{total distance covered}}{\text{time taken}}$$

The most common metric units of speed are kilometres per hour (km/h) and metres per second (m/s).

The only Imperial unit of speed in everyday use is miles per hour (mph).

> A car travelling at a constant speed covers 80 miles in two hours. The car travels 40 miles each hour so its speed is 40 mph (mph is short for miles per hour).

> When you travel, your speed is likely to vary.
> You can give an **average speed** for a whole journey. You do this by finding the distance covered then dividing it by the time taken.

Example 5

Amy ran for 10 minutes and walked for 10 minutes to get to the station.
She covered a distance of $1\frac{1}{2}$ miles.
What was her average speed in mph.

> To find a speed in mph, the distance must be in miles and the time in hours. So convert 20 min to hours.

Total distance = 1.5 miles.
Total time = 20 minutes = $\frac{1}{3}$ hour
$1.5 \div \frac{1}{3} = 1.5 \times \frac{3}{1} = 4.5$
Average speed = 4.5 mph.

> To divide by a fraction, turn it upside down and multiply.

Example 6

Convert a speed of 50 mph to km/h.

> Use 5 miles = 8 kilometres.

50 mph = 50 × (8 ÷ 5) km/h
       = 80 km/h

> 5 miles = 8 km, so 1 mile = 8 ÷ 5 km.
> This gives 50 miles = 50 × (8 ÷ 5) km.

Exam practice 15D

1 a Write down the speed shown on this dial.
   b Write down the speed on this dial.

> Remember to include the units.

2

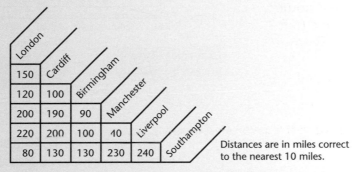

Distances are in miles correct to the nearest 10 miles.

> To find the distance between Cardiff and Liverpool, go down the Cardiff column until you are in the Liverpool row.

   a Use this distance chart to find the distance between
      i   Cardiff and Liverpool   ii London and Manchester.
   b A car travelled from Birmingham to Liverpool in 1 hour 45 minutes.
      Work out the average speed of the car in mph to the nearest 10 mph.
   c Convert the distance between Cardiff and Southampton to kilometres, correct to the nearest 10 km.
   d A car takes 3 hours to travel from Cardiff to Southampton. Find the average speed of the car in km/h to the nearest 10 km/h.

3 Ashad cycled 30 km in 2 hours. He rested for 30 minutes, then cycled 25 km in 75 minutes.
   Find his average speed for the journey.

4 Use this conversion graph to convert
   a 20 m/s to km/h
   b 50 km/h to m/s.

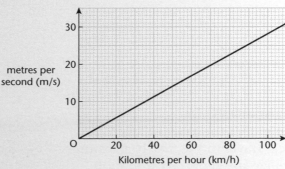

15.5 Distance–time graphs

A **distance–time graph** shows a journey.
The vertical axis shows distance and the horizontal axis shows time.

> A distance–time graph is also called a **travel graph**.

Example 7

This graph shows Gail's journey from home to work.
She left home at 7.30 a.m. and cycled to the station.
She caught a train to a station near her work and walked the rest of the way.

a How far is Gail's work from home?
b How long did Gail wait for a train?
c How long did Gail's journey to work take?
d What was the average speed of Gail's journey to work?
Give your answer to 1 d.p.

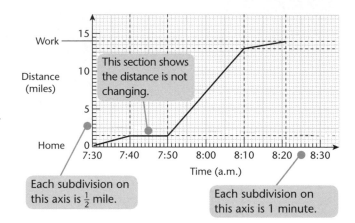

a 14 miles

> Gail's work place is at the top end of the graph. Read across from here to the distance axis.

b 10 minutes

> Gail's distance from home does not change while she waits. This is the flat section. It starts at 7.40 and ends at 7.50.

c 51 minutes

> She started at 7.30 and arrived at 8.21.

d Distance = 14 miles
   Time = 51 minutes = $\frac{51}{60}$ hours
   $14 \div \frac{51}{60} = 14 \times \frac{60}{51} = 16.47...$
   Average speed = 16.5 mph to 1 d.p.

> Press
> 1 4 × 6 0 ÷ 5 1 =

Exam practice 15E

1 This graph shows a car journey between two towns.

> Make sure you know what each subdivision on each axis means.

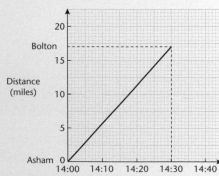

a How far is Bolton from Asham?
b How many minutes does the journey take?
c How far did the car travel in the first 10 minutes?
d Work out the average speed of the car in mph.

> Remember to give units in your answers.

2   This graph shows Henry's journey from Birmingham to Manchester.
    He leaves home at 10.30 and stops at a services on the way.

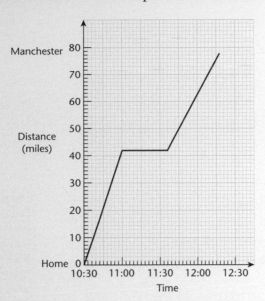

a   How far was Henry's journey to Manchester?
b   How far was the services from Henry's home?
c   How long did Henry stay at the services?
d   Work out Henry's speed from leaving the services to
    arriving in Manchester. Give your answer in mph to
    1 decimal place.

3   This graph shows Kim's journey to school.
    She leaves home at 08.35 and cycles to a friend's house.
    She waits for her friend and then they cycle to school together.

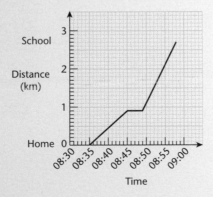

a   What is the time when Kim gets to her friend's house?
b   How far is it from Kim's home to the school?
c   Work out the speed for the last part of the journey.
d   Find Kim's average speed for the whole journey.
    Give your answer to 1 d.p.

4 This graph shows Freda's journey from work to a warehouse, and back to work.

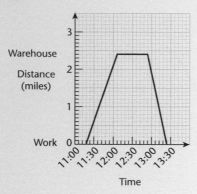

a How far is the warehouse from work?
b How long did Freda stay at the warehouse?
c How long did the journey back to work take?
d How far did Freda travel in the first six minutes after leaving the warehouse?
e Was Freda's speed greater on the journey to the warehouse or the journey back to work?
   Give a reason for your answer.

> The part of the graph that goes down shows the journey from the warehouse back to work. It shows the distance from work getting less as time increases.

5 Adam leaves home at 07:30 and drives 8 miles to work.
   He arrives at 07:45.
   Draw a graph to show his journey.

Use a copy of this grid.

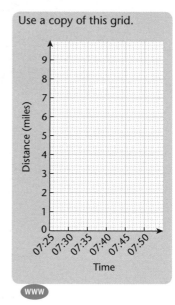

6 Dwaine walks from home to Pete's house.
   He waits 5 minutes for Pete to join him.
   They then walk together to the cinema which is 800 metres from Dwaine's home. They arrive at 18.53.
   a This graph shows Dwaine's walk from home to Pete's house.

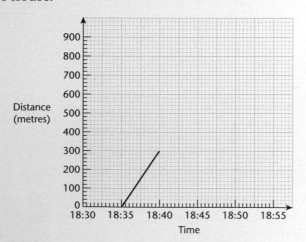

Copy and complete the graph to show Dwaine's journey from home to the cinema.
   b How far is the cinema from Pete's house?

7   Frank drives from his house to the bus station to pick up his daughter.
He waits for ten minutes. They then drive back home at a constant speed, arriving there at 12.49.
   a   This graph shows part of Frank's journey.

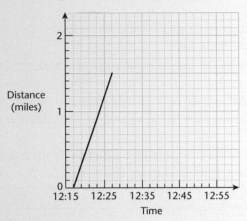

   Copy and complete the graph to show Frank's journey.
   b   Work out Frank's speed from the bus station to home.
   c   How far does Frank travel between 12.39 and 12.49?

8   This graph shows Gordon's journey from one set of traffic lights to another.

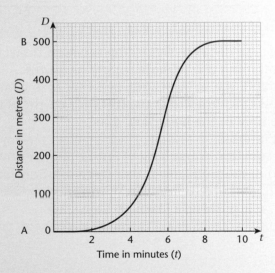

   a   How long did Gordon take to travel between the two sets of lights?
   b   How do you know that both sets of lights were red when Gordon reached them?
   c   How far apart are the two sets of lights?
   d   Find Gordon's average speed between the two sets of lights.

Summary of key points

- You can solve simultaneous equations by finding the point where the lines of the equations intersect.
- The solutions of a quadratic equation such as $x^2 - 3x + 1 = 0$ are the values of x where the graph of $y = x^2 - 3x + 1$ crosses the x-axis.
- When you read values from the scales on the axes of a graph, make sure you know what each subdivision means.
- You can draw a conversion graph using two sets of information, such as 5 cm = 2 inches and 10 cm = 4 inches. Plot these as points and draw a straight line through them.
- You can work out the speed for a journey or part of a journey from a travel graph. Read the time taken and the distance travelled from the scales on the axes.

Most students who get GRADE E or above can:
- can use a conversion graph
- know what a horizontal line on a distance–time graph means.

Most students who get GRADE C can also:
- use a distance–time graph to find the average speed for a journey.

Glossary

Average speed	the total distance divided by the total time
Compound measure	combining two or more simple measures
Conversion graph	a graph that converts one quantity to another
Distance–time graph	shows a journey with the distance on the vertical axis and the time in the horizontal axis
Intersect	cut or cross
Quadratic equation	an equation containing x^2 but no higher power of x
Simultaneous equations	two or more equations that have solutions in common
Speed	distance covered in one unit of time
Travel graph	a graph showing a journey

16 Transformations

This chapter will show you:
- ✓ how to recognise line symmetry
- ✓ how to draw the reflection of a shape in a mirror line
- ✓ how to recognise rotational symmetry and give the order
- ✓ how to draw the rotation of a shape by a given angle about a given point
- ✓ the meaning of a vector
- ✓ how to translate a shape from one position to another
- ✓ how to give a translation of a shape as a vector
- ✓ how to recognise transformations that are combinations of reflection, rotation and translation.

Before you start you need to know:
- ✓ how to find the coordinates of a point
- ✓ how to plot a point given its coordinates
- ✓ how to give the equation of a straight line
- ✓ the names of special triangles and quadrilaterals
- ✓ how to use a protractor to measure angles

16.1 Line symmetry

These shapes are **symmetrical**. They all have **line symmetry**. The dotted line is a **line of symmetry**.

If the shape is folded on the dotted line, one half of the shape will fit exactly over the other half.

Exam practice 16A

1 Which of these shapes have line symmetry?

A

B

C

2 On a copy of each shape mark any lines of symmetry and say how many there are.

If you are not sure if a shape has a line of symmetry, cut out a copy and try folding it.

a    b   c

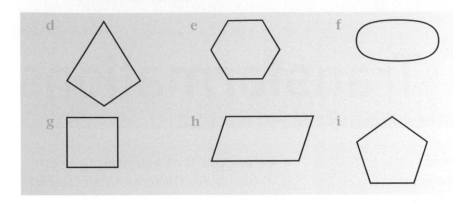

16.2 Reflection

This sketch shows a reflection of a triangle in a mirror.

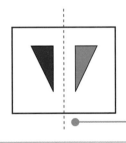

The triangle and its reflection are symmetrical about the **mirror line**.

This line is called the mirror line.

Example 1

Draw the reflection of the red shape in the mirror line.

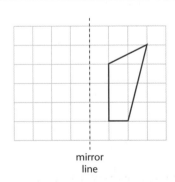

mirror line

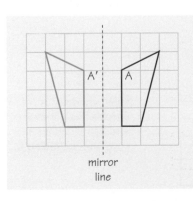

mirror line

One vertex of the shape is marked A. The reflection of A in the mirror line is the point A′. A′ is the same distance from the mirror line as A is, but on the opposite side of it. The line AA′ is perpendicular to the mirror line.

Example 2

a Write down the coordinates of
  i A   **ii** B   **iii** C.
b Draw the reflection of △ABC in the
  mirror line.
c Write down the coordinates of the reflection of
  i A   **ii** B.

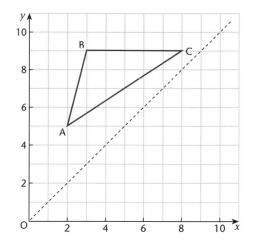

a **i** (2, 5)   **ii** (3, 9)   **iii** (8, 9)

b

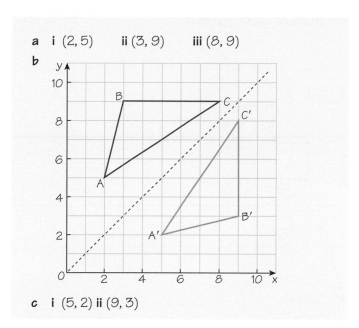

> Plot A′ such that the mirror line is the perpendicular bisector of AA′.
> Do the same with B and C.

c **i** (5, 2) **ii** (9, 3)

Exam practice 16B

1 Use a copy of each diagram to draw the reflection of the shape
   in the mirror line.

   a 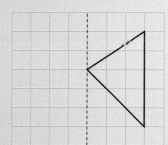   **b**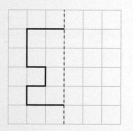

   > The dotted lines are the mirror lines.

   > The reflection of a point is the same distance behind the mirror line as the point is in front of it.

2 Copy the diagram and draw the reflection of each shape in the
   mirror line.

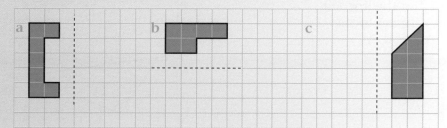

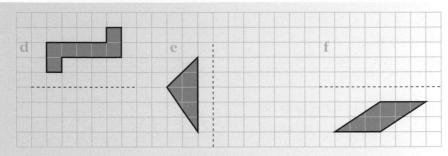

d   e   f

3   On a copy of the diagram draw the reflection of each shape in
    the mirror line.

a 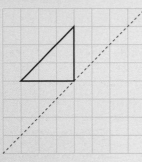   b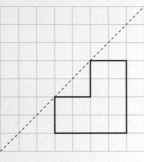

c 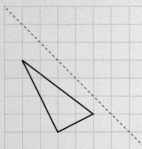   d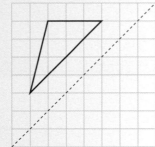

4   a   What is the mathematical name of this shape?
    b   Write down the coordinates of
            i A   ii B   iii C   iv D.
    c   On a copy of this diagram draw
        the reflection of ABCD in the
        line PQ.
    d   What are the coordinates of the
        reflection of i B   ii D?

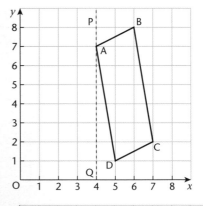

5   a   Write down the coordinates of
            i X   ii Y   iii Z.
    b   On a copy the diagram draw the
        reflection of △XYZ in the line PQ.
    c   What are the coordinates of the
        reflection of i X   ii Y?

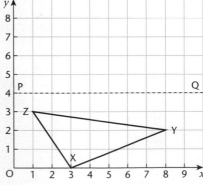

16.3 Transformations

A **transformation maps** (moves) an object to another position. It may also change its shape.

A reflection is an example of a transformation. To describe a reflection fully you need to give the mirror line.

> This reflection changes the position of the red triangle to the position of the green triangle.
>
>
>
> This is described as 'the reflection that maps A to B'.

Example 3

Describe fully the reflection that maps triangle ABC to triangle PQR.

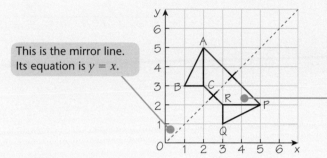

> This is the mirror line. Its equation is $y = x$.

> To describe the transformation fully, you need to give its name and give the equation of the mirror line.

> First you need to find the mirror line. You can do this by joining two pairs of corresponding vertices. Then mark the midpoints of these lines. The mirror line goes through these points.

The transformation is a reflection in the line $y = x$.

Exam practice 16C

1   Describe fully the transformation that maps triangle A to triangle B.

a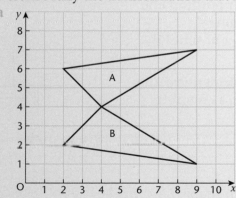

> First find the mirror line. Join two pairs of corresponding vertices and mark their midpoints. The mirror line goes through these points.

b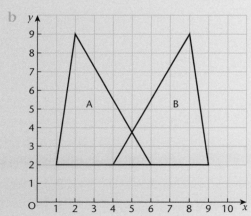

2   Describe fully the transformation that maps triangle A to triangle B.

a
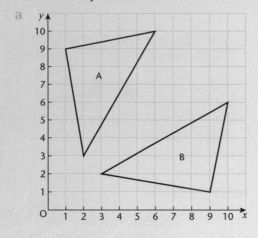

b
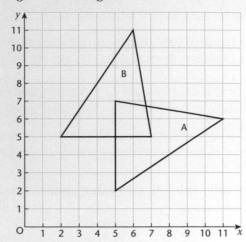

The equation of the straight line that goes through the points whose x and y coordinates are equal is $y = x$.

16.4 Rotational symmetry

Some shapes can be rotated about a point to another position and still look the same. This is called **rotational symmetry**.
The **order of rotational symmetry** is the number of times the shape looks the same in one complete revolution.

If you rotate this shape about the point X it will look identical after each quarter turn. It will look the same four times in a complete revolution so it has rotational symmetry of order 4.

Example 4

Write down the order of rotational symmetry of each shape.

a

b
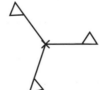

a   2

This shape looks the same after a half-turn, then again after a full turn. It has rotational symmetry of order 2.

b   3

This shape looks the same after $\frac{1}{3}$ of a turn, $\frac{2}{3}$ of a turn and a full turn. It has rotational symmetry of order 3.

Some shapes have both line symmetry and rotational symmetry.

Example 5

a Copy this shape. Shade 1 more square so that
the final shape has 2 lines of symmetry.
Does your shape have rotational symmetry?
If so, what is the order of this symmetry?

b Now shade 2 more squares so that the final shape
still has rotational symmetry of order 2, but has no line symmetry.

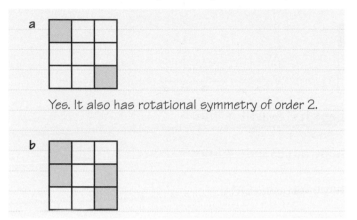

a

Yes. It also has rotational symmetry of order 2.

> This shape has line
> symmetry about both
> diagonals of the large
> square.

b

> This shape has
> rotational symmetry of
> order 2.

Exam practice 16D

1 For each shape write down
  i   the order of rotational symmetry
  ii the number of lines of symmetry.

  a 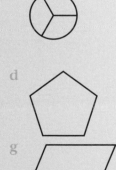   **b**   **c**

  d 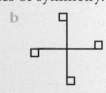   **e**   **f**

  g 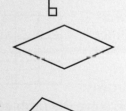   **h**    **i**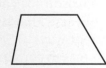

2 What is the mathematical name of the shapes in 1(c)–(i)?

www   3 For each shape
  i   write down the order of rotational symmetry
  ii on a copy of the shape draw all the of lines of symmetry.

  a    **b**   **c**

4   For each shape write down
    i   the number of lines of symmetry
    ii   the order of rotational symmetry.

a
b
c

WWW
5   Use a new copy of this block of 9 squares for each part of the question.

    a   Shade 1 more square so that the shape has exactly 1 line of symmetry.
    b   Shade 1 more square so that the shape has exactly 2 lines of symmetry.
    c   Shade 1 more square so that the shape has rotational symmetry of order 2.
    d   Shade 3 more squares so that the shape has rotational symmetry of order 4.

WWW
6   a   Copy this diagram and shade 1 more square so that the shape has rotational symmetry of order 2.

    b   Peter says that there are 2 ways to shade 1 more square so that the final shape has just 1 line of symmetry.
UAM
        Is Peter correct? Give a reason for your answer.

WWW
7   a   Kay says she can put spots in the centre of 4 squares so that the final shape has 4 lines of symmetry **and** rotational symmetry of order 4.
UAM
        Is Kay correct? Give a reason for your answer.

    b   Jim agrees with Kay but says that he can solve the problem in two completely different ways.
UAM
        Is Jim correct? Give a reason for your answer.

Enrichment task

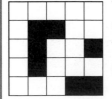

This is one-quarter of a blank grid for a 10 by 10 crossword.

The completed grid has rotational symmetry of order 4.

Copy the grid and complete it.

16.5 Rotation

You can change the position of an object by rotating it about a point.
The amount it turns is the **angle of rotation**.

The point about which a shape turns is the **centre of rotation**.
This is often one of the **vertices** of the shape but can be any point.

> The position of the orange triangle is found by rotating the purple triangle through a quarter-turn (90°) anticlockwise about A.
> The position of the green triangle is given by rotating the purple triangle through a half-turn (180°) about A.

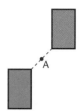 

If no direction is given, the rotation is anticlockwise.

> **Anticlockwise** means' in the opposite direction to the direction the hands of a clock turn'.
>
> **Clockwise** means 'in the same direction as the hands of a clock turn'. For half a turn it doesn't matter whether the rotation is clockwise or anticlockwise.

Example 6

The purple shape is rotated to the green shape.
Write down
a   the angle and direction of rotation
b   the letter that marks the centre of rotation.

> Choose a pair of corresponding sides. You can see that C is the turning point and that the angle is 90°.

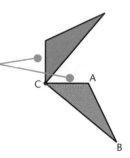

a   90° anticlockwise.

b   C

Exam practice 16E

1   The red shape is rotated to the green shape.
Write down
   i   the angle and direction of rotation
   ii   the letter that marks the centre of rotation.

> 'Direction' means 'clockwise' or 'anticlockwise'.
>
> You can use tracing paper and a pin to help with these questions.

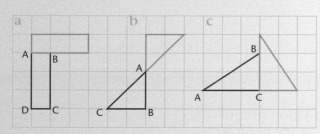

www 2 Use a copy of the diagram to draw the shape that P is mapped
into when it is rotated about A by the given angle.

a 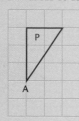   b    c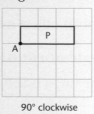

180°   90° anticlockwise   90° clockwise

3 Describe fully the rotation that maps A to B.

a 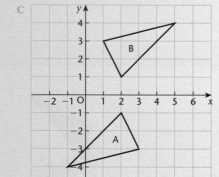   b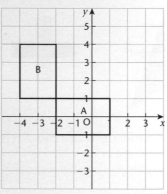

> You need to give the
> coordinates of the
> centre of rotation and
> the angle through
> which the shape is
> turned. Don't forget to
> state the direction of
> turning.

c 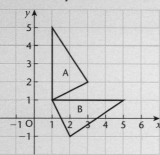   d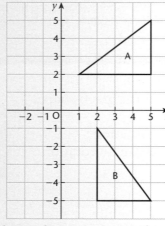

www 4 On a copy of the diagram draw the shape that A is mapped to
when it has been rotated about the given point by the given
angle. Mark your transformed shape B.

a 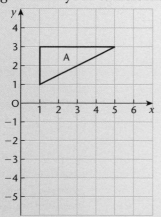   b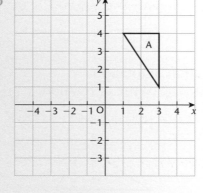

A rotation of 90° clockwise   A rotation of 180°
about the point (1, −1).   about the point (0,1).

c
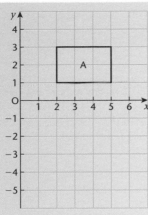

Rotation of 90° clockwise
about the point $(0, -1)$.

d
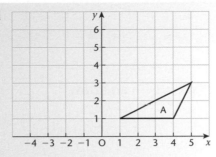

Rotation of 90° anticlockwise
about the point $(-1, 0)$.

Enrichment task

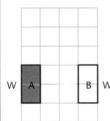

John wants to move his desk from A to B. This move can only be made by rotating the desk through 90° about one of its corners. He can do this as many times as he likes.

In position A the desk faces the window. In position B it must face the opposite window.

On a copy of the diagram, show how he can make this move, marking each point of rotation with a cross.

16.6 Vectors

A **vector** has length and direction.

When vectors are drawn on squared paper you can show them by the number of squares you need to go across and the number you need to go up or down.

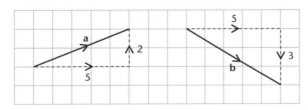

The vector **a** shows a movement of 5 to the right and 2 up.

You write this as $\mathbf{a} = \begin{pmatrix} 5 \\ 2 \end{pmatrix}$

The vector **b** shows a movement of 5 across and 3 down so $\mathbf{b} = \begin{pmatrix} 5 \\ -3 \end{pmatrix}$

> The top number represents movement across (+ to the right and − to the left). The lower number represents movement up or down (+ up and − down).

Example 7

A (2, 1) is the starting point of the vector $\begin{pmatrix} 4 \\ 3 \end{pmatrix}$.

a Plot the point A.

b Draw the vector $\begin{pmatrix} 4 \\ 3 \end{pmatrix}$. Mark it with an arrow.

$\begin{pmatrix} 4 \\ 3 \end{pmatrix}$ means go 4 to the right then 3 up.

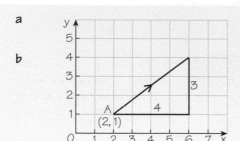

Exam practice 16F

1   Write the following vectors in the form $\begin{pmatrix} p \\ q \end{pmatrix}$.

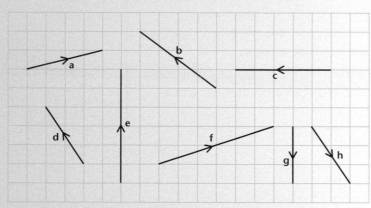

2   Draw these vectors on squared paper.
    Label each vector with its letter and an arrow.

$\mathbf{a} = \begin{pmatrix} 5 \\ 2 \end{pmatrix}$ $\mathbf{b} = \begin{pmatrix} -3 \\ 2 \end{pmatrix}$ $\mathbf{c} = \begin{pmatrix} 4 \\ -3 \end{pmatrix}$ $\mathbf{d} = \begin{pmatrix} 10 \\ 4 \end{pmatrix}$

$\mathbf{e} = \begin{pmatrix} -7 \\ 0 \end{pmatrix}$ $\mathbf{f} = \begin{pmatrix} 3 \\ 3 \end{pmatrix}$ $\mathbf{g} = \begin{pmatrix} 1 \\ 2 \end{pmatrix}$ $\mathbf{h} = \begin{pmatrix} -3 \\ -3 \end{pmatrix}$

What do you notice about   i **a** and **d**   ii **f** and **h**?

3   Plot the point, then draw the vector starting
    from that point.
    Write down the coordinates of the other end.

Use a grid like this.

a   (1,3), $\begin{pmatrix} 2 \\ 4 \end{pmatrix}$ b   (−1, 4), $\begin{pmatrix} 2 \\ 3 \end{pmatrix}$

c   (2, 6), $\begin{pmatrix} -3 \\ 4 \end{pmatrix}$ d   (3, 4), $\begin{pmatrix} -4 \\ -3 \end{pmatrix}$

e   (−5, 0), $\begin{pmatrix} 5 \\ -3 \end{pmatrix}$ f   (0, 6), $\begin{pmatrix} 4 \\ -2 \end{pmatrix}$

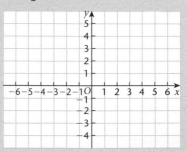

16.7 Translation

You can change the position of a shape by sliding it along a straight line.
This is called a **translation**.

The purple triangle moves to the position of the green triangle by sliding 3 squares to the right.
This translation is described by the vector $\begin{pmatrix} 3 \\ 0 \end{pmatrix}$.

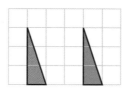

This translation moves a vertex 4 squares to the right and 1 up.
It is described by the vector $\begin{pmatrix} 4 \\ 1 \end{pmatrix}$.

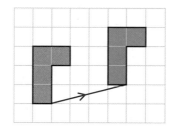

> A translation moves an object. It does not reflect and it does not rotate.

Exam practice 16G

1   Describe the translation that maps triangle A to triangle B.

a 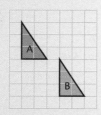   b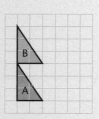

> You can describe a translation either by giving the number of squares moved left or right and up or down, or by giving a vector.

c 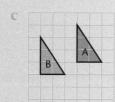   d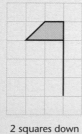

2   On a copy draw the result of translating the given shape along the marked line by the number of squares given.

a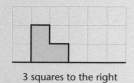

3 squares to the right

b

2 squares down

c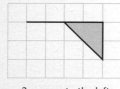

2 squares to the left

3 a What is the mathematical name
      of the shape ABCD?

   b Write down the coordinates of
      i A   ii C.

   c The shape ABCD maps to A'B'C'D'.
      Write down the vector that gives
      this translation.

   d Write down the coordinates of
      i A'   ii C'.

   e Ceri said that the vector that translates

      A'B'C'D' to ABCD is $\begin{pmatrix} -4 \\ -1 \end{pmatrix}$

UAM

      Is Ceri correct? Give a reason for your answer.

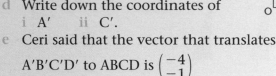

4 Triangle ABC is translated so that A translates to A'.

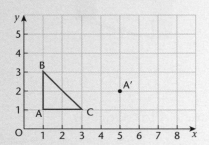

   a Write down the vector that gives this translation.

WWW

   b On a copy the diagram, draw the translation of △ABC using
      this vector.

   c B transforms to B' and C to C'.
      Label the transformed triangle A'B'C'.
      Write down the coordinates of
      i B'   ii C'.

5 Triangle ABC is translated so that A translates to A'.

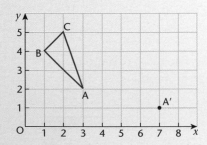

   a Write down the vector that gives this translation.

WWW

   b Copy the diagram and draw the translation of △ABC using
      this vector.
      Label the transformed triangle A'B'C'.

   c Write down the coordinates of
      i B'   ii C'.

16.8 Combining transformations

To move a shape from one position to another sometimes needs more than one transformation.

Example 8

Give the letter of the shape that the purple rectangle is mapped to when the shape is

a   translated 1 square to the right and 5 squares down

b   rotated about O through 90° anticlockwise

c   reflected in the line $y = x$

d   reflected in the y-axis then reflected in the x-axis.

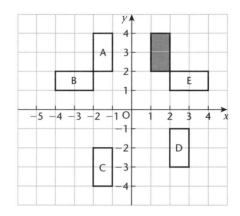

a   D

b   B

c   E

d   C

Do the transformations even if you think you know the correct rectangle. This will act as a check.

Do the reflection in the y-axis, then reflect the new shape in the x-axis.

Exam practice 16H

1

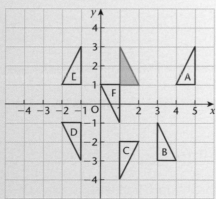

Give the letter of the shape that the green triangle is mapped into when it is

a   reflected in the y-axis

b   reflected in the line $x = 3$

c   translated 2 squares to the right and 4 squares down

d   rotated about O through 180°

e   reflected in the line $x = 3$ then translated 6 squares to the left.

Use a copy of the diagram to do these transformations. Not all the triangles are needed.

2

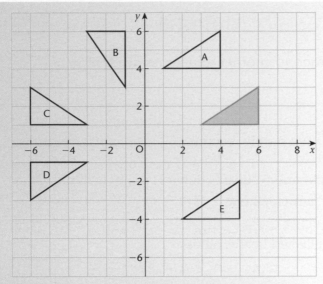

Describe fully the transformation that maps the green triangle on to

a E   b A   c B   d D   e C.

You need to give the name of the transformation as well as either a mirror line, a vector, or a centre and angle of rotation.

3

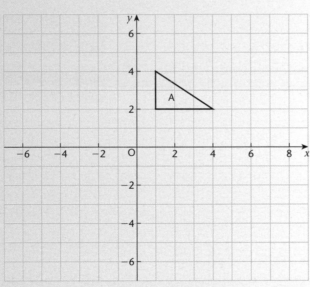

www

On a copy of this diagram draw the shape that A is mapped to when it is

a   reflected in the line $y = x$
b   reflected in the y-axis and then translated 3 squares down
c   rotated by 180° about O
d   reflected in the x-axis then rotated by 90° anticlockwise about O.

Summary of key points

- When a shape is reflected in a mirror line, the shape and its reflection are symmetrical about the mirror line.
- The mirror line is the perpendicular bisector of the line joining a point on the shape to the corresponding point on its reflection.
- A shape has rotational symmetry if it can be rotated about a point to a different position but still look the same.
- The order of rotational symmetry is the number of times the shape looks identical in one complete turn.
- A translation moves a shape without reflecting or turning it.
- A translation can be described by a vector.
- When you describe a transformation, you must give its name.
- For a reflection you must give the mirror line.
- For a rotation you must give the centre and angle of rotation and say whether it is clockwise or anticlockwise.
- For a translation you must describe the movement.

Most students who get GRADE E or above can:
- reflect a triangle in the x- or y-axis.

Most students who get GRADE C can also:
- describe a transformation fully.

Glossary

Angle of rotation	the angle through which a shape is turned
Axis of symmetry	a straight line about which a shape is symmetrical
Centre of rotation	the point about which a shape turns
Line of symmetry	the line that divides a shape into halves, one of which is a mirror image of the other
Line symmetry	describes a shape that can be folded so that one half fits exactly over the other
Maps	moves a shape to a new position
Mirror line	a line about which a shape and its reflection are symmetrical
Order of rotational symmetry	the number of times a shape looks the same in one complete turn
Symmetrical	a shape that has line symmetry
Transformation	an operation that changes the position or shape of an object
Translation	changing the position of a shape by sliding it along a straight line
Vector	a straight line that has length and direction
Vertex (plural vertices)	the corner of an object

17 Enlargement

This chapter will show you:
- ✓ the meaning of ratio and proportion
- ✓ how to enlarge a shape
- ✓ what the centre of enlargement means
- ✓ the meaning of similar figures
- ✓ how to make and read scale drawings
- ✓ the meaning of three-figure bearings
- ✓ what a locus is

Before you start you need to know:
- ✓ how to plot points and give the coordinates of a point
- ✓ how to cube and square numbers
- ✓ how to transform a shape by reflection, rotation and translation
- ✓ what congruent means
- ✓ how to find the perimeter and area of a shape
- ✓ how to use Pythagoras' theorem
- ✓ how to convert between units of length
- ✓ how to measure angles
- ✓ the relationships between angles on a straight line, round a point and with parallel lines
- ✓ how to draw parallel lines
- ✓ how to construct the perpendicular bisector of a line segment

17.1 Ratio

Ratio is a way of comparing quantities.

A ———4 cm——— B   L ———6 cm——— M

You can compare the lengths of these two lines by saying

'the ratio of the length of AB to the length of LM is 4 cm : 6 cm'

> 4 cm : 6 cm is read as 4 cm to 6 cm.

You can reduce the size of the numbers in a ratio by simplifying.
Simplifying ratios is very similar to simplifying fractions.

Example 1

Simplify: **a** 4 cm : 6 cm   **b** 20 cm : 1 m

a 4 cm : 6 cm =
$\quad$ 4 : 6
$\div 2$ $\quad$ $\div 2$
$\quad$ = $\quad$ 2 : 3

> You can simplify the ratio by leaving out the units.
> You can always leave out the units as long as they are the same for both quantities.

> You can now simplify 4 : 6 by dividing each number by 2.

b $20\,cm:1\,m = 20\,cm:100\,cm$

$= 20:100$

$= 1:5$

> You must write both lengths in the same units first.

> You can simplify by dividing each number by 20. Look for a number that divides exactly into both parts of the ratio.

Exam practice 17A

1 Simplify these ratios.
   a 10:50   b 40:200
   c 15:20   d 12 cm:8 cm
   e $3\,m:2\frac{1}{2}\,m$ f 0.2 mm:1.8 mm
   g 4 inches:1 foot   h 1.5 mm:2.5 cm
   i 2 m:20 cm

> For **e** you need to double both parts.
> For **f** you can start by multiplying both parts by ten.

2

   Find the ratio of the length of the side of square A to the length of the side of square B.

> Make sure that the numbers in the ratio are in the same order as the words.

3 Find the ratio of the length of this field to its width.

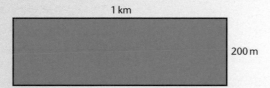

17.2 Enlargement

An **enlargement** is a transformation that maps a shape to another shape by multiplying all the lengths by the same number.
This number is called the **scale factor**.

> When the scale factor is larger than 1, the shape gets larger.

> When the scale factor is less than 1, the shape gets smaller.

> To enlarge a shape by a scale factor of 4 you have to make all the lengths 4 times longer.

> To enlarge a shape by a scale factor of $\frac{1}{2}$, you have to make all the lengths half as long.

> The word 'enlargement' is used for making a shape larger and for making it smaller. The scale factor tells you which it is.

> Square B is an enlargement of square A.
>
>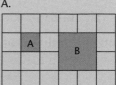
>
> The sides of B are twice the length of the sides of square A. The scale factor is 2.

Example 2

In the diagram rectangles B and C
are enlargements of rectangle A.
a   What is the scale factor of the enlargement that maps A to B?
b   What is the scale factor of the enlargement that maps A to C?

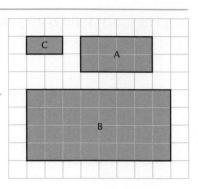

a   2   The sides of B are twice as long as the corresponding sides of A.

b $\frac{1}{2}$ The sides of C are half the length of the corresponding sides of A.

You can also enlarge a solid.

Example 3

Draw an enlargement of the solid A with a scale factor of 2.

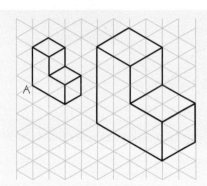

You need to draw your shape so that all its
edges are twice as long as those of A.
It is drawn on isometric paper so every grid line
is 5 mm long including the slanting ones.

Exam practice 17B

1   Give the scale factor for each of these enlargements.
    The green shape is an enlargement of the blue shape.

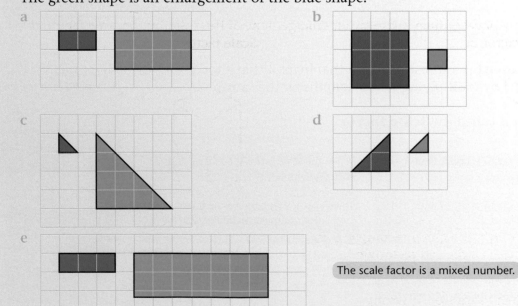

a

b

c

d

e

The scale factor is a mixed number.

2   The green solid is an enlargement of the blue solid.
    Give the scale factor for each enlargement.

   a 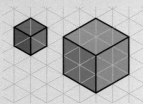   b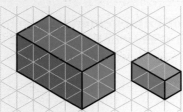

3   On a copy of each diagram, draw an enlargement of the shape by the scale factor given.
   a   Scale factor 2.   b   Scale factor $\frac{1}{2}$.

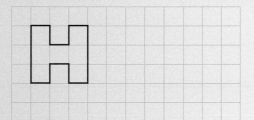

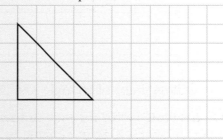

   c   Scale factor 3.   d   Scale factor $\frac{1}{4}$.

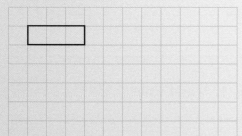

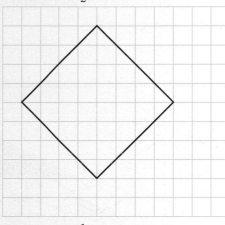

4   On a copy of each diagram, draw an enlargement of the solid by the scale factor given.
   a   Sale factor 2.   b   Scale factor $\frac{1}{2}$.

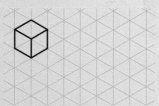

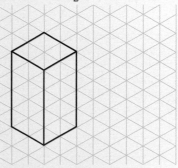

5   Kingston says 'the green rectangle is an
    enlargement of the red rectangle.'

    Explain why Kingston is wrong.

17.3 Centre of enlargement

The **centre of enlargement** is a point. Lines are drawn from this point to each **vertex** of the shape and then extended to give the vertices of the enlarged shape.

$$\begin{pmatrix} \text{length of the lines} \\ \text{to the vertices of the} \\ \text{enlarged shape} \end{pmatrix} = (\text{scale factor}) \times \begin{pmatrix} \text{length of lines to} \\ \text{the vertices of the} \\ \text{original shape} \end{pmatrix}$$

In this diagram the green triangle is an enlargement of the blue triangle. The scale factor is 3, and centre of enlargement is the point (0, 1).

This point is the centre of enlargement.

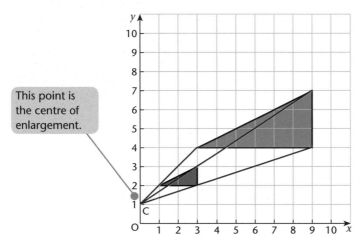

The red lines are drawn from C to the vertices of the blue triangle. They are then extended so that they are 3 times as long to give the vertices of the green triangle.

Example 4

Draw the enlargement of triangle ABC with centre (1, 2) and scale factor of $\frac{2}{3}$.

Mark the centre of enlargement. Draw lines from P to A, B and C. These are called **guide lines**.

To enlarge by a scale factor of $\frac{2}{3}$, you need to find the point on PA that is $\frac{2}{3}$ of its length from P. You can do this by counting grid lines. A is 6 grid lines above P, so the point you want is 4 grid lines above P ($\frac{2}{3} \times 6 = 4$).
Do the same for the other lines then join these points.

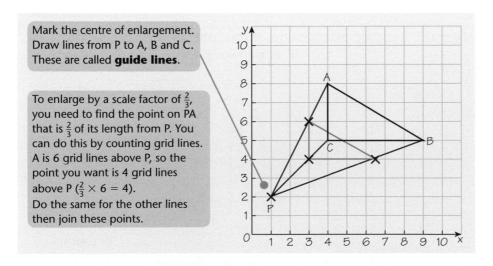

You can find the centre of enlargement by drawing lines through corresponding pairs of vertices.

Example 5

PQRS is an enlargement of ABCD.
Describe the enlargement.

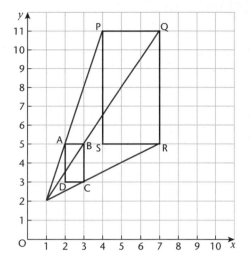

To describe an enlargement, you must give the scale factor and the centre of enlargement.

The scale factor is 3.

The centre of enlargement is the point (1, 2).

You can find the centre of enlargement by joining the vertices of the enlarged rectangle to the corresponding vertices of the small rectangle and extending them until they meet. This point is the centre of enlargement.

Exam practice 17C

www

1 On a copy of the diagram, draw the enlargement of each shape:
   a centre (1, 1), scale factor 3
   b centre (0, 2), scale factor $\frac{1}{2}$

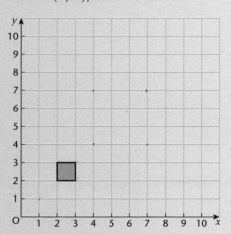

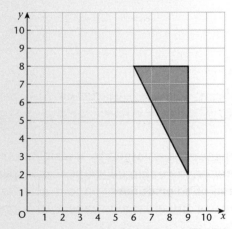

   c centre (1, 1) scale factor 2

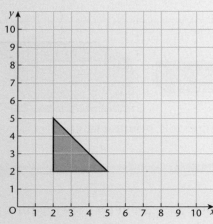

The enlarged triangle overlaps the yellow triangle.

2 Describe the enlargement that maps A to B.

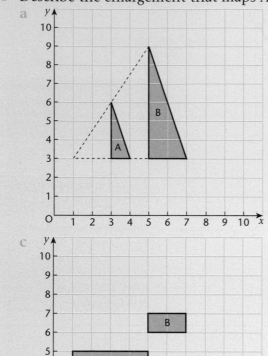

a

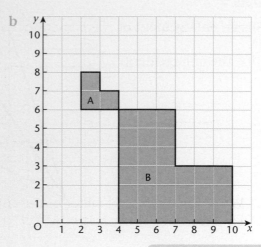

b

c

> To describe an enlargement, you must give the scale factor and the centre of enlargement.

> To find the centre of enlargement you need to draw guide lines. They are drawn for you in part **a**.

17.4 Perimeter, area and volume

When a shape is enlarged by a scale factor a,
perimeter of the enlarged shape $= a \times$ (perimeter of original),
area of the enlarged shape $= a^2 \times$ (area of original),
volume of the enlarged shape $= a^3 \times$ (volume of the original).

> The scale factor is 3:
>
>
>
> Perimeter of face B (12 cm)
> $= 3 \times$ perimeter of face A(4 cm)
> Area of face B (9 cm²)
> $= 3^2 \times$ area of face A (1 cm²)
> Volume of cube B (27 cm³)
> $= 3^3 \times$ volume of cube A (1 cm³)

Example 6

Cuboid P is an enlargement of cuboid Q.
The scale factor is 4.
Work out the ratio   volume of P : volume of Q.

Volume of P $= 64 \times$ volume of Q

Volume of P : Volume of Q $= 64 : 1$

> The scale factor is 4 so the volume of P $= 4^3 \times$ volume of Q.

Exam practice 17D

1   Rectangle ABCD is an enlargement of rectangle PQRS.

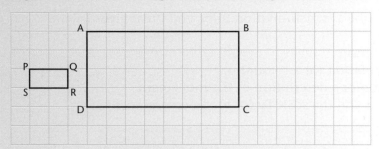

> You can count squares to find this ratio. Alternatively you can use
> Area ABCD = (scale factor)^2 × Area PQRS.

a   Write down the scale factor of the enlargement.
b   Find the ratio of the area of ABCD to the area of PQRS.

2   Triangle LMN is an enlargement of triangle PQR.

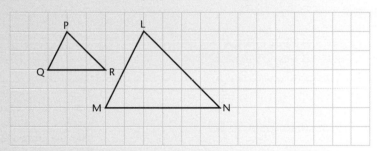

a   Find the scale factor of the enlargement.
b   The area of triangle PQR is 3 cm^2.
    Work out the area of triangle LMN.

3   Parallelogram ABCD is an enlargement of parallelogram WXYZ.

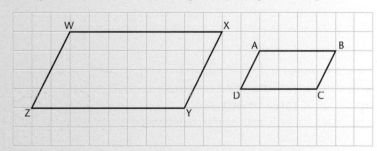

a   Write down the scale factor of the enlargement.

> Be careful. Read the question carefully.

b   Find the ratio   i $\dfrac{\text{perimeter ABCD}}{\text{perimeter WXYZ}}$ ii $\dfrac{\text{area ABCD}}{\text{area WXYZ}}$.

4   Solid B is an enlargement of solid A.

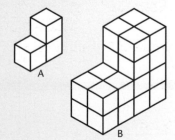

a   Give the scale factor.
b   The volume of A is 3 cm^3.
    Work out the volume of B.

17.5 Describing a transformation

When you are asked to describe a transformation fully, you must give
- the mathematical name
- the mirror line for a reflection
- the centre and angle of rotation for a rotation
- the vector for a translation or a description of the movement
- the centre of enlargement and the scale factor for an enlargement.

Class discussion

What is the mathematical name of this triangle?

3 cm   3 cm

3 cm

What are the properties of this triangle?
Which of these properties stay the same when the triangle is transformed
a by a reflection   **b** by a rotation
c by an enlargement   **d** by a translation?

Exam practice 17E

Describe fully the transformation that maps A to B.

1
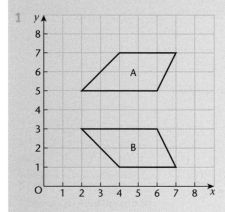

2
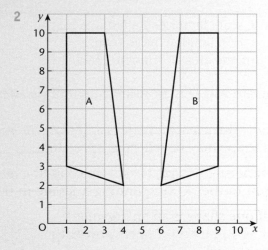

3
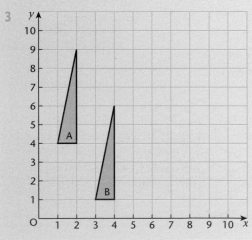

4
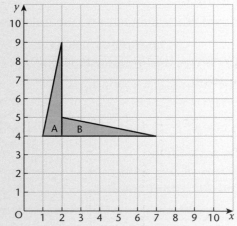

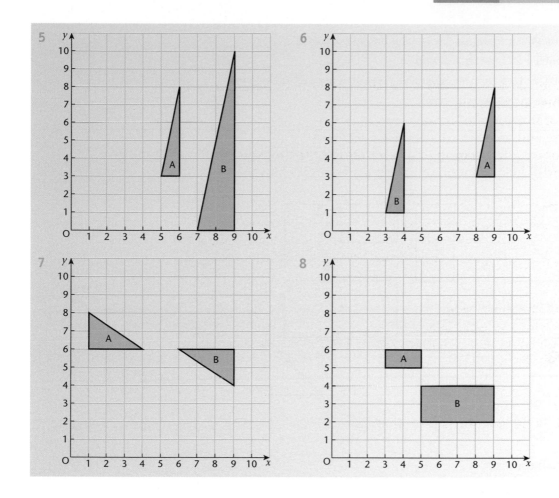

17.6 Similar shapes

Two shapes are **similar** when one is an enlargement of the other. The enlarged shape may be reflected or rotated.

When two shapes are similar, their corresponding angles are equal and the lengths of their corresponding lines are in the same ratio.

You can tell if one shape is an enlargement of another by seeing if their **corresponding** sides are proportional.

Corresponding means in the same position in each shape.

When two quantities are in the same ratio, they behave in the same way. If one quantity is doubled, so is the other, if one quantity is halved, so is the other, and so on. Quantities that are related in this way are **proportional**.

Example 7

Write down the letters of the rectangles that are similar. Explain your answer.

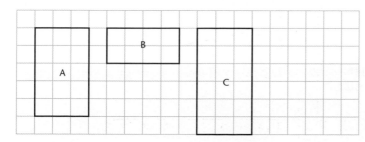

Compare the ratios of length to width.
For A, length : width = 5 : 3.
For B, length : width = 4 : 2 = 2 : 1.
For C, length : width = 6 : 3 = 2 : 1.

B and C are similar because their sides are proportional.

Length : width = 2 : 1 for both B and C.

A is not similar to B or C because the sides of A are not in the same proportion as the sides of B and C.

Exam practice 17F

1

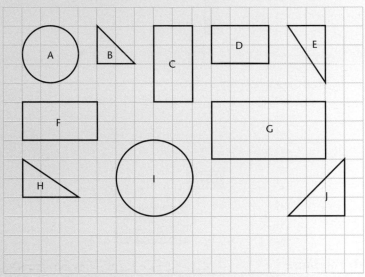

Name a shape that is

a   similar to A

b   congruent to F

c   similar to G

d   similar to B.

2

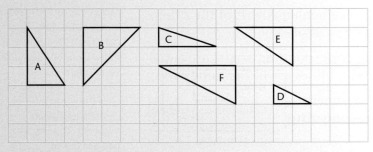

Which two of these triangles are

a   similar, but not congruent   b   congruent?

3   Write true or false for each statement.
Sketch an example to illustrate those that you think are false.

a   All circles are similar.

b   All rectangles are similar.

c   All squares are similar.

d   All equilateral triangles are similar.

e   All right-angled triangles are similar.

f   All regular hexagons are similar.

g   All isosceles triangles are similar.

4 This diagram shows two rectangles.

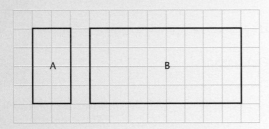

Write true or false for each statement.
a A and B are congruent.
b A and B are similar.
c B is twice as long as A.
d The perimeter of B is four times the perimeter of A.
e The area of B is four times the area of A.

17.7 Scale drawings

A **scale drawing** is a drawing with the same proportions as the real thing but with a different size.
A scale drawing of a shape is similar to the real shape.

> A scale drawing is an enlargement usually by a fractional scale factor.

A scale is given. This tells you what a length on the drawing represents on the ground.

> A scale where 1 cm represents 4 m is equivalent to a scale factor of $\frac{1}{400}$.

Example 8

This is a scale drawing of a house and garden.
It is drawn on a 1 cm grid.
Find the width of the garden.

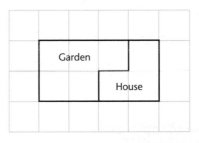

Scale: 1 cm represents 8 m.

The garden is 2 cm wide on the drawing.
The width of the garden is 2 × 8 m
= 16 m.

> The scale tells you that 1 cm on the drawing is 8 m on the ground.
> So 2 cm on the drawing is 2 × 8 m on the ground.

A map is a scale drawing.
The scale may be given the same way as a scale drawing or it may be given as a ratio.

A **map ratio** tells you the ratio of distances on the map to distances on the ground.

Example 9

A road on this map is 5 cm long.
How long is the road on the ground?

The road on the ground is 5 × 100 000 cm long.

$5 \times 100\,000\,cm = 500\,000\,cm$
$= 5000\,m$
$= 5\,km$
So the road is 5 km long.

The scale on the map is 1 : 100 000.
This is the map ratio.
It means that a line on the map shows a line on the ground that is 100 000 times longer.

Exam practice 17G

1   Greg draws the floor plan of his kitchen on a 1 cm grid.
   a   How long is the kitchen floor from A to B?
   b   Work out the floor area of Greg's kitchen.

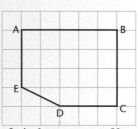

Scale: 1 cm represents 50 cm

2   This is a scale drawing of a village.

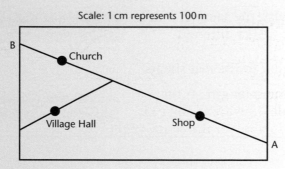

Scale: 1 cm represents 100 m

   a   Measure the line AB.
   b   AB shows the road through the village.
       How long is the road between A and B?
   c   Sally walks from the church to the shop.
       How far does she walk?

3   This is part of a street map.
    David walks from one end of
    Berry Road to the other.
    How far does he walk?
    Give your answer in metres.

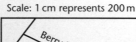
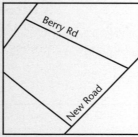

Scale: 1 cm represents 200 m

4   The map ratio of a map is 1 : 10 000.
    The distance between two towns on the map is 25 cm.
    How far apart are the towns? Give your answer in kilometres.

5   This is the floor plan of a flat.

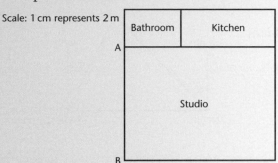

Scale: 1 cm represents 2 m

a   Work out the width of the actual studio (AB on the diagram).
b   Find the area of the actual kitchen.

6   Giles drew this sketch of a plot of land.

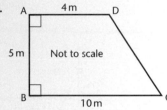

a   A scale drawing is made using a scale of 1 cm to represent 1 m. What is the length of AB on the scale drawing?
b   Draw another sketch showing the measurements you need to use to make a scale drawing.
c   Construct an accurate scale drawing of the plot.

> A sketch is not accurate.
> You cannot use a sketch to measure lengths or angles.

7   This sketch shows the cross-section of a roof.

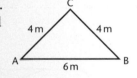

a   Use a scale of 1 cm to represent 0.5 m and draw another sketch showing the measurements you need to use to make a scale drawing of the roof.
b   Construct an accurate scale drawing of the roof.
c   What is the mathematical name for the shape of the cross-section?

> Not to scale.

17.8 Three-figure bearings

A **bearing** gives the direction from one place to another place.
There are two ways of giving a bearing.

A **compass direction** gives the direction as a point on a compass.
The main compass points are north, east, south and west.

A **three-figure bearing** gives the direction as an angle measured clockwise from north.

A three-figure bearing must have three figures. This bearing is 055°.

Example 10

This map shows three villages.
a Write down the bearing of Fordham from Denton.
b Work out the bearing of Denton from Fordham.
c Find the bearing of Fordham from Eastly.

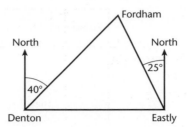

a   040°   The angle shown is 40°. You need to add a zero in front to give a three-figure bearing.

b   180° + 40° = 220°

You need to start at Fordham. Draw a North line here. The angle you want is the clockwise angle from the north line to the line going to Denton. This is 180° + 40°.

These two angles are alternate angles so they are equal.

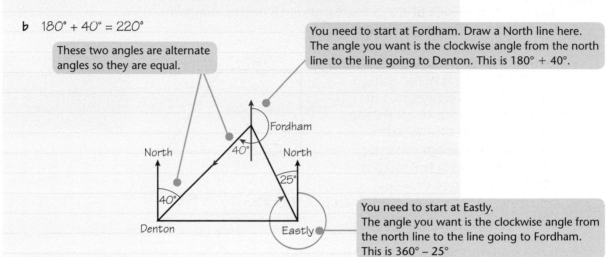

You need to start at Eastly.
The angle you want is the clockwise angle from the north line to the line going to Fordham.
This is 360° − 25°

c   360° − 25° = 335°

Exam practice 17H

1 a   Write down the three-figure bearing of A from B.

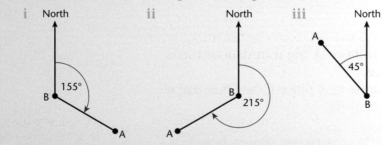

b   Work out the three-figure bearing of M from L.

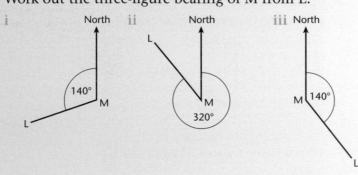

2   This map shows three villages, A, B and C. It is drawn to scale.
    B is due south of A.
    a   Work out
        i   the bearing of A from C
        ii the bearing of C from A.
    b   Measure angle ABC.
    c   Work out the bearing of
        B from C.
    d   Measure AB and write
        down its length.
    e   Village A is 10 kilometres
        due north of village B.
        Work out the scale of the map.

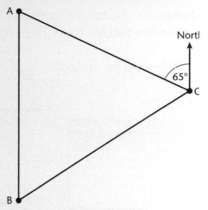

You need to add a 'north' line at the point you want the bearing from.

3   The diagram shows a sketched
    map of the positions of three
    buildings in a village.
    The church is due west of the shop.
    a   Construct an accurate scale
        drawing of this map.
        Use a scale of 1 cm to
        represent 100 m.
    b   Use your drawing to find the bearing of the shop from the
        school.

17.9 Loci

A **locus** (plural **loci**) is all the points that obey a rule.
A locus can be a straight line or a curve or an area.

Example 11

The seats on a roundabout are 2.5 metres from the centre, C.
a   Draw the path that a seat A follows as the roundabout turns.
    Use a scale of 1 cm to 1 metre.
b   What is the mathematical name for the path that A follows?

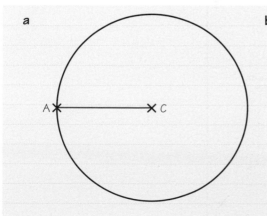

b   The path that A follows is
    a circle.

The rule is that A must always be exactly 2.5 m from C. This means that the path A follows is a circle with radius 2.5 m.

Example 12

T is a tree in a field. A cable has to be buried in the field. It must be
more than 7.5 m from the tree and more than 10 m from the trees on
the edge AB.
Shade the area where the cable can be buried.

Scale: 1 cm represents 5 m

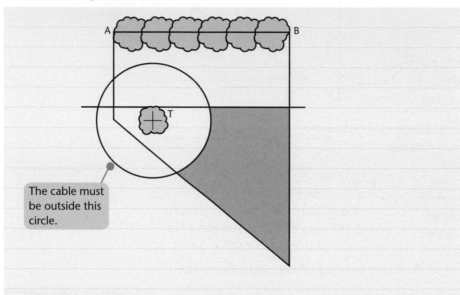

The cable must
be outside this
circle.

The points that are
7.5 m from T are on a
circle, centre T, radius
7.5 m. Using the scale
given, you need to
draw a circle with
radius 1.5 cm.
The points that are
10 m from AB are on a
line parallel to AB at a
distance of 10 m from
AB. On the drawing,
the line is 2 cm from
AB.

Exam practice 17I

1   The diagram shows a goat tethered to a pole. The tether is
    2 metres long.
    On a copy of the diagram, shade the area that the goat can reach.

Scale: 1 cm represents 0.5 m

2   The diagram shows a circular flower bed and a single garden
    fence panel. Alec is sitting at a point A behind the fence.
    Beth is walking about behind the fence in such a way that Alec
    cannot see her.
    Shade the locus of the point representing Beth.

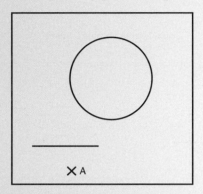

3   One end of a chain, 2 metres long, is attached to the collar of a
    guard dog. At the other end is a ring which can slide on a fixed
    wire 5 metres long. Assuming that the dog's collar is always the
    same distance above the ground, sketch the locus of the point of
    attachment on the collar.

4   This diagram shows two towns, R and S.
    a   Find the actual distance between R and S.
    b   A road is to be built so that it is always equal distances from
        R and S.
        Draw the path of the road on a copy of the diagram.

> All the points on the
> perpendicular bisector
> of a line segment are
> the same distance from
> each end of the line
> segment.

Scale: 1 cm represents 1 km

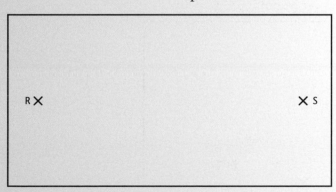

c   The local council wants to build an estate.
    This estate must be more than 3 km from S and less than
    1 km from both sides of the new road.
    Shade the area where they can build the new estate.

5   This is a scale drawing of the front garden of Priyantha's house.
    She wants to plant a tree.
    The tree must be more than 3 m from the front of the house and
    it must be more than 1 metre from the path.
    On a copy of the diagram shade the area where Priyantha can
    plant the tree.

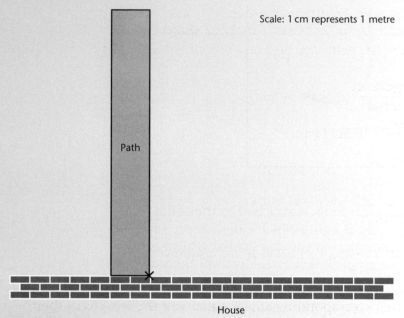

Scale: 1 cm represents 1 metre

6   Use another copy of the diagram for question **5** for this question.
    Priyantha buys a lawn mower. It has a cable 6 m long.
    She can plug the cable into a socket marked X on the diagram.
    Shade the area that Priyantha cannot reach with this lawn mower.

Summary of key points

- You can simplify a ratio by leaving out the units, as long as both parts have the same units, and by dividing both parts by the same number.
- An enlargement with a scale factor greater than 1 makes a shape larger and an enlargement with a scale factor less than 1 makes a shape smaller.
- The relationships between perimeter, area and volume of an enlargement and the original are:

$$\frac{\text{perimeter of enlargement}}{\text{perimeter of original}} = \text{scale factor},$$

$$\frac{\text{area of enlargement}}{\text{area of original}} = (\text{scale factor})^2,$$

$$\frac{\text{volume of enlargement}}{\text{volume of original}} = (\text{scale factor})^3$$

- To describe a transformation fully you must give
  - the mathematical name
  - the mirror line for a reflection
  - the centre, direction and angle of rotation for a rotation
  - the vector for a translation
  - the centre of enlargement and the scale factor for an enlargement.
- Similar shapes have their corresponding angles equal and the lengths of their corresponding lines in the same ratio.
- To find a bearing, start by drawing a north line from the point you are finding the direction from.

Most students who get GRADE E or above can:
- enlarge a shape by a whole number scale factor
- measure an angle to find a bearing.

Most students who get GRADE C can also:
- enlarge a shape by any positive scale factor from a given centre of enlargement
- describe a transformation fully.

Glossary

Bearing	the direction from one place to another place
Centre of enlargement	the point from which lines are drawn to the vertices of the original shape and extended to give the vertices of the enlarged shape
Compass direction	a direction given in terms of north, south, east and west
Corresponding	in the same position in each shape
Enlargement	a transformation that makes a shape larger or smaller
Guide lines	lines drawn from the centre of enlargement to the vertices of a given shape. The corresponding vertices of an enlarged shape lie on these lines.

Glossary (continued)

Locus (plural loci)	all the points that obey a rule
Map ratio	the scale of a map given as a ratio
Proportional	quantities that are in the same ratio
Ratio	a way of comparing quantities
Scale drawing	a different sized drawing in the correct proportions
Scale factor	the number that tells you how much to enlarge a shape
Similar	two shapes are similar when one is an enlargement of the other
Three-figure bearing	a direction given as a clockwise angle measured from the north
Vertex (plural vertices)	the corners of a shape

Examination practice papers

Paper 1   Time allowed: 1 hour 15 minutes   Calculators are not allowed

1 Select the most suitable answer for each part.

  (a) The weight of a bag of crisps

    28 grams   28 kilograms   28 milligrams   *(1 mark)*

  (b) The height of a man

    175 millimetres   175 centimetres   175 metres   *(1 mark)*

  (c) The amount of juice in a carton of drink

    25 litres   25 centilitres   25 millilitres   *(1 mark)*

  (d) An obtuse angle

    60°   90°   160°   *(1 mark)*

2 (a) (i) Write down the next number in the sequence

        3   6   9   12   *(1 mark)*

    (ii) If the sequence was continued, the number 300 would appear.
          Explain why 300 would appear.   *(1 mark)*

  (b) (i) Write down the next number in the sequence

        50   48   46   44   42   *(1 mark)*

    (ii) If the sequence was continued, the number 23 would **not** appear.
          Explain why 23 would not appear.   *(1 mark)*

3 (a) Write down all the factors of 18.   *(2 marks)*

  (b) Write down all the multiples of 4 between 19 and 39   *(2 marks)*

4 (a) A ————————————— B

    Measure the length of AB.

    (i)   Write your answer in millimetres.   *(1 mark)*

    (ii) Write your answer in centimetres.   *(1 mark)*

  (b) (i) Use your compasses to draw a circle with centre A and radius AB. *(1 mark)*

    (ii) Mark and label a point P on the circumference of the circle.   *(1 mark)*

(c) A square CDEF is drawn.

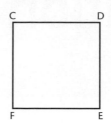

(i)   Mark and label the mid-point M of side DE.   *(1 mark)*

(ii) Name a pair of parallel lines.   *(1 mark)*

(iii) Name a pair of perpendicular lines.   *(1 mark)*

5

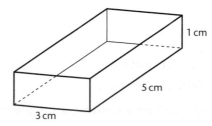

(a) Write down the coordinates of the points O, A and B.   *(3 marks)*

(b) Mark and label the points C $(-3, -1)$ and D $(0, -3)$ *(2 marks)*

6 Here is a flow chart.

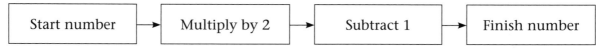

| Start number | → | Multiply by 2 | → | Subtract 1 | → | Finish number |

(a) Find the finish number if the start number is $5\frac{1}{2}$.   *(1 mark)*

(b) Find the start number if the finish number is 21.   *(2 marks)*

7 Here is a diagram of a small open box.

1 cm

5 cm

3 cm

Draw on the grid an accurate diagram of the net of the box.

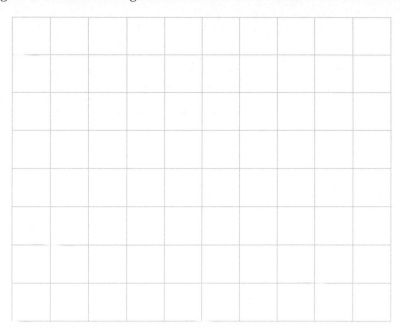

(3 marks)

8 (a) Simplify

    (i) $a + 5a$ *(1 mark)*

    (ii) $4x + 2y - 2x + 3y$ *(2 marks)*

  (b) Expand and simplify

    (i) $5(d - 3)$ *(1 mark)*

    (ii) $c(c^2 + 1)$ *(2 marks)*

9 (a)

    a cm

    b cm b cm

    a cm

The perimeter (P) of the parallelogram is given by the formula

$$P = 2a + 2b$$

    (i)   Find P when $a = 6$ and $b = 4$.

        State the units of your answer.   *(3 marks)*

    (ii) Find a when $P = 36$ and $b = 5$.   *(3 marks)*

  (b) (i)   How many lines of symmetry does a parallelogram have?   *(1 mark)*

      (ii) What is the order of rotational symmetry of a parallelogram?   *(1 mark)*

10 Here is an isosceles triangle.

AB = AC

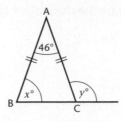

Calculate x and y.   *(3 marks)*

11 (a) Complete this table of values for the equation $y = 2x - 3$.

x	-1	0	1	2	3
y	-5	-3		1	3

(1 mark)

(b) (i)   Draw the graph of $y = 2x - 3$ on the axes below.

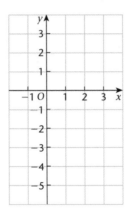

(2 marks)

(ii)   Draw the line $y = 2$ on the same axes.   *(1 mark)*

(iii) Write down the coordinates of the point of intersection between
$y = 2x - 3$ and $y = 2$.   *(1 mark)*

12

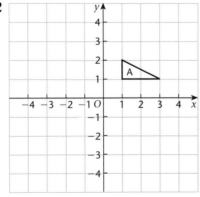

(a) Reflect triangle A in the y-axis.   *(1 mark)*

(b) (i)   Translate triangle A one square to the right and five squares down.   *(1 mark)*

(ii)   Write down the translation vector for (i).   *(1 mark)*

(c) Rotate triangle A through 180° about the Origin.   *(3 marks)*

13 Which of these fractions is nearest to the value $\frac{1}{2}$.

$$\frac{2}{5} \qquad \frac{23}{40} \qquad \frac{9}{20}$$

You **must** show your working. *(3 marks)*

14 Convert 5.6 cubic centimetres to cubic millimetres. *(2 marks)*

15 (a) You are given that $-2 \leqslant 2n \leqslant 7$ and that n is an integer
   Work out all the possible values of n. *(3 marks)*

   (b) Solve $4x - 5 > 5$ *(2 marks)*

16 Simplify

   (a) $b^4 \times b$ *(1 mark)*

   (b) $m^8 \div m^2$ *(1 mark)*

Paper 2   Time allowed: 1 hour 15 minutes   Calculator allowed

1 Read the value that the arrow is showing.

(a)

(1 mark)

(b)

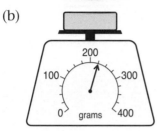

(1 mark)

(c)

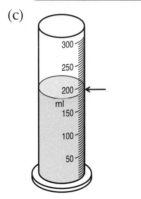

(1 mark)

2

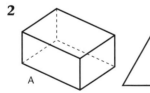 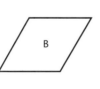 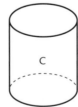 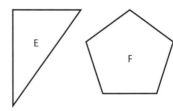

Match each diagram with these names.

equilateral triangle	cuboid	cylinder
right-angled triangle	pentagon	rhombus

(6 marks)

3 The rule for hiring a bouncy castle is

> # £15
> ## plus £6 per hour

(a) Jenny hires the bouncy castle for 4 hours.
    Work out how much she pays.   *(2 marks)*

(b) Amir hires the bouncy castle and pays £57.
    How many hours did he hire the bouncy castle for?   *(3 marks)*

4 (a) Draw the reflection of the shape in the mirror line.

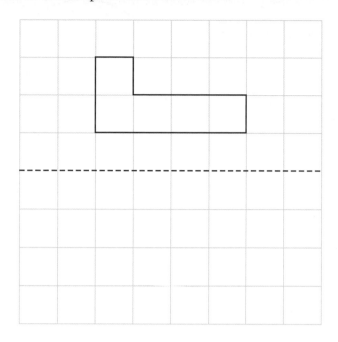

(2 marks)

(b) (i)   Which three of these shapes are congruent?

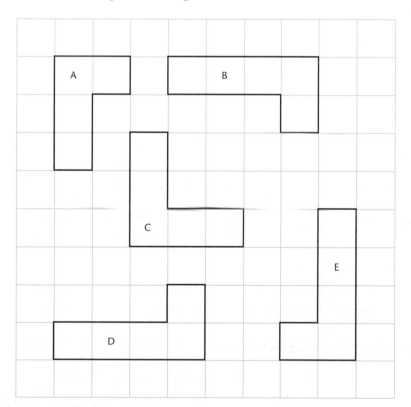

(3 marks)

(ii)   These shapes are drawn on a 1 cm grid. Work out

area shape A + area shape B + area shape C   *(2 marks)*

5 Here is a circle with centre O.

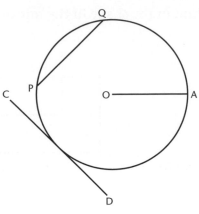

(a) Name the lines OA, PQ and CD.   *(3 marks)*

(b) A diameter of a circle is _____ as the radius of a circle.
     Which words go in the blank space?
     Choose from

          half as big   the same size   twice as big   *(1 mark)*

6 (a) Complete the missing parts of this pattern.

$$21^2 - 20^2 = 41$$
$$20^2 - 19^2 =$$
$$19^2 - \quad =$$ *(2 marks)*

(b) Write down the next term in this sequence

          16, 25, 36, 49, 64   *(1 mark)*

(c) The nth term of a sequence is $\frac{1}{2}n + 5$
     Work out the first three terms of the sequence.   *(2 marks)*

(d) What is the formula for the nth term of the sequence

          4, 8, 12, 16, 20, 24   *(1 mark)*

7 (a) Work out angle x.

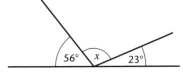

                                                                      (2 marks)

(b)

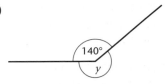

(i)   What type of angle is y?
      Choose from
                right   reflex   obtuse   acute   *(1 mark)*
(ii) Work out angle y.   *(2 marks)*

(c) Work out angle z.

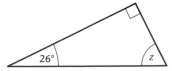

                                                                      (2 marks)

8 Solve

   (a) $6x = 12$ *(1 mark)*

   (b) $x - 3 = 3$ *(1 mark)*

   (c) $5c + 4 = 6 + c$ *(3 marks)*

   (d) $\frac{a}{3} + 5 = 15$ *(2 marks)*

9 (a) Draw an enlargement, scale factor 2, of this trapezium.

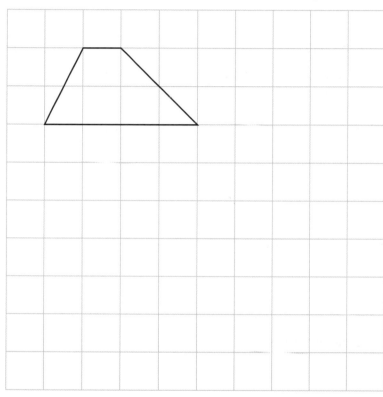

                                                                (2 marks)

   (b) How many times bigger is the area of the enlarged trapezium than the original trapezium?   *(2 marks)*

10

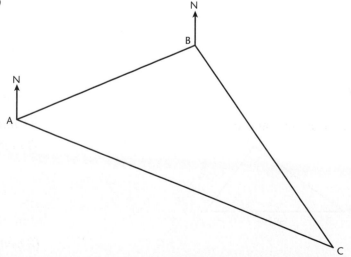

   (a) Measure and write down the bearing of B from A.   *(1 mark)*

   (b) Measure and write down the bearing of C from B.   *(1 mark)*

   (c) Measure and write down the bearing of A from C.   *(1 mark)*

11 A train journey begins at 8.00am.
Details of the journey are:

8.00am to 8.30am;
train travels a distance of 15 miles

8.30am to 9.00am;
train stops at a station

9.00am to 10.00am;
train travels a distance of 60 miles

Draw a distance-time graph for
the journey

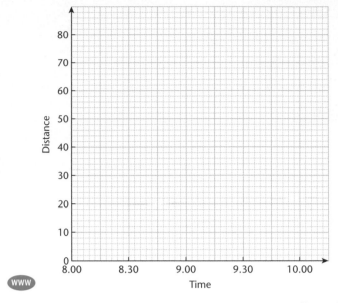

(3 marks)

12 Calculate the value of *x*.

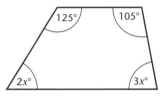

(4 marks)

13 Factorise

(a) $6p + 9$ *(1 mark)*

(b) $t^2 - 2t$ *(1 mark)*

14 Explain clearly why the interior angle of a regular octagon is 135°   *(2 marks)*

15 Calculate the area of these shapes.

(a)

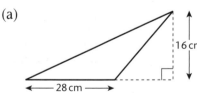

(2 marks)

(b)

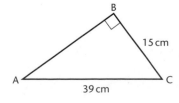

(2 marks)

16 Calculate the length of AB.

(3 marks)

Answers

Exam practice 1A

1 a 100   b 42   c 100
   d 200   e 300   f 135
2 a 58   b 205
3 She subtracted 8 not added it.
4 a 2   b 4   c 9   d 0   e 8   f 2
5 He added 2 to 4 and to 5. He should only add it once.

Exam practice 1B

1 a 45   b 130   c 266   d 927
   e 336   f 510   g 567   h 1270
2 4000 g
3 432, 2592
4 a 4   b 4   c 5
5 It should be $260 - 26 = 234$.
6 a 370   b 35 000   c 12 000   d 270 000
   e 560   f 11 200   g 393 000   h 370 000
7 $7 \times 0 = 0$ so the last digit must be 0.
8 a 9   b 16   c 9   d 27
   e 37   f 23   g 57   h 14
9 He needs 7 boxes. 10 each in 6 boxes + 1 box for the 8.
10 a 6, r 2   b 13, r 1   c 11, r 2   d 12
    e 8   f 16   g 31, r 2   h 13, r 1
11 a 18   b 30   c 32   d 84
    e 6   f 14   g 9   h 2
12 She multiplied both 3 and 2 by 4, whereas she should have only multiplied their product by 4

Exam practice 1C

1 a 26   b 7   c 7   d 0   e 56   f 18
2 a 18   b 4   c 14   d 4   e 32   f 25

Exam practice 1D

1 a 2, 6, 8, 14   b 5, 21   c 2, 5   d 6, 21
2 a 1, 2, 7, 14
   b 1, 2, 3, 4, 6, 8, 12, 24
   c 1, 2, 4, 7, 8, 14, 28, 56
   d 1, 3, 9, 27
3 2, 3, 5, 7, 11, 13, 17, 19
4 a $2 \times 2 \times 2 \times 5$
   b $2 \times 2 \times 7$
   c $2 \times 2 \times 2 \times 7$
5 a No, 45 does not divide exactly by 7.
   b e.g. 14, 28
6 a 4, 7   b 2 or 11   c 15, 20   d 7, 11
7 e.g. $2 + 3 = 5$
8 a 1, 3, 5, 15   b 1 and 3

9 a 1 and 7   b 1, 2 and 4
10 a e.g. 24   b e.g. 30   c e.g. 16
11 a 34 and 51   b e.g. 51
12 a 2 and 8   b 21
    c 12, 24 and 36
    d 2 or 17   e 14
13 a 60   b 270   c 19   d 63   e 15

Exam practice 1E

1 a 16   b 64   c 8
   d 81   e 1000   f 6
2 The two numbers on the left hand side must be the same.
3 a 10   b 10   c 225   d 169
4 a 9   b 11   c 12   d 15   e 14
5 $3 \times 3 \times 3$ is not 9
6 2 is not a square number so does not have an even number as its square root.
7 a 81   b 125   c 11, 13, 29   d 42   e 13
8 $\sqrt{64} = 8$, the cube root of 64 is 4.
9 a 152   b 100   c 125   d 97

Exam practice 1F

1 a 2^2 b 4^3 c 7^4 d 10^5
2 a 32   b 49   c 27   d 10 000
   e 1 000 000
3 $4^3 = 4 \times 4 \times 4 = 64$
4 a $2^2 \times 7^2$ b $2^2 \times 3^3$ c $2^2 \times 3^2 \times 5^2$
   d $3^2 \times 5 \times 7^4$ e $5^2 \times 13^3$ f $3^3 \times 5^7 \times 7^2$
5 a 72   b 900   c 700   d 540
6 The base numbers are different so the indices cannot be added.
7 a 64   b 1 000 000
8 $(5^2)^3 = 5^6$
9 a i 10^1 ii 10^3 iii 10^5 iv 10^9
   b i one hundred
      ii ten thousand
      iii two million
      iv five hundred thousand five hundred
10 5^2; $5^2 = 25$, $\sqrt{121} = 11$
11 a 2^1 b 2^2 c 2^5 d 2^6
12 3^5; $3^5 = 243$, $5^3 = 125$
13 a $2^2 \times 3^2$ b $2^3 \times 3^1$ c $2^2 \times 7^1$ d $2^2 \times 5^2$
14 $\sqrt{169}$, $\sqrt{225}$, 2^4, 4^3, 14^2

Exam practice 2A

1 a $\frac{1}{3}$ b $\frac{2}{3}$ c $\frac{3}{4}$ d $\frac{3}{4}$ e $\frac{5}{8}$
   f $\frac{1}{4}$ g $\frac{3}{5}$ h $\frac{5}{9}$ i $\frac{4}{9}$

2 a e.g. 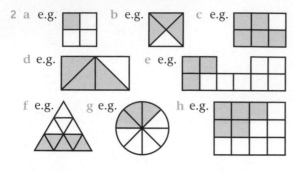 b e.g. c e.g.

d e.g.

e e.g.

f e.g. g e.g. h e.g.

3 The unshaded area is larger than the yellow area.

Exam practice 2B

1 Missing values are:
   a 15   b 4   c 3   d 16
   e 7   f 4   g 3   h 3

2 a $\frac{4}{14}$ b $\frac{14}{24}$ c $\frac{10}{16}$ d $\frac{2}{12}$

3 e.g. $\frac{12}{27}$

4 $\frac{3}{4}$

5 a $\frac{4}{12}$ b $\frac{9}{12}$ c $\frac{10}{12}$

6 a $\frac{25}{30}$ b $\frac{24}{30}$ c $\frac{20}{30}$

7 Missing values in order are:
   a 6, 12   b 9, 20   c 3, 10   d 3, 8

8 a  b

   c   d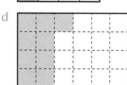

   e f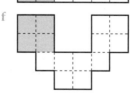

9 $\frac{6}{9}$, $\frac{7}{9}$; $\frac{7}{9}$

10 $\frac{4}{9} = \frac{16}{36}$, $\frac{5}{12} = \frac{15}{36}$ so $\frac{4}{9}$ is bigger than $\frac{5}{12}$.

11 a $\frac{2}{5}$ b $\frac{1}{2}$ c $\frac{4}{5}$ d $\frac{3}{4}$

12 a $\frac{1}{4}$, $\frac{3}{10}$, $\frac{2}{5}$ b $\frac{11}{18}$, $\frac{7}{9}$, $\frac{5}{6}$

Exam practice 2C

1 a $\frac{1}{2}$ b $\frac{3}{4}$ c $\frac{2}{3}$ d $\frac{1}{3}$ e $\frac{2}{3}$ f $\frac{3}{4}$
   g $\frac{4}{5}$ h $\frac{1}{2}$ i $\frac{2}{3}$ j $\frac{1}{5}$ k $\frac{1}{4}$ l $\frac{1}{14}$
   m $\frac{1}{5}$ n $\frac{1}{5}$ p $\frac{7}{10}$ q $\frac{1}{4}$

2 a $\frac{1}{2}$ b $\frac{3}{4}$ c $\frac{1}{3}$ d $\frac{1}{2}$ e $\frac{4}{9}$ f $\frac{1}{4}$
   g $\frac{2}{5}$ h $\frac{1}{8}$ i $\frac{2}{3}$

3 $\frac{5}{15}$, $\frac{20}{100}$, $\frac{12}{36}$

Exam practice 2D

1 a £15   b £33   c 12 m
   d 20 litres e 140 people f 55 kg

2 10

3 20 sq cm

4 £8

5 a $\frac{1}{3}$ b 1

6 312 miles

Exam practice 2E

1 a 0.32   b 2.7   c 5.149

2 a $\frac{1}{2}$ b $\frac{1}{4}$ c $\frac{1}{8}$ d $\frac{2}{5}$ e $\frac{3}{4}$ f $\frac{7}{25}$ g $\frac{3}{8}$

3 £3.65

4 a 3.8 miles
   b 9.9 miles
   c i 14.6 min   i 21.9 min

5 a 250   b 16.2   c 38 500   d 17.5
   e 0.48   f 0.175   g 0.28   h 0.017

6 £135

7 a £28.97   b £35.88   c £10.86 (nearest p)

Exam practice 2F

1 a i   260   ii 4770   iii 20 500   iv 100
   b i   24.6   ii 2.6   iii 56.7   iv 0.2
   c i   0.27   ii 22.81   iii 4.50   iv 0.01
   d i   300   ii 5   iii 0.7   iv 0.02

2 25.47

3 a 0.333   b 0.078   c 1.141   d 5.124

4 a 0.625   b 0.6   c 0.7   d 0.85

5 a 0.43   b 0.83   c 0.11   d 0.27

6 a $\frac{1}{3}$ b 0.25   c $\frac{7}{10}$ d $1\frac{5}{8}$

7 $\frac{1}{6} = 0.1\dot{6} = 0.1666...$

8 £13.33

9 a $\frac{1}{2}$ b $\frac{5}{3}$ c $\frac{3}{2}$ d $\frac{1}{5}$ e $\frac{2}{3}$

10 a 0.1   b 2.3   c 0.2   d 1.7   e 0.1

11 reciprocal of 5 is $\frac{1}{5} = 0.2$

Exam practice 2G

1 a 0.25   b 0.45   c 0.175
   d 0.075   e 0.054

2 a $\frac{1}{2}$ b $\frac{1}{4}$ c $\frac{3}{5}$ d $\frac{3}{8}$ e $\frac{1}{3}$

3 a 46%   b 52%   c 150%   d 26.5%
   e 75%   f 75%   g 80%   h 70%
   i 62.5% j 250%

4 Missing values are:
   $\frac{1}{5}$, 0.2, 87.5%, 0.875, 175%, $1\frac{3}{4}$, $\frac{5}{8}$, 0.625

5 $\frac{1}{3} = 33\frac{1}{3}\%$

6 60%

7 $\frac{5}{8}$; $\frac{5}{8} = 62.5\%$

8 $\frac{2}{5}$, 52%, 0.72

Exam practice 2H

1 a £60   b 8p   c £12
   d 100 kg e £60   f 20 m
   g £1.75   h 11p   i 75p

2 385
3 a £2.50   b £47.50
4 50 miles
5 2800
6 60 sq cm

Exam practice 2I

1 a 9 (3^2) b 7 c 5 d 100 000
   e 14 f 81 (9^2) g 8 (2^3) h 3
2 Yes $2^2 = 4$ so $\sqrt{3} < 2$.
3 a 0.57 b 0.73 c 0.42 d 0.07 e 0.18
4 a 58.3% b 42.9% c 55.6%
   d 9.1% e 48.4%
5 a $\frac{20}{9}$ (2.22) b 0.07 c 0.13
   d 0.14 e 0.52
6 a $\frac{1}{11}$, 0.59, 78% b $\frac{8}{15}$, 80%, 1.2
7 $\frac{1}{20}$, $\frac{1}{20} = 5\%$
8 $\sqrt{31}$; $5.1^2 = 26.01$, $\sqrt{31} = 5.57$
9 a £46.53 b i 9 ii 9
10 a 2500 b 410 c 73 000 d 1250
11 a 125 000 000 000 b 129 600 000 000
   c 1 406 250 000

Exam practice 3A

1 a $2x$ b $3y$ c $4a$ d $2t$
   e xz f x^2 g v^2 h xt
2 a $6x$ b $10x$ c $18x$ d $30x$
   e $12y$ f $4a$ g $12t$ h $21y$
3 The left-hand side is equal to $2 \times 4 \times x \times x$
   which equals $8x^2$, not $8x$
4 a $2x$ b $2y$ c $4a$ d $5s$
   e x f $3b$ g s h x
5 a $15a^2$ b $15p^2$ c $8x^2$ d $20a^2$
   e x^3 f $6st$ g p^3 h x^2y

Exam practice 3B

1 a $2x$ and $10x$ b y^2 and $2y^2$
   c $4x$ and $6x$ d $2a$ and $7a$, $3a^2$ and $4a^2$
2 a $2 + 2x$ b $5t - 4$ c $7y - 4$
   d $-x - 4$ e $y + 6$ f $x^2 + 2x$
   g $ab - 4a + b$ h $7x^2 - 4$ i $6 - 2x + 5y$
3 a $3x$ b $2x$ c $9y$ d $4x$
   e $2x$ f x g $9a$ h $8q$
   i $6n$ j $4x$ k a l $11t$
4 a $9 - a$ b $8x + 5$ c $5x + y$
   d $12p - 10$ e $11a + 2b$ f $x + 4$
   g $3a + 10$ h $7x + 6y$ i $5ab + 4a$
5 $2x + x = 3x$
6 a $x^2 + 8x$ b $a^2 + 3a$
   c $2a^2 + 2a$ d $x^2 + 2xy$
   e $5p^2 + 2p$ f $y - y^2$
   g $7x^2 + 10x + 4$ h $a^2 + 11a + 8$
   i $4t^2 + 2t + 8$

Exam practice 3C

1 a -5 b -10 c -3
   d -5 e -1 f -11
   g $4a$ h $-x$ i $-5y$

2 a 1 b -3 c -5
   d -7 e -2 f x
   g $3x$ h $-3a$ i $-8b$
3 a 8 b 4 c 11
   d -4 e 4 f $11x$
   g $2y$ h $-9a$ i $-2p$
4 a 1 b $-2x$ c y
   d 0 e $3t$ f $-6d$
   g $7x^2 - 7x + 4$ h $a^2 - 5a + 8$ i $4t^2 - 8t + 8$
5 a $4 - 5a$ b $9x - 11$ c $3x - 3y$
   d $5 - 3p$ e $-x - 2y$ f $2 - 2x$
   g $5 + 5s$ h $8x + 8$ i $2x + 5y$
6 $-2x - 2x = -4x$

Exam practice 3D

1 a -12 b 8 c 20 d 16
   e -18 f -15 g -16 h 25
   i -2 j 2 k -7 l 5
2 a $-8x$ b $-6x$ c $-16x$ d $-2y$
   e $3a$ f $-2a$ g $-x$ h $6a$
   i $-10t^2$ j $-3ab$ k xy l $15t^2$
3 a 12 b 8 c $8ab$
   d $-2x^2$ e $24xy$ f $-5a^2$
4 a 14 b 23 c 1
   d $-4x$ e $-6y$ f b
   g a h $-x$ i t
5 a false b true c false
   d true e false f false

Exam practice 3E

1 a 3^7 b 7^8 c 5^7 d x^5
   e x^7 f a^6 g l^8 h p^6
2 a and b $x^4 \times x^2 = x^6$
3 a 3^3 b 2^2 c 7 d 3^3
   e x^5 f x^4 g 1 h y^2
   i 4^4 j p^5 k 3^3 l x^2
4 a 2^6 b x^8
5 a No, $(y^3)^2 = y^{3 \times 2} = y^6$.
   b No, $b^7 : b^7 \times b^1 = b^5 \times b^4 = b^9$.
6 a x^2y b $2x^3$ c $4v^3$ d $3n^1$
   e $2a^2b$ f $2abc$ g $8bc^2$ h $6a^3b$
7 a 1 b x^5 c $2x^7$ d a^4
   e $3x^6$ f $3x^2$ g $2x^9$ h $4x^8$
   i $3x^7$ j $8t^2$ k $6v^7$ l $4b$
   m 5^5 n x^5 p a^5
8 a true b false c false

Exam practice 3F

1 a $5x + 10$ b $6x - 9$ c $8a + 24$
   d $10 - 6x$ e $14 - 7x$ f $10a - 15b$
   g $28y - 12y^2$ h $8x - 2x^2$ i $6x - 18x^2$
   j $6x - 2xy$ k $3a^2 + 6ab$ l $6p^2q - 4pq^2$
   m $x^3 + 2x$ n $4y^3 - 3y$ p $a^3 + a^2$
2 a $2a^2 - 8a + 9$ b $3x^2 - 7x - 8$
   c $6x - 6y$ d $x^2 + 7x + 10$
   e $3x^2 + x - 2$ f $8x^2 - 10x + 3$
   g $x^2 + xy + 6y^2$ h $5x - 13y$
   i $-x^2 + 5x - 4$

3 a $x^2 - 3x - 4$ b $a^2 - 2a - 35$
   c $x^2 + 7x + 12$ d $y^2 + 6y + 8$
   e $x^2 + 3x - 10$ f $b^2 + 12b + 35$
   g $x^2 - 3x + 2$ h $p^2 + p - 20$
   i $a^2 - 7a + 12$
4 a $2x^2 + 3x + 1$ b $2x^2 + 7x + 6$
   c $3x^2 + 14x + 8$ d $6s^2 + st - 2t^2$
   e $14y^2 + 69y + 27$ f $4t^2 - 13t + 3$
   g $x^2 - 4$ h $9x^2 - 1$
   i $10 - 9y + 2y^2$ j $x^2 + 6x + 9$
   k $x^2 - 10x + 25$ l $4x^2 + 4x + 1$
   m $9x^2 - 6x + 1$ n $4x^2 + 12x + 9$
   p $16 - 24x + 9x^2$

Exam practice 3G

1 a $1, 2, 4$ b $1, 2, 3, 4, 6, 12$
   c $1, 3, x, 3x$ d $1, 2, 7, 14, x, 2x, 7x, 14x$
   e $1, x, x^2$ f $1, 2, t, 2t, t^2, 2t^2$
2 a $1, 2$ b $1, 3$ c $1, 5$
   d $1, 3$ e $1, x$ f $1, 4$
3 a $3(x + 2)$ b $3(x - 4)$ c $4(2x + 1)$
   d $2(x + 3)$ e $5(2 + x)$ f $8(2b + 1)$
   g $7(x - 2)$ h $5(x + 1)$ i $4(b + 3)$
   j $3(y + 3)$ k $9(x - 2)$ l $7(2 - 3x)$
4 a $x(x + 3)$ b $a(a - 2)$ c $x(x + 5)$
   d $t(t - 6)$ e $v(v + 2)$ f $x(2 - x)$
   g $x(4 + x)$ h $x(5 - x)$ i $x(2x - 1)$
   j $a(2a + 5)$ k $2x(3 - x)$ l $2x(2 + x)$
5 a $2(x + y)$ b $x(x - y)$ c $5(a + 2b)$
   d $a(b + c)$ e $x(2x + y)$ f $y(x + y)$
   g $2(x^2 + 2y^2)$ h $x(x^2 - 2)$
6 a $2(x + y + 2)$ b $2(a + 2b - c)$
   c $2(2a^2 + a - 4)$ d $3(xy + 2x + 4)$
   e $3(x + 2x^2 + 3)$ f $a(b + c + d)$

Exam practice 3H

1 a 9 b -3 c -11
2 a 22 b -3 c 2
3 a 1 b -7 c 9
4 a 14 b 9 c 14
5 a 6 b 0 c 0
6 a 14 b 13 c -1
7 a 10 b 2 c 10
8 a 6 b 6 c 0.75
9 a 3 b 5 c 3.75
10 a 2 b -11
11 a 15 b 8 c 18 d 6
12 a 6π b 3π c 18π
13 a 12π b 18π c 54π

Exam practice 4A

1 a 7 b 23 c 8
   d 13 e 12 f 20
   g 12 h 20 i 12
2 a -2 b -1 c -9
   d -1 e -3 f -2
3 a 12 b 7 c 2
   d 2 e 11 f 7
   g -1 h -2 i -3
   j -2 k 15 l -3

Exam practice 4B

1 a 4 b 8 c 12
   d 60 e 20 f $\frac{2}{5}$
   g 10 h 40 i $3\frac{1}{2}$
   j 4 k $3\frac{1}{3}$ l $\frac{3}{4}$
2 a i $5x$ ii 3 b i $7x$ ii 3 c i $3x$ ii 4
3 a 10 b 2 c $2\frac{1}{3}$
   d 30 e 10 f 72
4 a 10 b 20 c 36
   d 12 e 35 f 60
   g 36 h 40 i 28
   j 24 k 48 l 5

Exam practice 4C

1 a 2 b 1 c 3 d 2
   e 2 f $2\frac{1}{4}$ g 3 h 3
   i 2 j 4 k $1\frac{1}{8}$ l $\frac{1}{2}$
2 a 1 b 3 c -1 d -2
   e $1\frac{1}{3}$ f 1 g 1 h $\frac{1}{6}$
   i $-\frac{1}{2}$ j $-\frac{1}{7}$ k $2\frac{2}{5}$ l $-2\frac{1}{4}$
3 a 10 b 30 c 5 d 21
   e 3 f -6 g -15 h 20
   i 2 j 16 k -18 l $7\frac{1}{2}$

4 x isn't equal to $6 + 4$, it is equal to $\dfrac{6 + 4}{2}$

Exam practice 4D

1 $5c$ pence   2 $30\,n$ pence
3 $(x - 3)\,$cm   4 £$(C + 5)$
5 £$(2p + 4)$ 6 $(2x + 6)\,$cm
7 $(x + y - 3)$ pens   8 $(5a + 4b)$ pence
9 $(4x + 3y)\,$cm
10 If x stands for the number
   a $x + 4$ b $3x$ c $x - 6$
   d $2x + 5$ e $\frac{1}{2}x - 10$.
11 If x is the number of beads in each box, total number of beads left is $2x - 10$.
12 If a plain muffin costs x pence, total cost is $(2x + 5)$ pence.

Exam practice 4E

1 a $25n$ pence
   b i $25n = 300$ ii 12
2 a $(4 - x)\,$m
   b i $4 - x = 2.5$ ii 1.5 iii $1.5\,$m
3 a $20c$ pence
   b i $20c = 300$ ii 15 iii 15p
4 $x + 5 = 8.5$, $x = 3.5$
5 a $x - 25$ b $x - 25 = 105$ c 130
6 a $(200 - 3c)$pence   b $200 - 3c = 80$ c 40p
7 $6\,$cm
8 a 13 b 8 c 6 d 2
9 $60°$
10 $50°$
11 $54°, 108°, 162°, 54°, 162°$

Exam practice 4F

1 a 4 b -2 c 6 d -5
   e 11 f 3 g 3 h $-\frac{1}{3}$

2 a $\frac{1}{2}$ b $-\frac{1}{7}$ c $\frac{3}{4}$ d -4
   e 1 f 1 g -1 h 1
3 a $(x - 2)$ m   b $(3x - 10)$ m
   c $x - 2 = 3x - 10, x = 4$ d 12 m

Exam practice 4G

1 a 2 b $\frac{1}{2}$ c $2\frac{5}{7}$
   d 2 e 0 f $-2\frac{1}{2}$
   g $4\frac{1}{2}$ h $1\frac{1}{2}$ i 1
2 a 5 b 9 c $-4\frac{1}{2}$ d $\frac{1}{2}$
   e $-5\frac{1}{2}$ f $1\frac{2}{3}$ g $\frac{6}{7}$ h 4
   i 22 j $1\frac{3}{10}$ k $-\frac{11}{13}$ l 13
   m $\frac{5}{11}$ n $-\frac{9}{8}$
3 a 4 b 7 c -5 d $12\frac{1}{2}$ e $\frac{2}{3}$ f 22
4 a $(3x - 150)$p   b $210 = 3x - 150, 120$p
   c 120p
5 6
6 $-2(x - 3) = -2x + 6$ and $4 - 6 = -2$ not 2

Exam practice 4H

1 3.6 2 3.1
3 1.4 4 2.3
5 2.7

Exam practice 4I

1 a $x < 4$ b $x < 5$ c $x > 3$
   d $x < 6$ e $x > -3$ f $x > 2.5$
   g $x \geqslant 5$ h $x \geqslant 3$ i $x \leqslant 14$
   j $p < -3$ k $x > 2$ l $s \geqslant -2$
2 a $x < 3$ b $x > 2\frac{2}{3}$ c $x < 2$
   d $x \leqslant 8$ e $x < 2$ f $y > 2$
   g $a \geqslant 3$ h $x \leqslant 5$ i $x > 1\frac{2}{3}$
   j $t < 4\frac{2}{3}$ k $k \geqslant 6$ l $y \leqslant 2\frac{1}{4}$
3 a $7, 8, 9$ b $-2, -1, 0, 1$ c $4, 5, 6$
   d $3, 4$ e $0, 1, 2, 3$ f $0, 1, 2$
   g $2, 3$ h $-3, -2, -1, 0, 1$ i 1

Exam practice 5A

1 a and f are acute, b and c obtuse, d and e reflex
2 a $270°$ b $540°$ c $30°$ d $54°$
3 a $30°$, acute   b $240°$, reflex   c $150°$, obtuse
4 a 6 b 2 c 6 d 9
5 a i acute   iii $36°$
   b i obtuse   iii $108°$
   c i reflex   iii $230°$
   d i acute   iii $33°$
   e i reflex   iii $334°$

Exam practice 5B

Where reasons are given they are for example.
Any valid reason is acceptable.
1 a $23°$ b $66°$
   c $135°$ d $55°$
2 Their sum is not 180°.
3 Their sum is 100° not 90°
4 116, supplementary
5 67, supplementary
6 53, complementary or straight line
7 180, straight line
8 46, straight line
9 113, angles at a point
10 30, angles at a point
11 59, angles at a point
12 67, angles at a point
13 $s = u = 127$, supplementary and vertically opposite, $t = 53$, vertically opposite
14 $360 - 100 = 2r$
     $260 = 2r$
     $r = 130$
15 No, supplement of 20° is 160°, which is obtuse.
16 Yes, supplement of 35° is 145°, complement of 65° is 25° and the difference between these is 120°.
17 $41°$

Exam practice 5C

Where reasons are given they are for example.
Any valid reason is acceptable.
1 a $c°$ b $b°$
2 a $f°$, they are corresponding angles.
   b $180°$, they are angles on a straight line.
3 a $g°$ b $h°$ c $h°$
4 a $v°$ b $v°$ c $x°$
5 70, corresponding angles
6 105, vertically opposite angles
7 65, corresponding angles
8 108, alternate angles
9 46, alternate angles
10 120, vertically opposite angles
11 80, corresponding angles, angles on a straight line
12 125, corresponding angles, angles on a straight line
13 125, corresponding angles, angles on a straight line
14 84, corresponding angles, angles on a straight line
15 $x = 75$, alternate angles, $y = 25$ angles on a straight line
16 43, alternate angles (twice)
17 115, corresponding angles, angles on a straight line
18 $f = 135$, corresponding angles, angles on a straight line, $g = 45$, angles on a straight line

Exam practice 6A

Where reasons are given they are for example.
Any valid reason is acceptable.
1 60, angles in a triangle
2 52, angles in a triangle
3 60, angles in a triangle
4 115, angles in a triangle
5 47, angles in a triangle
6 15, angles in a triangle
7 55, exterior angle = sum of two interior angles
8 101, angles in a triangle
9 109, exterior angle = sum of two interior angles
10 106, angles on a straight line, exterior angle = sum of two interior angles

11 79, exterior angle = sum of two interior angles
12 $s = 40$, $r = 106$, angles in a triangle, exterior angle = sum of two interior angles
13 30, angles in a triangle
14 $22\frac{1}{2}$, angles in a triangle
15 $m = 126$, $n = 54$, exterior angle = sum of two interior angles, supplementary angles
16 $j = 70$, $k = 50$, vertically opposite angles, angles in a triangle

Exam practice 6B

1 a isosceles   b right-angled
   c equilateral   d isosceles
   e equilateral
2 All angles are 60°.
3 Third angle is 70°, so two angles are 70°.
4 Yes, third angle is $180° - 37° - 53° = 90°$.
5 Yes, third angle is 65°, so triangle is isosceles.
6 44, angles of a triangle
7 70, angles of a triangle, base angles of isosceles triangle
8 82, angles of a triangle
9 60, angles of an equilateral triangle
10 73, base angles of isosceles triangle
11 120, exterior angle of an equilateral triangle
12 84, isosceles triangle, angles of a triangle
13 $h = 65$, $i = 115$, isosceles triangle, angles on a straight line
14 $j = 50$, $k = 80$, angles on a straight line, base angles of isosceles triangle, angles of a triangle
15 25, isosceles triangle, vertically opposite angles
16 a doesn't equal $40 + 40$, it equals $180 - (40 + 40)$.
   b $a = 180 - (40 + 40)$
      $a = 100$

Exam practice 6C

1 45   2 110   3 83   4 65
5 119   6 106   7 68   8 115
9 32   10 57   11 68   12 71

Exam practice 6D

1 90   2 122   3 110
4 36   5 60   6 68
7 83   8 45   9 112
10 $a = b = 36$
11 $f = 74$, $g = 44$, $h = 118$
12 $c = 42$, $d = 18$, $e = 18$
13 $p = 38$, $q = 35$, $r = 73$
14 $i = 127$, $j = 59$
15 a   b   c

16 a parallelogram   b rectangle
   c rectangle   d square
   e rhombus
17 a demonstration, this is a special case
   b no
18 yes, opposite angles are equal and adjacent angles add up to 180°.

Exam practice 6E

1 117   2 100
3 82   4 34
5 a 60°   b 45°   c 30°   d 20°
6 a 108°   b 135°   c 150°   d 162°
7 a 18   b 12   c 8
8 a 6   b 9   c 8
9 a yes   b no   c yes   d no
   (yes only if 360° ÷ exterior angle is a whole number)
10 a yes   b no   c yes   d yes
   (yes only if 360° ÷ (180° − interior angle) is a whole number)
11 a 60   b 135
12 a a hexagon   b $p = 60$
   c $q = 120$
13 a 108   b 36
14 a 120°   b 30°, 30° c 30°
15 a 120°, 120°, 60°, 60°   b a trapezium

Exam practice 6F

1 a yes   b no   c yes   d yes
   e yes   f yes   g no   h no
2 D and F
3 A and C; F and H
4 B, C, D and F
5 a 37°   b 5 cm
6 a 110°   b 4 cm
7 a 20 cm   b 110°
8 a a pentagon
   b He has assumed that the pentagon is regular
9 a a hexagon   b ABF or BCD   c ABF

Exam practice 6G

1 a diameter   b radius
   c chord   d arc
2 a chord   b diameter
3 a radius   b chord
4 a tangent, touches the circle at one point (E)
   b chord, a straight line joining two points on the circle
5 a tangent, touches the circle at one point (R)
   b chord, a straight line joining two points on the circle
6 a segment   b semicircle
   c sector   d quadrant
7
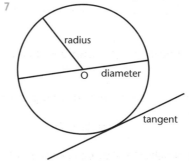

8 a i AD   ii e.g. DC   iii AB or BC   iii e.g. OA
   b Yes, OA, OC and OD are all radii

Exam practice 7A

1. 72°   2 6.6 cm   3 5.6 cm
4. 5.2 cm   5 61°   6 5.6 cm
7. 33°
8. Yes, BC can have two positions. $\angle ACB$ can be acute or obtuse.
9. –
10. 9.3 cm
11. c 11.5 cm

Exam practice 7B

1. yes, SSS 2 yes, AAS 3 yes, SAS 4 no
5. yes, RHS 6 yes, SAS 7 yes, AAS 8 yes, SSS

Exam practice 7C

1. b 3.8 cm
2. b 7.1 cm
3. b 3.6 cm

Exam practice 7D

1. d 30°
2. d 45°
3. b 6.9 cm
4. b 8.5 cm
5. b 7.3 cm
6. c 4.8 cm
7. c yes
8. c no
9. c midpoint
10. b 90°   c right-angled isosceles triangle
12. b 7.2 cm
13. b 7.1 cm
14. b 12.9 cm

Exam practice 8A

1. 240   2 £500
3. 6 h 20 min
4. a 2400 cu cm   b 250 cu cm
5. 70 cm
6. a 72   b 8
7. a 960   b 5
8. a £155   b 800

Exam practice 8B

1. Charge = £40 × number of days + £50
2. Total charge = £30 × number of hours + cost of parts
3. a 96
   b Number of bottles = 12 × number of boxes
4. $N = 20n$
5. $A = l \times w$
6. a Time (minutes) = 2 × number of sausages + 1
   b $t = 2n + 1$
7. $C = n \times c$ 8 $P = 2l + 2w$
9. a 33
   b i number of nails = 3 × number of panels + 3
       ii $N = 3 \times n + 3$ where N is the number of nails and n the number of panels

10. a 170
   b i Number of chairs = number of tickets + 20
       ii $N = n + 20$ where N is the number of chairs and n the number of tickets sold

Exam practice 8C

1. a 160   b 5
2. a 4   b 6300
3. a 90   b 3.5
4. 32
5. a 2   b 7   c 11
6. a 2   b 1
7. a 10   b 2500
8. a 4   b 1   c 20
9. a 24   b −37   c −5
10. a 52   b 29
    c yes, $2^2 + 3^2 = 4 + 9$ and $(-2)^2 + (-3)^2 = 4 + 9$
11. a 40 cm²   b 2.5 cm²   c 4 cm
12. a 24π cm³   b 0.08π cm³

Exam practice 8D

1. a $n = T - 6$ b $b = N + 3$ c $r = \frac{1}{2}d$
   d $b = \dfrac{A}{l}$ e $d = \dfrac{C}{\pi}$ f $s = \dfrac{d}{t}$
   g $y = 2x$ h $t = \dfrac{s}{w}$ i $x = \frac{1}{3}(y - 2)$
   j $p = \frac{1}{5}(t + 40)$ k $p = \frac{1}{3}(r + 4)$ l $y = \frac{1}{2}(c - x)$
   m $x = \dfrac{y - c}{m}$ n $A = \dfrac{3V}{h}$ p $b = \frac{1}{2}a + 4$
   q $a = \frac{1}{3}(w + 6b)$
2. a $t = n + 20$ b $n = t - 20$
3. a $w = \frac{1}{4}(N - 4)$ b 8 ft
   c The number of stones needed is always a multiple of 4.
4. a $b = \dfrac{2A}{h} - c$ b 6

Exam practice 9A

1. a 7 cm   b 4 cm   c 4 cm   d 6 cm
2. a 45 mm b 67 mm c 33 mm d 64 mm
3. 6 ft $1\frac{1}{2}$ in
4. a 6000 m b 100 mm c 10 km d 7.6 km
5. a 7 cm   b 4.5 m   c 8 m   d 56 m
6. a 2000 mm   b 17.8 cm
   c 3500 m   d 730 cm
7. a 3 ft   b 3 yd
8. a 64 km b 104 km c 320 km
9. a 250 miles   b 40 miles   c 100 miles
10. 2 metres
11. a 30 cm b 24 in   c 75 cm   d 20 in
12. 120 cm, 1 m, 30 in, 2 ft
13. No, 80 miles ≈ 128 km
14. Yes, 6 ft ≈ 180 cm which is less than 2 m
15. a 15 cm   b 10 cm   c 1 m

Exam practice 9B

1. a 14 cm b 12 cm   c 14 cm
   d 18 cm e 12 cm   f 18 cm
2. a 24 cm b 360 mm c 1.6 km

3 a 16 cm b 20 cm c 73 cm d 42 cm
4 a 12 cm   b 18.9 mm   c 1.35 km
5 a isosceles b 5.7 cm   c 16 cm
6 15 cm   7 15 cm   8 12.9 cm
9 a x cm   b equilateral triangle
10 a rhombus   b 14 cm
11 a 24 cm   b 25 cm   c 33 m
   d 37 cm   e 168 cm   f 88 cm

Exam practice 9C

1 a 120 mm²   b 4.5 cm²   c 500 000 m²
   d 0.0056 km²   e 400 000 m²   f 5.64 cm²
2 a 247 acres   b 10 ha   c 50 ha
   d 74.1 acres
3 a 16 cm² b 32 cm² c 32 cm² d 31 cm²
4 1 cm² = 100 mm²
5 a H   b E   6 a 8   b 2

Exam practice 9D

1 a 36 cm²   b 8100 mm²   c 0.16 km²
2 a 60 cm²   b 1750 m²   c 33.5 cm²
3 40.5 cm²
4 a 192 cm²   b 65 cm²   c 37 cm²
   d 384 cm²   e 376 cm²   f 54 cm²
5 a 128 000 m²   b 12.8 ha
6 a 360 cm²   b 120 cm²   c 240 cm²
7 a 3500 cm²   b 2.82 m²

Exam practice 9E

1 a 6 cm²   b 8 cm²   c 4 cm²
   d 4.5 cm²   e 7.5 cm²
2 a 40 cm²   b 42 cm²   c 28.5 cm²
   d 160 cm²   e 42 cm²   f 22.5 cm²
   g 84 cm²   h 60 cm²   i 16 cm²
3 a 6 cm²   b 12 cm²   c 9 cm²
   d 12 cm²   e 12 cm²
4 a 40.5 cm²   b 32 cm²   c 72 cm²
   d 135 cm²   e 145 cm²   f 288 cm²
5 a 60 cm²   b 25.5 cm²
6 a 104 cm²   b 312 cm²   c 170 cm²
   d 84 cm²   e 126 cm²   f 252 cm²
7 34 m²
8 a 60 cm × 40 cm
   b 2400 cm²   c 1836 cm²   d 564 cm²
9 No, both areas are 8 × 12 cm² = 96 cm².
10 a trapezium and parallelogram
   b Yes, both areas are 5 × 6 cm² = 30 cm².
11 Yes, both areas are 18 cm².
12 a 35.2 cm²   b 52.8 cm²

Exam practice 9F

1 a 21 cm   b 9 m   c 27 mm
2 a 60 cm   b 48 m   c 180 mm
3 225 cm
4 a 24 cm   b 72 cm
5 a 60 cm   b 2.5 m   c 32 mm
6 a 8π cm   b 9π m²   c $\frac{60}{\pi}$ cm
7 a i 22.0 cm   ii 11.0 cm   iii 2305.9 mm
   b i 56.5 cm   ii 52.2 cm   iii 471.2 m

8 282.7 cm
9 50.3 cm, 66.0 cm, 84.8 cm
10 a 25.7 cm   b 39.3 cm²
11 a 1520.5 m²   b 1134.1 mm²
12 a 227.0 cm²   b Yes, its area is 490.9 cm².
13 a 400 cm²   b 153.9 cm²   c 246.1 cm²
14 a 4590 cm²   b 4085.6 cm²   c 12 761.3 cm²
15 a 660.5 cm²   b 2017.0 cm²

Exam practice 10A

1 a 4   b 4   c 2   d 3 cm × 2 cm
2 a 4   b 8   c 8   d 3
3 a 6   b 2   c 4   d 3 cm
4 a 6   b 12   c 3   d 3
5 a 4   b 4   c 8   d 0
6 a Yes, all measure 4 cm × 3 cm.
   b Yes, all measure 4 cm × 4 cm.
   c Yes, 8 × 4 + 4 × 3 = 44.
7 a cube   b cuboid   c triangular prism
   d cylinder   e cuboid   f triangular prism
8 a 6   b 12   c 8
9 a 8   b 18   c 12

Exam practice 10B

1 b B and C
2 b B
3 a D and E   b AB
4 a

5 4 cm × 2 cm × 2 cm
6 b A and E
7

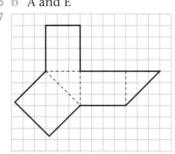

8 B, C and D
9 B and C
10 No, this will not give 6 faces.

Exam practice 10C

1 a   b

2 a   b

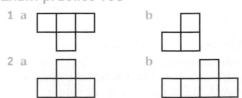

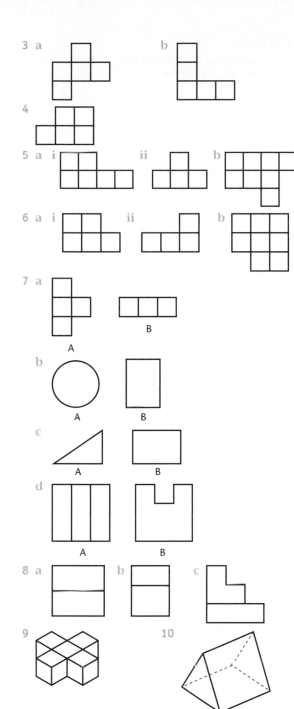

3 a   b

4

5 a i   ii   b

6 a i   ii   b

7 a   A   B

   b   A   B

   c   A   B

   d   A   B

8 a   b   c

9   **10**

Exam practice 10D

1   a   1800 cm²   b   390 cm²   c   662 cm²
    d   1225 cm²   e   95.5 m²   f   114 300 mm²
2   113.2 cm²
3   No. Surface area of 1 block is 136 cm².
    1 can will cover 10 000 cm² so 1 can will do
    10 000 ÷ 136 = 73.5 blocks.

Exam practice 10E

1   a   234 cm²   b   348 cm²
2   8.6 m²
3   a   960 cm²   b   18 300 cm²   (1.83 m²)
4   60 cm²

---

5   a   23.2 cm   b   232 cm²
6   a   50.3 cm²   b   301.6 cm²   c   75.0%
7   11.0 cm²
8   a   i   1.32 m²   ii   132 m²   b   606
9   a   The tallest, 271 cm² compared with 236 cm²
       and 245 cm².
    b   The first, 236 cm² compared with 245 cm²
       and 271 cm².
    c   The first, 324 cm² compared with 402 cm²
       and 352 cm².

Exam practice 11A

1   a   14, 16   b   64, 81   c   128, 256
    d   13, 16   e   1, 0   f   10 000, 100 000
    g   19, 23   h   17, 19   i   10, 5
    j   −6, −10
2   a $a = 16, b = 64$ b $a = 18, b = 30$
    c $a = 49, b = 16$ d $a = 1, b = -8$
    e $a = 6, b = 18$ f $a = -1, b = 14$
3   27, 81   4   22, 29
5   − 6, −11   6   16, 8
7   22, 46   8   26, 677
9   15, 31, 63
10   Every term must be a multiple of 5; 52 is not.
11   a   30, 84, 246
    b   There cannot be another number between
       84 and 246.
12   a   38, 70, 134
    b   No; there cannot be another number
       between 70 and 134.

Exam practice 11B

1   a

    b   Missing values are 13, 16, 19.   c   121
2   $x + 10, x + 12$
3   a

    b   Missing values are 7, 9, 11.   c   99
4   $4x + 14 = 34, 5x + 12 = 32$
5   a $x + 1 = 0, x = -1$
    b   Each equation is obtained by subtracting 1
       from both sides of the equation before and
       this does not change the value of x.
6   a   16   b   30 is not a square number.
7   a   Missing numbers are 16 and 25.   b   13
    c   81, number of blocks = (pattern number)²
8   a   Missing values are 16 and 20.
    b   32   c   80
    d   No. Every number is a multiple of 4.
9   a $9x, 11x$
    b $x + 16, x + 25$
    c $4x + 17, 5x + 16$
    d $16x = 32, 32x = 64$
    e $5(x - 1), 6(x - 3)$
    f $x - 2 = 2, x - 3 = 1$
    g   (6, 13), (7, 15)

Exam practice 11C

1 add 2 to the last term
2 a add 3 to the last term
   b subtract 2 from the last term
   c half of the last term
   d divide the last term by 10
   e add 6 to the last term
   f subtract 10 from the last term
3 a Missing values are 7, 9, 11.
   b add 2 to the last term
   c 5
4 a Missing values are 9, 16, 25.
   b squared
   c 81
5 a 3, 5, 7, 9
   b add 2 to the last term
   c Yes, adding 2 to an odd number always gives an odd number.

Exam practice 11D

1 a 2, 5, 8   b 9, 13, 17   c 6, 4, 2
   d 1, −2, −5   e 2, 6, 12   f 0, 3, 8
2 a 6, 11
   b 51
   c No. No whole number value for n gives $5n + 1 = 37$.
3 a 2, 5, 10   b 145
   c No whole number value of n gives $n^2 + 1$ as 100.
4 a 49, 48, 47   b 30
   c Every term is less than 50
5 a Missing values are 8, 10, 12, 14.
   b $2n + 2$ where n is the pattern number
6 a Missing values are 10, 12, 14, 16.
   b $2n + 4$ where n is the pattern number
   c 24   d 18
7 a Missing values are 6, 9, 12, 15, 18.
   b $3 \times$ pattern number   c $3n$
   d i 33rd
      ii Yes, 1. The largest value of n so that $3n < 100$ is 33.
8 a Missing values are 14, 20, 26, 32, 38.
   b $6n + 2$
   c 13 (there will be 2 empty places)

Exam practice 12A

1 a 8 cm³   b 24 cm³   c 36 cm³
   d 18 cm³   e 9 cm³   f 13 cm³
2 a 2 500 000 cm³   b 6000 mm³
   c 5 000 000 000 cm³   d 7 500 000 mm³
   e 79 mm³   f 8.5 cm³

Exam practice 12B

1 a 24 cm³   b 4500 cm³
   c 360 cm³   d 56.25 cm³
2 a 144 cm³   b 540 cm³   c 140.4 cm³
3 a 27   b i 8 cm³   ii 216 cm³
4 60 000 cm³
5 a no   b It is $2 \times 1.5 \times 0.15$ m³ = 0.45 m³.

6 a no
   b Volume of 1 cube = 0.001 m³ so volume of 100 cubes is 0.1 m³.
7 a no   b depth = $\frac{360}{12 \times 6}$ cm = 5 cm
8 a no
   b Volume = $5 \times 3 \times 0.3$ m³ = 4.5 m³ so 5 m³ will be enough.
9 a 6000 cm³   b 2080 cm²   c 143 cm

Exam practice 12C

1 a 70 cm³   b 84 cm³
   c 36 cm³   d 93 cm³
2 a 202.5 cm³   b 312 cm³   c 600 cm³
   d 36 cm³   e 390 cm³   f 504 cm³
3 a 385.6 cm³   b 125.7 cm³
   c 50.4 cm³   d 2.3 cm³
4 a 6283.2 cm³   b 6283.2 cm³
5 a 34 cm²   b 408 cm³

Exam practice 12D

1 a 4000 ml   b 2500 cm³
   c $\frac{1}{4}$ d 1500 ml
2 2 l
3 20 000 cm³
4 $\frac{3}{4}$
5 5000 cm³
6 a 4   b 10
7 a 80 m³   b 80 000
8 a yes
   b 40 litres is 40 ÷ 4.56 gallons = 8.77 gallons which is more than 8 gallons.
9 a yes   b 2 litres ≃ 3.5 pints
10 a 0.225 m³   b 225 litres
11 1.67 m³

Exam practice 12E

1 a 2000 g   b 3200 kg   c 7.46 kg   d 2.45 t
   e 0.5 kg   f 0.583 t   g 50 g   h 1.4 kg
   i 3 g   j 60 mg   k 8 g   l 7.5 kg
2 7.5 t
3 200 l
4 8 kg
5 11 pounds
6 Yes, 2 kg ≈ 4.4 pounds.

Exam practice 12F

1 588 g
2 476 g
3 3550 g (3 s.f.)
4 a yes
   b Mass of 2 litres is 2000×0.98 g = 1960 g = 1.96 kg.
5 a yes
   b Mass of platinum is 430 g compared with 425 g for gold.
6 7500 g
7 a 1000 cm³   b 0.8 g/cm³
8 2.7 g/cm³

Exam practice 12G

1 a true   b false   c true
  d true   e false   f false
2 a area   b length   c volume   d length
  e area   f volume   g area   h length
3 a cm^2 b cm   c cm^2 d cm^3
  e cm^3 f cm   g cm^2 h cm^2
4 $F = 2\pi^2abc$, $G = \pi a^2b$
5 Yes, 2 × number × length is a length not an area.
6 Bracket is volume units + area units which are incompatible.

Exam practice 13A

1 5 cm   2 13 cm
3 65 mm   4 4 cm
5 10 cm   6 7.2 cm
7 14.2 cm   8 12.0 cm
9 11.1 cm   10 20.0 cm
11 7.7 cm   12 10.2 cm
13 44.7 cm   14 14.8 cm
15 5 km   16 5.8 km
17 a 90°   b 136.0 m
18 14.8 cm   19 2.3 m
20 a 34 doesn't equal 5.8 and no degree of accuracy is given after the answer.
   b length of diagonal $= \sqrt{3^2 + 5^2}$
                        $= \sqrt{9 + 25} = \sqrt{34}$
                        $= 5.8$ (1 d.p.)
21 a rhombus (diagonals bisect at right angles)
   b i 3.75 cm   ii 15 cm

Exam practice 13B

1 10.5 cm   2 6.6 cm
3 4.5 cm   4 3.3 cm
5 12.7 cm   6 72 mm
7 18 cm   8 5.5 cm
9 25.4 mm   10 12.1 cm
11 73.3 m   12 4.9
13 a trapezium   b 0.7 m   c 1.1 m
   d 2.74 m²   e 4.4 m³

Exam practice 14A

1 a i (−2, 0)   ii (0, −4)
  b and c
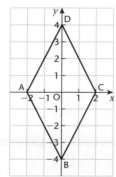
  d rhombus
2 a i (1, 2)   ii (5, −1)

b and c
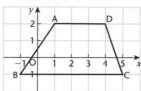
d trapezium

3
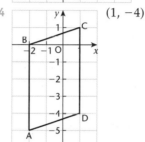
(−2, −3)

4
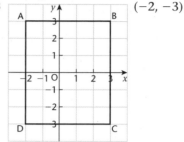
(1, −4)

5
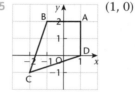
(1, 0)

6 a isosceles   b 4 units   c (1, 3)
7 a kite
  b
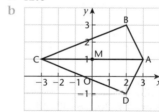
  c 6 units   d (0, 1)
8 a i ($\frac{1}{2}$, 5)   ii (0, 1)
  b This line is not perpendicular to both SP and RQ so is not the distance between the two opposite sides.
9 a isosceles triangle
  b
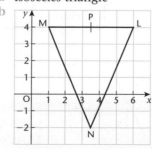
  c i ($3\frac{1}{2}$, 4)   ii 5 units   iii 6 units
  d 15 sq units   e 6.5 units

10 a trapezium
   b i 3 units   ii 8 units
   c 4 units
   d 22 sq units
   e 4.1 units
   f PQ is not perpendicular to SP and QR.

Exam practice 14B

1 a Missing values are 3 and 4.
   b
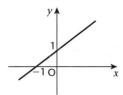

2 a Missing values are 2 and 1.
   b
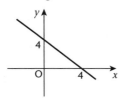

3 a Missing values are 0, 1, 2.
   b   c (3, 1)
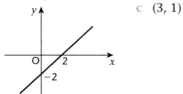

4 a Missing values are 2, 1, 0.
   b   c (2, 1)
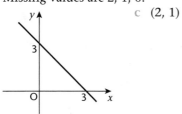

5 a Missing values are 1 and 3.
   b and c   d (3, 5)
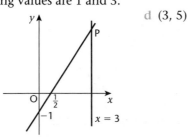

6 a and b   c (3, 2)
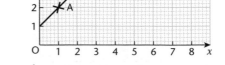

7 a   b $(\frac{1}{3}, \frac{1}{3})$
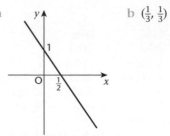

8 a   b (4, 3)
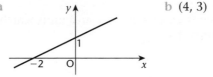

Exam practice 14C

1 a 3   b 2   c −1
   d −2   e $\frac{1}{2}$ f $-\frac{2}{3}$
2 $y = 3x - 1$ and $y = 4 + 3x$
3 No, their gradients are different (5 and −5)
4 a 1   b $\frac{1}{2}$

Exam practice 14D

1 a $y = -2$ b $x = 2$ c $y = -x$
2 a A (2, 8), B (1, 4)   b
   c 4
   d $y = 4x$

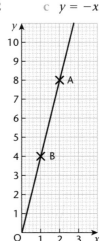

3 a A (1, 2), B (5, 6)
   b

c 1
d $y = x + 1$

4 a and b

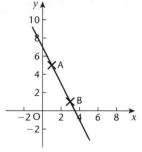

  c −2   d $y = -2x + 7$
5 a, b and e

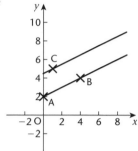

  c $\frac{1}{2}$ d $y = \frac{1}{2}x + 2$
  f $y = \frac{1}{2}x + 4\frac{1}{2}$

6 a and b

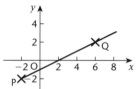

  c $\frac{1}{2}$ d $y = \frac{1}{2}x - 1$
7 a   b $y = -4x + 8$
                              c $y = -4x - 8$

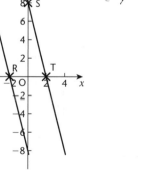

8 a $P = 8t + 15$ b £15   c £23
9 a

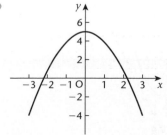

b £50   c £10
d $C = 10t + 50$ e £120

Exam practice 14E

1 a Missing values are 2 and 2.
   b

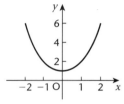

2 a Missing values are 2 and 5.
   b

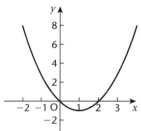

3 a Missing values are 3, −1, 0 and 8.
   b

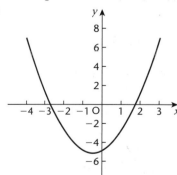

4 a Missing values are 1, −5, −5, 1, 7.
   b

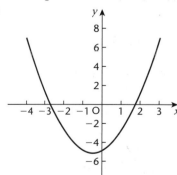

5 a Missing values are 1, 1, −4.
   b

Exam practice 15A

1 a Missing values are 5, 4, 2, 0.
  b   c x = 2.25, y = 2.75

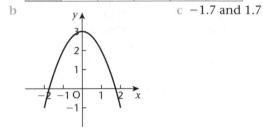

2 a Missing values 2, −1.
  b

c x = 3.7, y = 0.7

3 a Missing value is 1.
  b Missing value is 4.
  c

d x = 1.5, y = 2.5

Exam practice 15B

1 0 and 3
2 −2.8 and 1.8
3 a Missing values are −1 and −1.
  b

c −1.4 and 1.4

4 a Missing values are −0.5 and −1.
  b   c 0.3 and 1.7

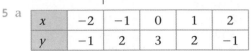

5 a

x	−2	−1	0	1	2
y	−1	2	3	2	−1

  b   c −1.7 and 1.7

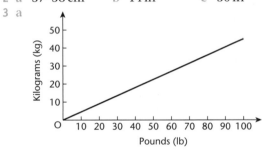

Exam practice 15C

1 a €30   b £38   c €79
2 a 37–38 cm   b 14 in   c 30 in
3 a

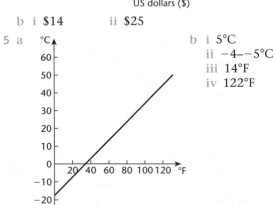

  b i 55 lb   ii 23 kg
4 a

  b i $14   ii $25
5 a   b i 5°C
                ii −4--−5°C
                iii 14°F
                iv 122°F

Exam practice 15D

1 a 47 mph   b 103 km/h
2 a i 200 miles   ii 200 miles
   b 60 mph   c 210 km   d 70 km/h
3 $14\frac{2}{3}$ km/h
4 a 72 km/h   b 14 m/s

Exam practice 15E

1 a 17 miles   b 30
   c 5.67 miles   d 34 mph
2 a 78 miles   b 42 miles
   c 36 min   d 52 mph
3 a 8:45   b 2.7 km
   c 12 km/h   d 7.0 km/h
4 a 2.4 miles   b 48 min
   c 30 min   d 0.48 miles
   e Back, 2.4 miles in 30 min compared with
     2.4 miles in 48 min.

5
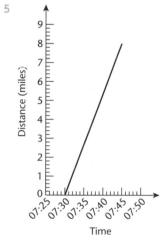

6 a
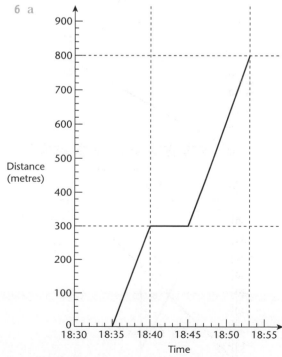
   b 500 m

7 a
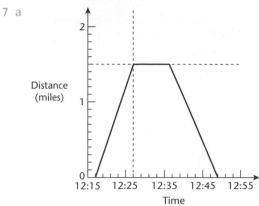
   b 7.5 mph   c 1.25 miles
8 a 8 minutes   b He stops twice
   c 500 m   d 3.75 km/h

Exam practice 16A

1 A and C
2 a
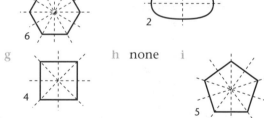

Exam practice 16B

1
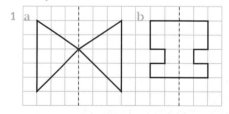

2
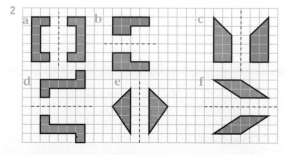

3 a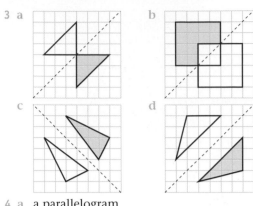
b
c
d

4 a a parallelogram
b i (4, 7)   ii (6, 8)   iii (7, 2)   iv (5, 1)
c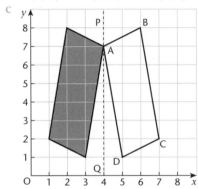
d i (2, 8)   ii (3, 1)

5 a i (3, 0)   ii (8, 2)   iii (1, 3)
b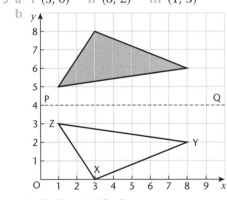
c i (3, 8)   ii (8, 6)

Exam practice 16C

1 a reflection in the line $y = 4$
b reflection in the line $x = 5$
c reflection in the line $y = x$
d reflection in the line $y = x$

Exam practice 16D

1 a i 3   ii 3   b i 4   ii 0
c i 4   ii 4   d i 5   ii 5
e i 2   ii 2   f i 2   ii 2
g i 2   ii 0   h i 1   ii 0
i i 0   ii 0

2 c square   d pentagon
e rhombus   f rectangle
g parallelogram   h kite
i trapezium

3 a i 0   ii 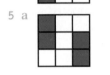   b i 2   ii
c i 3   ii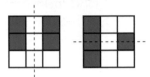

3 a i 2   ii 2   b i 4   ii 4   c i 0   ii 2
4 a 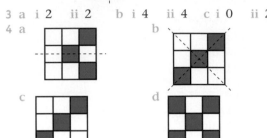 b
c
d

5 a   b Yes, as the diagrams show.

6 a and b

Exam practice 16E

1 a i 90° anticlockwise   ii A
b i 180°   ii A
c i 90° clockwise   ii C

2 a   b   c
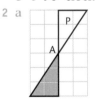

3 a rotation 90° clockwise about (1, 1)
b rotation 90° anticlockwise about (−2, 1)
c rotation 180° about (2, 0)
d rotation 90° clockwise about the origin

4 a

b

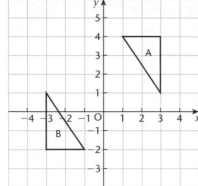

c

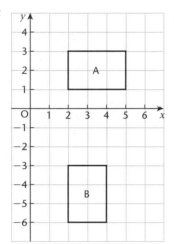

d

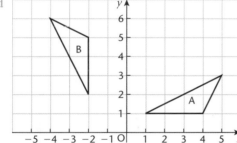

Exam practice 16F

1 $\mathbf{a} = \begin{pmatrix} 4 \\ 1 \end{pmatrix}$ $\mathbf{b} = \begin{pmatrix} -4 \\ 3 \end{pmatrix}$ $\mathbf{c} = \begin{pmatrix} -5 \\ 0 \end{pmatrix}$ $\mathbf{d} = \begin{pmatrix} -2 \\ 3 \end{pmatrix}$

$\mathbf{e} = \begin{pmatrix} 0 \\ 6 \end{pmatrix}$ $\mathbf{f} = \begin{pmatrix} 6 \\ 2 \end{pmatrix}$ $\mathbf{g} = \begin{pmatrix} 0 \\ -3 \end{pmatrix}$ $\mathbf{h} = \begin{pmatrix} 2 \\ -3 \end{pmatrix}$

2

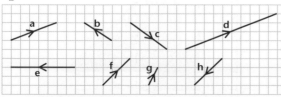

i   **d** is twice **a**
ii they have the same length but are in
    opposite directions

3 a, b, d and e

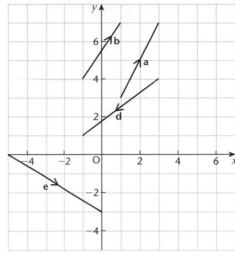

c and f

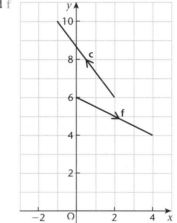

The coordinates of the other ends of the
vectors in alphabetical order, are (3, 7), (1, 7),
(−1, 10), (−1, 1), (0, −3), (4, 4).

Exam practice 16G

1 The translations are described by the vectors:

$\mathbf{a} = \begin{pmatrix} 3 \\ 0 \end{pmatrix}$ $\mathbf{b} = \begin{pmatrix} 3 \\ 3 \end{pmatrix}$ $\mathbf{c} = \begin{pmatrix} -3 \\ -1 \end{pmatrix}$ $\mathbf{d} = \begin{pmatrix} 0 \\ 3 \end{pmatrix}$

2 a   b   c

3 a   rectangle   b   i (1, 5)   ii (3, 1)

  c $\begin{pmatrix} 4 \\ 1 \end{pmatrix}$ d   i (5, 6)   ii (7, 2)

  e   Yes, the vector $\begin{pmatrix} -4 \\ -1 \end{pmatrix}$ is equal and opposite
      to the vector $\begin{pmatrix} 4 \\ 1 \end{pmatrix}$.

4 a $\begin{pmatrix} 4 \\ 1 \end{pmatrix}$ b

  c   i (5, 4)
      ii (7, 2)

5 a $\begin{pmatrix} 4 \\ -1 \end{pmatrix}$ b

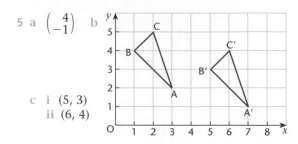

c i (5, 3)
   ii (6, 4)

Exam practice 16H

1 a E   b A   c B   d D   e E

2 a translation described by the vector $\begin{pmatrix} -1 \\ -5 \end{pmatrix}$

  b translations described by the vector $\begin{pmatrix} -2 \\ 3 \end{pmatrix}$

  c rotation about O by 90° anticlockwise

  d rotation 180° about O

  e reflection in the y-axis.

3

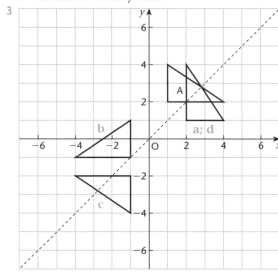

Exam practice 17A

1 a 1:5   b 1:5   c 3:4
  d 3:2   e 6:5   f 1:9
  g 1:3   h 3:50   i 10:1
2 5:9   3 5:1

Exam practice 17B

1 a 2   b $\frac{1}{3}$ c 4   d $\frac{1}{2}$ e $2\frac{1}{3}$

2 a 2   b $\frac{1}{2}$

3 a 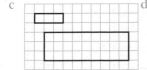 b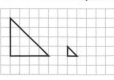

  c 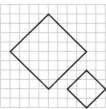 d

4 a 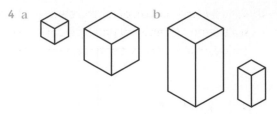   b

5 Length increased by 50% but width by 100% so red shape is not an enlargement.

Exam practice 17C

1 a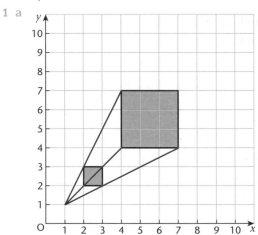

  b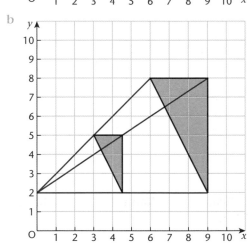

  c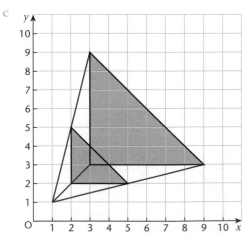

2 a scale factor 2, centre of enlargement (1, 3)
  b scale factor 3, centre of enlargement (1, 9)
  c scale factor $\frac{1}{2}$, centre of enlargement (9, 9)

Exam practice 17D

1 a 4   b 16 : 1
2 a 2   b 12 cm²
3 a $\frac{1}{2}$ b i $\frac{1}{2}$ ii $\frac{1}{4}$
4 a 2   b 24 cm³

Exam practice 17E

1 reflection in $y = 4$
2 reflection in $x = 5$
3 translation by the vector $\begin{pmatrix} 2 \\ -3 \end{pmatrix}$
4 rotation 90° clockwise about (2, 4)
5 enlargement, scale factor 2, centre of enlargement (3, 6)
6 translation by the vector $\begin{pmatrix} -5 \\ -2 \end{pmatrix}$
7 rotation 180° about (5, 6)
8 enlargement, scale factor 2, centre of enlargement (1, 8)

Exam practice 17F

1 a I   b C
  c C or F   d J
2 a D and F   b A and E
3 a true   b false   c true
  d true   e false   f true
  g false
4 a false   b true   c true
  d false   e true

Exam practice 17G

1 a 2.5 m   b $4\frac{3}{4}$ m²
2 a 7 cm   b 700 m   c 400 m
3 600 m
4 2.5 km
5 a 6 m   b 10 m²
6 a 4 cm
  b
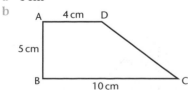
7 a
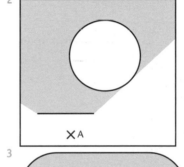
  c isosceles triangle

Exam practice 17H

1 a i 155°   ii 215°   iii 315°
  b i 040°   ii 140°   iii 320°
2 a i 295°   ii 115°
  b 57°   c 237°
  d 5 cm   e 1 : 200 000
3 b 050° (or 049°)

Exam practice 17I

1
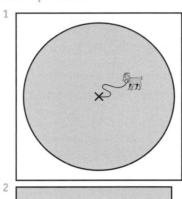
2

3
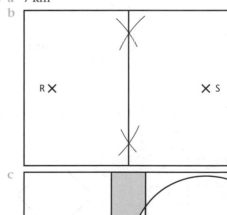
4 a 7 km
  b
  c
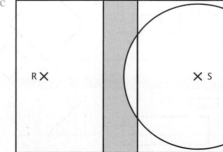

5

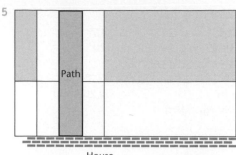

House

6

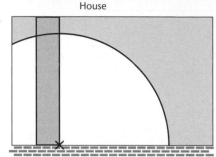

Examination practice papers
Paper 1

1 a 28 grams   b 175 centimetres
   c 25 centilitres   d 160°

2 a i 15
     ii because it is divisible by 3
  b i 40
     ii all the numbers in the sequence are even,
        23 is odd

3 a 1, 2, 3, 6, 9, 18   b 20, 24, 28, 32, 36

4 a i 40 mm   ii 4 cm
  b i and ii

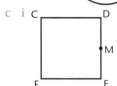

  c i

ii DE and CF or DC and EF
iii e.g. CD and DE

5 a O (0, 0), A (2, 3), B (−4, 1)
  b

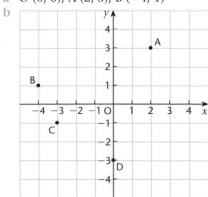

6 a 10   b 11

7

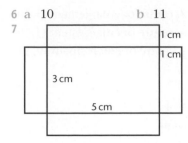

8 a i $6a$ ii $2x + 5y$
  b i $5d - 15$ ii $c^3 + c$

9 a i 20 cm   ii 13
  b i 0   ii 2

10 $x = 67, y = 113$

11 a missing value is -1
  b i and ii

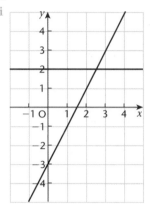

    iii $(2\frac{1}{2}, 2)$

12

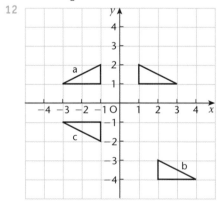

  b ii $\begin{pmatrix} 1 \\ -5 \end{pmatrix}$

13 $\frac{9}{20}$

14 5600 mm³

15 a $-1, 0, 1, 2, 3$
  b $x > 2.5$

16 a b^5
  b m^6

Paper 2

1 a 46 mph   b 225 grams
  c 185 millilitres

2 equilateral triangle D, cuboid A, cylinder C,
  right-angled triangle E, pentagon F, rhombus B

3 a £39   b 7 hours

4 a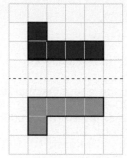

  b i B, D and E   ii 14 cm²

5 a radius, chord, tangent

  b twice as big

6 a 39, 18², 37   b 81

  c 5.5, 6, 6.5   d nth term is $4n$

7 a 101°

  b i reflex   ii 220°

  c 64°

8 a $x = 2$ b $x = 6$ c $c = \frac{1}{2}$ d $a = 30$

9 a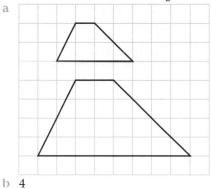

  b 4

10 a 067°   b 145°   c 292°

11

12 26

13 3(2p + 3)

  b $t(t - 2)$

14 exterior angle $= \frac{360}{8} = 45°$ so interior angle is 180° − 45° = 135°

15 a 224 cm²

  b 19.2 m² (3 s.f.)

16 36 cm

Index